The T

Love Child

They were making more than just love…

Praise for three bestselling authors – Jacqueline Baird, Anne Mather and Robyn Donald

About *The Italian's Runaway Bride*:
'Jacqueline Baird will delight readers with this highly passionate tale comprised of fiery characters, dramatic scenes and dynamite conflict.'
—*Romantic Times*

About Anne Mather:
'…Anne Mather has a layered premise, intense characters and provocative scenes.'
—*Romantic Times*

About Robyn Donald:
'Robyn Donald captures passion in its rawest form, mixes it with a sit-up-and-take-notice storyline, and features enticing characters guaranteed to knock your socks off.'
—*Romantic Times*

The Tycoon's Love Child

THE ITALIAN'S RUNAWAY BRIDE
by
Jacqueline Baird

SAVAGE INNOCENCE
by
Anne Mather

THE PATERNITY AFFAIR
by
Robyn Donald

MILLS & BOON®

All the characters in this book have no existence outside the imagination of the author, and have no relation whatsoever to anyone bearing the same name or names. They are not even distantly inspired by any individual known or unknown to the author, and all the incidents are pure invention.

Harlequin Mills & Boon Limited,
Eton House, 18-24 Paradise Road, Richmond, Surrey, TW9 1SR

THE TYCOON'S LOVE CHILD

The Italian's Runaway Bride, *Savage Innocence* and *The Paternity Affair* were first published in Great Britain by Harlequin Mills & Boon Limited in separate, single volumes.

ISBN 0 263 84474 9

05-0405

Printed and bound in Spain
by Litografia Rosés S.A., Barcelona

Jacqueline Baird began writing as a hobby when her family objected to the smell of her oil painting, and immediately became hooked on the romantic genre. She loves travelling and worked her way around the world from Europe to the Americas and Australia, returning to marry her teenage sweetheart. She lives in Ponteland, Northumbria, the county of her birth, and has two teenage sons. She enjoys playing badminton, and spends most weekends with husband Jim, sailing their Gp.14 around Derwent Reservoir.

Look out for the next passionate read
by Jacqueline Baird:
PREGNANCY OF REVENGE
Coming in June 2005, in Modern Romance™!

THE ITALIAN'S RUNAWAY BRIDE

by

Jacqueline Baird

CHAPTER ONE

KELLY MCKENZIE, skimpily clad in cut-off denim shorts and shirt, lay flat on her back on the lawn that sloped softly to the edge of Lake Garda, and sighed her contentment. It was the end of August; the sun was shining and life was great. Rolling onto her stomach, she looked back at the house, a glorious old stone building set some fifty yards from the water's edge. A terrace extended across the full width of the house, and at one end a cluster of cypress trees and shrubs cascaded over the stone balustrades. Shrubs that appeared to be moving, although there was not a breath of wind! How odd!

Then she saw him. Her blue eyes narrowed warily. It was the figure of a man half-hidden by the bushes; one hand was on the balustrade and he was leaning over, trying to peer into a window. In his other hand was an iron bar. Kelly's heart missed a beat. Suspicious didn't cover it... He looked downright dangerous.

Every muscle of her body filled with tension. She watched as he straightened up, his back to her. Dressed in a white vest and a pair of oil-stained khaki shorts, he looked thoroughly disreputable. He was tall—well over six feet—broad-shouldered with lean hips, and he had long legs that rippled with muscle and sinew as he moved.

A man who was moving furtively towards the steps up to the terrace and the entrance to the rear windows of the house...

Stay cool, girl, she told herself, you can handle this. Three months ago, when she'd bumped into an old school friend, Judy Bertoni, in Bournemouth, and Judy had offered her a job as a nanny to her son with the family in Italy for ten weeks, Kelly had leapt at the chance to spend a summer in the sun, before taking up her post as a research chemist with a government laboratory in Dorset in October.

It had seemed a great idea at the time, but now, faced with what looked like a very sinister intruder, Kelly was not so sure…

She was on her own. The family was in Rome, and Marta the housekeeper had taken the opportunity of her employer's absence to go and visit friends, after having warned Kelly to lock up carefully as there had been a spate of burglaries in the area.

Kelly fought down the panicked urge to leap up and run and sat silently watching the figure of the man move stealthily to the first step. The tyre iron in his hand said it all. He was obviously intent on breaking in.

Well, there was nothing for it, Kelly told herself: desperate situations required desperate remedies, and she'd been a keen gymnast in her youth and the university Thai kick-boxing champion two years running. While the intruder's attention was firmly fixed on the windows of the house she psyched herself into fighting mode. Slowly, silently she rose to her feet, adrenaline pumping through her veins.

Then, with a blood-curdling yell, she spun through the air like a whirlwind, and in a few deft kicks the would-be burglar was flat on his back and she had the tyre iron in her hand and her foot on his throat.

Gianfranco Maldini had spun around in surprise at the noise, then he'd had a fleeting image of silver-blonde hair and a very feminine form flying towards him, then all the air had left his lungs.

He could not believe it… A chit of a girl had quite literally dumped him flat on his back. Never in all of his thirty-one years had a woman done that to *him*. About to move, he glanced up the long shapely length of her and stilled. His testosterone took over from common sense.

Dio, but she was gorgeous. His dark eyes raked over her in a slow, intense scrutiny. From the top of her head, where silver-blonde hair had been scraped back into a pony-tail and tied with a ribbon, lingering on the perfect symmetry of her features, wild eyes, and a sultry mouth that was begging to be kissed, then lower, to where her high firm breasts pushed against the soft cotton shirt she had knotted under the luscious mounds. An expanse of smooth pale flesh revealed her tiny waist and the indentation of her navel, which the ridiculously ragged denim shorts could not hide, nor the long shapely legs.

For the first time in years Gianfranco was struck dumb; he felt himself instantly harden and that had not happened in years either, he thought wryly. But she was stunningly beautiful, vibrant with life, and the image of her flying through the air with such verve and grace was the most spectacular thing he had seen in a long time. What she was doing at Carlo Bertoni's he had no idea, but it might be a lot of fun to find out. He had not had a holiday in three years and uncomplicated fun had been sadly lacking in his life of late, he suddenly realised. A quick call to his office, and he could free up some time. New York could wait. Yes, he was going to pursue her, he decided with unconscious arrogance.

He could do without her foot on his neck, but he was in no hurry to get up. The view was stunning. She was standing legs apart, one leg bent at the knee to keep her foot on his throat and the other beside his shoulder. Her shorts did not cover all they should and he made the intriguing discovery that she was a natural blonde and he had to smile as he wondered if she knew what she was exposing.

Kelly lifted the tyre iron in her hand, finally getting a good look at the burglar. Thick black hair flopped over his broad forehead in soft curls and perfectly arched black eyebrows framed deep brown heavily lidded eyes. Only a slight crook in what once must have been a straight blade of a nose stopped him from being classically beautiful. But the whole added up to a ruggedly handsome man. A wickedly handsome man, she amended when his lips curved back over brilliant white teeth in a slow, sexy smile.

Kelly almost groaned out loud. Why was it that the most gorgeous male she had seen in her life was a thief? Even at her mercy, he had an aura of supreme male confidence about him that was hard to ignore. But that did not make him any less a burglar, she told herself staunchly. More likely it meant he was highly successful at his chosen occupation.

'Now, look here, buster, I know you came here to commit a burglary.'

'What?' Gianfranco exclaimed. Being caught off-guard and thrown to the ground was humiliating enough, but to be accused of being a thief was a step too far for a man of his pride and arrogance. In that second he vowed he would make the little madam pay for the insult.

'Don't play the innocent with me—it won't wash,' Kelly blundered on determinedly. 'But I am prepared to give you a chance. You didn't actually get around to stealing anything, so I will let you go, if you promise not to come back.'

The man on the ground shook his head in amazement. If the girl really thought he was a criminal, she was hopelessly naïve believing a genuine thief would just walk away.

'Was that a no?' Kelly demanded, seeing him shake his head. 'Because the alternative is I am going to hit you over the head with this iron bar, and call the police.'

'No—yes,' Gianfranco spluttered, his sense of humour totally deserting him as he noticed she was holding the damned tyre iron over her head. She was mad, and he had wasted too long lying on the ground admiring the view.

One minute Kelly was congratulating herself on keeping her head and control of the man and situation, the next, with a speed that defied gravity, their positions were reversed. Her head hit the ground with a thump and for a second she saw stars, and when her vision cleared she was pinned to the ground. Her hands were held above her head in one massive male hand, and a great body was splayed half over her, one long muscular leg flung across her own slender limbs.

'Get off me! You great brute!' she yelled, and started to struggle, but to very little effect. He was much bigger and much stronger. He simply tightened his hold on her wrists and with his free hand he caught her chin, holding her head firm as he stared down at her with angry brown eyes.

'Now, why would I do that?' Gianfranco asked mockingly. 'If I am the villain you imagine, do you really think I am going to let you go?'

Kelly wasn't thinking, she was panicking, the iron bar she'd taken off him had vanished, and his chest felt like iron pressing down on hers. In a last desperate attempt to dislodge him she tried bringing her knee up against his thigh, and opened her mouth to scream.

She almost succeeded, but a hard mouth crashed down on hers and choked off the scream in her throat. It was a kiss of sheer power, forcing her lips back against her teeth until she thought he would draw blood. If he'd wanted to frighten her he had succeeded, she thought numbly.

Then subtly the kiss changed. His mouth gentled on hers, moving over and over against the lush fullness of her lips, and, to her shame, slowly she felt herself succumbing to the intense sensual pleasure his kiss aroused. Involuntarily her lips parted on a soft, needy sigh, and helplessly she accepted the probing invasion of his tongue.

His hand dropped from her chin to curve around the fullness of her breast, and time stopped. Heat flared through every vein in her body. Seduced by the touch of his hand, the heat of his kiss, the musky male scent of him, she melted against him. It had never happened to her before, sexual excitement overwhelming her mind and body.

When he finally broke the kiss and lifted his head she stared up at him in hazy puzzlement, wondering why he had stopped. His hand fell from her breast and he stared down at her with eyes black with anger. She felt the hard proof of his arousal against her belly, and suddenly she came to her senses. What was she inviting by her helpless surrender to his kiss?

Gianfranco, with the part of his brain that still functioned, wondered what the hell he was doing, making love to a crazy English girl on the lawn of his friends' house in the middle of the day. Even though another much more basic part of him had responded instantly to the feel of her curvaceous body softening against him, it angered him. He was not the sort of man who ever lost control.

'Please let me go,' Kelly pleaded. Somehow he had inserted one long leg between her own and the heat and weight of him was no longer exciting but sexually threatening. This was a total stranger and a thief she was dealing with, and maybe worse, judging from the state of his body. 'Stop now,' she cried, fighting to stay calm. 'You know, you could go to prison for years for rape.'

'Santa Maria.' Incredulous dark eyes stared down into

the beautiful face of the woman beneath him. He had been accused of many things in his time, but a rapist certainly was not one of them. 'Are you completely mad?' he rasped scathingly.

'No.' The fact that his kiss had knocked her for a loop must have been an apparition, Kelly told herself. She knew what she had to do. He was angry and dangerous, she had to humour him until she got a chance to run.

'Who the hell are you? And what are you doing here?' Gianfranco demanded bluntly. Apart from driving him crazy, he thought wryly. He was very conscious of the soft subtle body…except it wasn't soft, but stiff with tension. He looked into the bluest eyes he had ever seen in his life, and saw she really was frightened, but doing her best to hide it. She actually believed the rubbish she'd been spouting.

'My name is Kelly McKenzie, and I am working here for the summer as a nanny to the owners' child.' If she could keep him talking, she had a better chance to escape. 'No one heard me scream, so if you let me go now I promise I will not report you.'

'*Basta.* Enough.' This farce had gone on long enough. Report him, indeed! Gianfranco saw her flinch, and determinedly forced himself to lower his tone. 'Well, Kelly McKenzie, I am not going to hurt you; I have never forced a woman in my life and I am not going to start with you. Understand?' She looked up into the dark attractive face, and wanted to believe him. 'Now, I am going to let go of you and we are going to sit up and discuss this mistake like two rational human beings. Agreed?'

She nodded, every muscle in her body tensing in anticipation of escape. The next moment he let go of her wrists and sat up, but before she could even move he had placed a strong arm around her slender shoulders and hauled her hard against him.

'Neither am I a burglar,' he continued quietly. 'So sit still and listen.'

She didn't have much option, with his hands linked in front of her, trapping her in the cage of his arms. But, with the imminent danger of rape fading from her mind, Kelly began to recover some of her usual feisty temperament.

'So you make a habit of wandering around other people's gardens with an iron bar?' She turned her head and arched one delicate eyebrow sardonically. Did the man take her for a complete idiot? she wondered. But to her surprise he started to chuckle, a deep, throaty sound that did uncomfortable things to her pulse rate again.

'Ah, Kelly, now I understand. I know Carlo Bertoni. I borrowed the tyre iron from him to fix a wheel on the boat trailer, down at the marina. I came around today to return it.'

She had never mentioned her employer's name and yet this man knew it, and she also knew Signor Bertoni kept a boat in the marina. Kelly almost groaned out loud. Such a simple explanation, but she had jumped to the worst possible scenario. Her own father had always used to tell her she had too much imagination for her own good. This time she had surpassed herself. The man spoke English but with an Italian accent. Obviously he must work at the harbour in Desenzano, and as he continued she felt the colour rise in her face.

'The security gate was open so I called at the door, and when no one answered I walked around the back with the intention of leaving the iron on the terrace. I didn't want to take it back with me, because I have another call to make further around the lake at Bardolino. That was until I saw this wild woman come flying at me like a circus tumbler and she immediately accused me of being a thief.'

'Oh, my God! I am sorry.' Kelly swivelled around, raising very relieved sparkling blue eyes to his. 'So you're not a thief but a sailor, and you work at the port in town.'

Gianfranco's lips quirked at the corners in the briefest of grins; he had never met a woman in his life before with the ability to jump to conclusions so readily. It crossed his mind to correct her but, looking down into her surprisingly guileless face, and lower to the soft thrust of her breasts, he remembered his earlier decision to have some fun. Plus, it still rankled she had floored him so easily.

'Yes, I do sail, and I have been working on a boat all morning.' He didn't lie, but neither was he telling the truth.

'I suppose this is the busiest time of year here on Lake Garda, what with all the tourists. Then, of course, there is the big race next week—the contestants come from all over the world, I understand.' Her employer was going to sail in the twenty-four-hour race. 'I suppose that is how you speak such good English.' Kelly was babbling, she knew, but she was so relieved he wasn't a criminal, just an ordinary person like herself. Now no longer afraid of him, she suddenly had a terrific urge to simply relax in the curve of his arm.

'Maybe,' he said with a smile, his dark brown eyes glittering as they met her trusting blue. 'But allow me to introduce myself. Gianfranco…'

'How do you do, Signor Franco?' Nerves and a racing pulse made her jerk out her hand, a tentative smile illuminating her lovely face. 'May I call you Gian?'

'Gianni. I prefer Gianni.' And, with her hand swallowed up in his, he dragged her to her feet. 'So, Kelly, no more misunderstandings. Friends…as you English say, shake on it.'

Very formally they shook hands, but she could see the dancing lights in his deep brown eyes and she chuckled. Then she laughed out loud; the strength of his handclasp, the slight calluses she could feel against her soft palm, obviously from manual labour, convinced her he was telling the truth. 'I can't believe I thought you were a robber,' she spluttered, and then the spluttering stopped as he drew her close into the long length of his body.

'A kiss to seal our friendship.' And his dark head swooped down, his mouth claiming hers in a long, tender kiss.

When he finally eased her away from him she was trembling, bemused; her dazed blue eyes sought his, and as she watched his heavy-lidded eyes narrowed, masking his expression, and just for a second she wondered if she had accepted his explanation a little too easily.

'I am afraid I have to leave in a minute, but, now we have established we are friends, will you have dinner with me tonight? Or will Signor Bertoni object?' Gianfranco asked lightly, tucking her hand under his arm and leading her slowly around the side of the house.

'I'd love to,' Kelly accepted with alacrity. 'I have the next week free, because Signor Bertoni and his wife and son Andrea have gone to visit his parents in Rome.' Her tongue was running away with her, she knew, but with his fingers linked with hers, and her arm pressed against his side, a tingling sensation sizzled through her whole body; she felt as if she had been plugged into an electric socket. The sudden sensual shock to her system was something completely outside her experience.

'How old are you?' Gianfranco interrupted her rambling explanation, glancing down at the beautiful but nervous girl at his side with some amusement. He was far too astute not to recognise that her feverish response to his kiss had shocked her more than it had shocked him. Even so, he hadn't felt such an instant powerful attraction to a woman in years. She obviously did not have vast experience of the male sex, and it would be his pleasure to expand her education. He slashed her a smile, and felt a brief twinge of guilt; she didn't look much more than a teenager.

'I'm twenty-one.' Kelly beamed up at him. 'Why, how old are you?'

'Thirty-one—probably too old for you.'

'Not at all,' Kelly denied quickly. 'Judy is twelve years younger than Signor Bertoni, and they are very happily married. In fact, she would do anything for him. That is why I am here on my own. Judy likes to impress her in-laws by looking after her son herself when she visits them.'

Kelly had no idea how much she was giving away by her announcement, but to the man at her side it was a warning. Kelly McKenzie was not the type for a brief fling. She clearly believed in marriage and happy-ever-after and he knew he was on dangerous ground. But, looking down at her animated features and her luscious body, Gianfranco squashed his doubts. He wanted her, and he was a man who always got what he wanted…

Eight o'clock in the evening and Kelly's first surprise was Gianni's arrival on a large roaring motorbike. They dined on baked lake trout, sitting on the terrace of a small *trattoria* in a tiny village high up in the mountains. Far below them, the dark waters of Lake Garda shimmered in the moonlight, a perfect setting for a romantic meal.

It was well after midnight when they took their leave and got back on the bike. Kelly wrapped her slender arms around him, clasping her hands together at his waist and clinging tightly to him as he expertly manoeuvred the motorbike along the winding road back to Desenzano.

Handing Gianni back the crash helmet he had insisted she wear, Kelly was suddenly deflated that the evening was almost over. She looked up at the house and then back to Gianni. Should she ask him in? But it wasn't her house, and she had only just met him. 'Thank you for a lovely evening,' she began formally, but Gianni solved her problem by placing the helmets on the seat of the bike and drawing her slowly into his arms.

'The pleasure was all mine,' he husked softly, 'and, if you will permit me, I have a few days' holiday and I would like to spend them showing you around the lake.'

'Yes, please,' she agreed breathlessly, completely bemused by the slumbering sensuality in his dark eyes, and when he bent his head and kissed her her fate was sealed. He was everything she had ever wanted, dreamed of, she realised, and nothing else mattered in the world but to be in his arms, where she just *knew* she belonged.

CHAPTER TWO

THE next four days they spent touring on the motorbike to some of the lesser-known beauty spots. Places that only the locals knew, according to Gianni.

Kelly was fascinated and thrilled in turn; they laughed and teased, and talked. She discovered he lived on the other side of Desenzano, with his mother; his father had been dead for some years. It made sense because Kelly knew that the other side of the marina was the old town, so obviously Gianni was a local, and it was quite usual for an Italian male to live at home until he married.

Every day that passed her passion for Gianni grew, until finally she admitted to herself she was in love for the first time in her life.

Kelly lay flat on her back on the blanket Gianni had provided for their picnic. It was a beautiful spot—a small grassy clearing on the edge of the lake. They'd had to ride the bike through the trees to find it. But Gianni had assured her they were not trespassing. Slipping off her shorts and shirt to reveal a tiny blue bikini, she'd run into the cool water of the lake with Gianni chasing her. She could still feel the imprint of his large nearly naked body against hers as he had wrapped two strong arms around her and his firm mouth had closed over hers to kiss her breathless.

She turned her head slightly. Gianni was lying beside her, one arm outstretched and the other loosely curved around the top of her head. She watched the slow rise and fall of his mighty bronzed chest with helpless fascination. They had eaten lunch, fresh bread, a whole roast chicken, and fruit and cheese. Now he looked as if he was asleep and she could admire him to her heart's content.

Her eyes wandered with awe over his sinfully sexy body—tanned, with a smattering of soft black body hair over his chest arrowing down beneath the wicked black trunks that cupped his sex and not much more. She was beginning to regret not asking him into the house that very first night, because the next day Marta had returned and so now she couldn't, and she ached for him with fervour she could barely control.

Restlessly she sat up. Judy had called this morning—they were coming back the next day, Saturday, and her freedom to meet Gianni would be seriously curtailed. Helplessly her eyes strayed back to the man at her side and she frowned.

'Why the frown?' Gianni queried lazily, lifting heavy-lidded eyes to hers.

She had thought he was asleep and, catching the dark gleam in his slumbrous eyes, she knew he had been aware of her watching him, and liked it. Her heart jumped, and her nipples tightened against the brief cotton covering in unwitting response.

Drawing her knees up to her chin, and wrapping her arms around them, hiding as much of her body as she could, she fixed her eyes on the lake and said, 'The family are coming back tomorrow.' She had no real reason to be afraid their relationship would end simply because her brief holiday was ending. But she was… 'This is the last day of my holiday, I suppose,' she said with a brief attempt at a smile.

'Then we must not waste it,' Gianni drawled huskily, and, reaching up, he caught her shoulders and tumbled her round and down on top of him, his mouth finding hers with unerring accuracy. 'Open your mouth,' he husked against her lips, but he did not need to ask as she was more than willing.

Gianni's strong hands swept down the length of her slender body, shaping her waist and hips, her thighs, and trailed back up, one to settle on her buttocks, the other to inch up over her breast. His fingers slipped beneath her bikini top, his thumb grazing over one pert nipple, and she gasped into his mouth as her breast hardened at his touch. She felt his great body's instant reaction, and instinctively she straddled him, wanting his masculine hardness at the most sensitive part of her. She squirmed on top of him, only two bits of cloth separating her from the possession she ached for.

'*Dio*, I want you,' Gianni rasped. 'I have to have you.' He swallowed a groan.

She was all fire and light in his arms; the provocative sexiness of her incredible body moving against him made him dizzy with a raw, primitive desire he could barely control. It was years since he had made love to a girl out in the open, and he knew he should not do it now. He was a well-known man, the lake was full of boats, perhaps even paparazzi, which was the last thing he needed. He'd never realised until the last few days how difficult it was for lesser mortals to find somewhere to take a woman to bed. He should stop this now. But as he felt her breast swell into his hand, the soft, slightly tentative stroke of her tongue on his throat, he was lost.

Gianni rolled her over onto her back and nudged her thighs apart to settle himself in the cradle of her hips, his hands seeking the halter-neck of her top. He wanted to feast on her beauty, to touch and taste every delectable inch of her. But first his mouth angled over her pouting lips in a kiss of wild, hungry passion. Then he heard it…

Suddenly Kelly found herself staring up into the bright sun glinting down from a clear blue sky. Gianni had leapt up, a string of what had sounded very like curses escaping from his mouth in a low, furious undertone.

She sat up. Gianni was striding to the edge of the trees, where a much older man stood with a shotgun over his arm. She couldn't hear what was said, and in any case she was too embarrassed. She hadn't heard the other man approach. Thank heaven Gianni had or the poor old fellow might have got the shock of his life.

Horribly embarrassed by what had nearly happened, she jerked to her feet. Never mind what Gianni had said, she just *knew* they must be trespassing, and they had been caught. Panic-stricken, she began bundling everything together, visions of languishing in an Italian jail leaping into her mind.

'I don't believe it,' Gianni muttered furiously under his breath, swinging around and striding back to pick up his shorts and shirt and pull them on.

'We are trespassing, aren't we?' Kelly demanded, her face flushed, her hair disheveled. She had no notion of how wonderful she looked to Gianni as she struggled into her own shorts and top.

A wry smile parted his firm mouth. He'd just been caught by the security guard he employed to keep an eye on the grounds and hunting lodge he owned. At least the man was doing his job properly, but it was no consolation to Gianni, who was aching in actual pain with frustration. Not for the first time in the last few days he wondered if the pretence was worth it. But he was so used to women throwing themselves at him because of his wealth and name that it made a refreshing chance to be treated like a regular guy. But if he had told Kelly who he was, and taken her to his house and his bed, he would not now be suffering the burning torment of frustration her delectable body had aroused in him.

'Sorry, Kelly. But I will make it up to you tonight, I promise.' His mind was made up: tonight he would tell her the truth. Bending down, he picked up the blanket and the food box in one hand and held the other one out to her.

He glanced down at her silver head, her hand so trustingly in his, and he felt a bit of a bastard. She was a truly lovely girl, both inside and out. He knew she wanted him; she could not hide her reactions. Neither could he, he thought drily, willing his body to subside. But he was not into denial so it would have to be tonight, because tomorrow he was leaving. He had work commitments piling up around his ears, never mind the fact the Bertoni family were returning.

Gianfranco was a sophisticated, experienced man of the world and Kelly, at twenty-one, was obviously no innocent. She was incredibly responsive and went wild in his arms, though sometimes she actually looked surprised at her own reactions. He knew without conceit that he could have had her the first day he'd met her.

He stopped, puzzled for a moment at his own restraint. He was not a man who went in for one-night stands—he usually took a woman out three or four times before taking her to bed. He had to like the woman he was sleeping with, and he certainly liked Kelly. He was looking forward to a new affair as it had been three months since the end of his last relationship. Plus, he wanted to discover if she was as much a gymnast in bed as she was out of it!

His sudden halt about a yard away from the motorbike caught Kelly by surprise and she kept moving. Her hand fell from his, and, turning, she grinned up at him.

'Don't look so worried.' He was watching her as she spoke with an oddly speculative gleam in the dark eyes that met her own. 'We weren't arrested, and it could have been worse,' she offered with a grin. 'At least the chap didn't shoot at us.'

Gianni's lips quirked. He chuckled and then laughed out loud. 'You are so good for me, Kelly. Come on…' And, handing her a helmet, he added, 'Mount up and let's ride.'

'Now, that's an offer few girls could refuse.' She gave him a very sexy wink.

'Get on the bike,' Gianni ordered. 'Before I change my mind,' he teased her with a blatantly salacious grin, his dark eyes sweeping her slender form from the top of her head to her toes. She really was very lovely; she made him feel like a teenager again. She looked like one herself in cut-off denim shorts. It suddenly occurred to him that he'd never seen her wear anything but shorts or trousers. A necessity on a bike, but he could not help wondering what she would look like sleek and groomed in the kind of designer dress his usual girlfriends favoured. He found himself voicing his thoughts. 'Tonight, wear a dress.'

'On a bike? You *are* joking?' Kelly chuckled, swinging one shapely leg over the saddle.

'No, no, I'm not.' Straddling the bike, he glanced back over his shoulder. 'Tonight we will ride in style. I'll collect you at eight in a car.'

Kelly clasped her hands around his waist and hung on tight as he revved up the engine. Usually she wallowed in the warm protection of his huge body as they rode along the road, but not today. Instead her brain ran a hasty inventory of her wardrobe and she realised she had absolutely nothing to wear!

When she heard the doorbell ring Kelly waved goodbye to a frowning Marta and dashed down the marble hall to the entrance door. She was praying Gianni would approve of the pale pink silk-lined chiffon dress that she had bought that afternoon from a sale rack in a very expensive boutique in the town.

Gianni's reaction was all she'd hoped for. His dark eyes widened and an arrested expression crossed his ruggedly attractive face. 'You look absolutely stunning, Kelly.'

'I did as you said. I wore a dress,' Kelly responded softly, her heart swelling with love and pride, her eyes drinking in the sight of him. A pale green shirt fitted perfectly across his broad shoulders, open at the neck to reveal the tanned column of his throat. Cream pleated cotton trousers skimmed his lean hips and long strong legs, and on his feet were brown hide loafers.

She looked back up at his face and her breath caught in her throat. He was so handsome, and somehow different, older than the devil-may-care biker she had fallen in love with.

Gianfranco was silent for a long moment, his dark eyes narrowing assessingly on her face and shapely body. The long silver-blonde hair was swept up on top of her head, revealing a diamond crucifix glinting at her throat. The jewels were genuine. The elegant pink dress and shoes were designer wear. He should know—he had bought enough clothes for females over the years.

His dark brows drew together in a frown. Maybe she knew who he was. Who was fooling whom? he wondered wryly. Tonight she looked older than her twenty-one, a mature, sophisticated lady, and hey, if she liked to play games, all the better; she obviously knew the score.

'Gianni.' Kelly had an uneasy feeling that she had upset him somehow, and she wondered if everyone in love felt this roller-coaster ride between high and low. Her stomach did flip-flops and her pulse raced at the sight of him, but he only had to frown and she was worried sick.

A relieved if slightly cynical smile parted his firm lips.

'Kelly, *cara.*' He drawled the endearment and, taking her arm, added, 'Come on, let's go eat.'

Encouraged by the endearment, and a minute later seated in the passenger seat of a big blue Volvo car, she asked as Gianni slid behind the driving wheel, 'This is a nice car; is it yours?'

'My family's.' Bending over, Gianni pressed a swift, hard kiss on her mouth. 'Don't worry, I have not stolen it,' he quipped.

'I would not dream of thinking such a thing,' Kelly said drolly.

'Of course not.' One dark brow arched sardonically in her direction and they both chuckled, remembering their first meeting.

Kelly's earlier fear was quickly dismissed, and half an hour later, when he took her hand as he helped her out of the car, she looked up with interest at the large grey stone house set in a small clearing surrounded by trees. 'Where are we?' Kelly queried. It did not look like a restaurant. A single window was lit, the light spilling out over a terrace, and there was not a soul in sight.

'I did think of taking you to the most expensive restaurant in the area.' Gianni turned her to face him, and added, 'But I thought of something more private,' he husked in a deeply sensual tone.

The butterflies in Kelly's stomach started a stampede, but she was where she wanted to be, with Gianni, and, lifting her head, she beamed up at him. 'Admit it. You couldn't afford it,' she challenged him teasingly. 'So you decided to break into a house in the woods.'

'Your imagination will get you into trouble one day, sweetheart,' he drawled cynically, but the gleam of laughter in the dark eyes as they met hers belied his cynicism. 'We don't have to break in—I have a key. The house is owned by the company I work for, and I have permission to use it.'

'Oh, so it's empty,' she murmured weakly, and swallowed hard, knowing once she entered the house she was tacitly agreeing to furthering their intimate relationship.

'I'm not going to lie to you, Kelly. I want you; you know that,' he said softly. 'But I promise I will not do anything you don't want me to,' Gianni assured her with a smile. 'Now, come on, dinner is waiting. I was up here earlier and prepared it.'

'You can cook?' she asked as he pushed open the door and with a hand at her back urged her forward into the house.

'I can do anything,' Gianni said arrogantly, and before she knew his intention he had spun her around into his arms and kissed her long and hard. When he finally lifted his head her eyes, wide and worshipping, clung to his.

'We had better eat,' he said roughly, 'while we still can.'

Kelly knew exactly what he meant. Her hunger for him was growing by the second. She did not know this sensual, needy woman she had become with Gianni. But her mind was made up—she was going to take the chance and find out…

They ate out on the terrace by candle-light. Gianni was a marvellous host, but Kelly had to laugh at the food.

'You call that cooking?' she jibed as she forked the last mouthful of potato salad into her mouth. He had served melon with Parma ham, followed by prawns with salad, then cold cuts of meat with more salad. 'There was not a single dish that needed cooking, you fraud. I bet you simply bought the lot in the delicatessen in town.'

'Maybe so, but it worked—I needed to get you alone,' he drawled with a lascivious grin, and filled her glass with white wine yet again.

She lifted laughing blue eyes to his. 'You are incorrigible.'

'I know.' His brown eyes danced with devilment as they met hers, and for a moment the shared humour united them, but subtly the mood changed and their eyes meshed. 'Kelly,' Gianni murmured her name, 'we don't have much time left; your employer is back tomorrow and I have to go to Genoa; I will be away for a few days.'

Her heart sank. 'You're going away.' Their holiday idyll was at an end, but it did not mean their relationship had to end, she told herself staunchly.

'It will be at least a week before we can see each other again.' He reached out to her, his hands palm up on the table. 'Shall we go inside?'

Her heart lifted: he did intend seeing her again. She glanced up into his deep brown eyes, and what she saw there made her pulse race. She knew all evening had been leading to this moment. They had laughed and joked, but the underlining sexual tension had been growing stronger and stronger. She knew what he was offering, and she knew if she took his hands there would be no going back.

She placed her glass on the table, and put her hands in his.

Gianni lifted them both to his mouth, pressing a soft kiss to the centre of each palm before rising to his feet.

Feeling Kelly tremble, Gianni pulled her up and into his arms. She was so soft, so warm, so his! he thought triumphantly as he claimed her lush, pouting lips with his own.

'Gianni,' she moaned his name, her slender body quivering with a need, a want she could not control. She looked up into his night-dark eyes and knew it was the same for him.

'Yes, my sweet Kelly,' he husked as he lifted her off her feet and carried her up the stairs to the bedroom, all the time pressing brief kisses to her lips, her cheek, her eyes, nuzzling the curve of her neck.

'*Dio!* Kelly, you have no idea how much I ache for you,' he groaned, lowering her down the long length of his body and holding her slightly away from him. 'I don't think I can wait any longer.' He caught her shoulders and eased the straps of her dress down over her arms. His brilliant brown eyes holding hers, she felt the gentle stroke of his fingers on her bare flesh right through to her bones.

'I want to see you naked.' He slid the dress down her body to pool at her feet.

Standing before him in tiny lacy briefs, Kelly shuddered as his hands slid back up her hips and shaped the indentation of her waist, and watched as his dark eyes dropped to savour the glory of her near-naked body. His hands tightened around her waist. The bones of his face were taut with passion and for the briefest second she was afraid.

He sensed her fear, and loosened his hold. His hands skimmed over the silk slide of her skin to her breasts. 'You are incredible, so responsive, so beautiful.' Her skin was as pale as ivory, her body toned to perfection, with high full breasts tipped with delicate rosebuds. His body hardened to steel, and want raced through him like a tidal wave. 'No woman has ever affected me the way you do, Kelly.' He bent his head towards her, his breath brushing her lips. 'But if you want me to stop, say so now,' he murmured, and kissed her lightly. He did not trust himself to do more.

Kelly swayed into him, her lips parting on a trembling sigh, her fingers reaching for his shirt buttons. 'I don't want you to stop,' she whispered against his mouth. 'Not ever.'

Their mouths met in a hungry, ravishing kiss that blanked every doubt from her mind—all she could think, feel and taste was Gianni. His head lifted and he eased her away from him. She followed his movements with longing in her brilliant sapphire eyes, and in seconds Gianni was naked.

Fascination kept her still, her eyes roaming over his body in wonder. He was magnificent, like a sculptured god to her innocent gaze. She dragged a breath into her air-starved lungs and caught that musky fragrance of masculine arousal. She saw his sex surging from the curling black nest of his groin, and wild colour flooded over every inch of her skin.

Gianni, reaching out for her, hesitated for a second and stepped back, his dark eyes narrowing. 'You're blushing as though you had never seen a naked man before.'

'The curse of the McKenzies, my father always said. He was ginger-haired and always blushed.' She was babbling, she knew, but without Gianni's touch to reassure her she suddenly felt exposed. 'My mother suffered from the same affliction, and I take after both my parents.'

'Hush.' Gianni silenced her ramblings by drawing her into his arms. 'I like it,' he said, and quite unexpectedly he felt rotten. Kelly knew next to nothing about him, not even his real name. He must tell her.

'And I like you,' Kelly murmured as he held her close to his naked body. She was drowning in a million sensations. She did not care that the light was still on; in fact, she knew the picture of him in all his nudity would live with her to her dying day. She stroked her slender hands up his spine, down over his buttocks. He felt like satin and steel, hot and hard, and she ached to know every inch of him.

Gianni's great body shuddered as her small hot hand slid like silk up his spine. He swung her up into his arms and carried her to the bed, dropped her down on it.

Breathless, she smiled up at him, a slow, soft curve of her incredibly sexy mouth. Her sapphire-blue eyes, shining like stars, met his, and she reached two slender arms out to him.

'My full...' Name, he was going to say, but her lithe naked body spread on the bed was too much. '*Dio, sì*, Kelly,' he said in a strangled voice. It could wait, but he couldn't, and he joined her on the bed.

Her heart racing, Kelly curved her hands around his shoulders, letting her fingers curl into the soft black hair at the nape of his neck, urging him down to her. 'Yes,' she breathed. A tremulous little gasp caught in her throat, and anticipation made her moan out loud as he covered her face with tiny kisses before finally claiming her mouth. She felt his kiss, the stroke of his hand down to cup the fullness of her breast in every cell in her body. Excitement surged through her, making her arch against him with a soft whimper of need. Her fingers dug into his skin as he lowered his head, trailing a fiery line of kisses down her throat to her breast, his mouth closing over one hard tip, suckling and tasting, until she cried out with pleasure.

With a wantonness that amazed her, her body responded to his every touch. He was a magnificent male animal, power and virility in every line of his huge body. He nudged her legs apart with one of his own, and she gasped as his long fingers delved between her thighs, but her legs moved wider, welcoming the intimate caress.

Her hands slipped down to clutch his hips, one small hand stroking across his thigh, revelling in the different textures of skin and soft curling body hair, and tentatively to the core of his manhood.

Gianni instantly reared back. 'Kelly,' he grated, his massive chest heaving. He wanted to take it slowly. He wanted it to be good for her, the best ever. He did not ask himself why.

'Don't stop,' Kelly begged, her blue eyes, dark with need, fixed on his hard face. 'Please, please,' she moaned.

Gianni slid his hands beneath her hips and lifted her to him. His need for her sang in his blood, raced through his veins. There was a roaring in his ears and any notion of taking it slowly was obliterated.

With one swift thrust he entered her, sheathing himself inside her. Kelly cried out as a fierce pain ripped through her. For a second Gianni froze, but before she could react to the pain with a low groan he surged into the hot, sleek centre of her again and again, and slowly the pain subsided. Euphoria took over as he drove her higher and higher to some destination she had only ever dreamed about.

Afterwards Kelly wrapped her arms around his neck, hugging his great body, relishing his weight on her as the sounds of their frantic breathing became regulated. She could not find the words to describe how he made her feel. He had captured her heart and soul. 'I love you,' she sighed, and with a murmur of pleasure kissed his sweat-slicked shoulder, still wanting more.

Gianni said something harsh and guttural in Italian and tore himself from her arms and leapt off the bed. 'You were a virgin,' he grated incredulously, his dark eyes narrowing down to where she lay naked on the bed. 'Why the hell did you not tell me?' he demanded with barely contained rage. He could not believe he had lost control so totally *and* maybe fallen for the oldest trick in the book…

CHAPTER THREE

'I NEVER thought,' she murmured, her new-found euphoria dwindling at the repressed fury in his tone. Towering over her, the lover of a moment ago was gone, and in his place was a furious naked man; his hard eyes clashed with hers and the dark menace of his expression made her inwardly wince. Kelly did not understand what she had done wrong. Her mouth dried, and she dampened her top lip with her tongue, tearing her gaze away from the violence in his.

'You never thought!' snorted Gianni, shaking his dark head in disgust.

Kelly had no defence. She could not help having been a virgin, and it had never entered her head to mention the fact. How naïve could one get? she thought, feeling sick with a mixture of embarrassment and humiliation. 'Obviously I made a mistake,' she said in a flat little voice, forcing the words past trembling lips; suddenly she quite desperately wanted to cry.

'*I* certainly did,' he muttered between clenched teeth as he began to pull on his clothes. 'A virgin.' His black brows drew together in a frown as he surveyed her slender body spread-eagled on the bed where he had left her, the blush of passion tinting her pale skin. 'Cover yourself, for God's sake!'

The electric light that she had not objected to before now seemed to be fixed like a spotlight on her naked body. Jerking up into a sitting position, she grabbed the sheet and tugged it up under her chin. 'I'm sorry.' But she was not apologising to him, she was sorry for herself—his reaction had turned what she had thought was a wonderful experience into something shoddy and shameful.

Kelly saw it all clearly now. Gianni had been looking for a holiday fling, and she, poor fool that she was, had thought it was love, the real thing…

'Sorry. You're sorry!' Gianni snarled. 'What about me? Is it too much to hope you are on the Pill, or can I expect a paternity suit in a few months' time?'

As soon as the words left his mouth he knew he was being cruelly unfair. He should have used protection. But he had been so out of his head with wanting Kelly that for the first time in his life he had forgotten. He had lost control, and not only that, he thought, as his dark eyes, bright and hard as jet, raked over her huddled figure on the bed: he had taken her virginity and not even satisfied Kelly sexually, something else he never failed to do with his usual lady-friends. It was a massive blow to his ego. But then, he had known the moment he'd set eyes on her she would drive him crazy, and she had. He needed to think, and think hard, and he could not do it with Kelly sitting like a broken doll on the bed.

'Sorry, Kelly—' he reached out a hand to her '—I should not have said that.' Whether she was a clever little fortune-hunter or not, she did not deserve his anger.

Pregnant! Paternity! While she had thought love, he had been counting costs. All the colour drained from her skin, and cold beads of sweat broke out across her upper lip; she had the horrible conviction she had just made the biggest mistake of her life. How could she have been such a gullible, careless fool? Galvanised into action by his outstretched hand, Kelly knocked it away and shot out of the other side of the bed. Wrapping the sheet around her shivering body, she raised stormy eyes to his across the wide expanse of the bed, anger, hot and hard, coming to her rescue.

'Oh, please, don't apologise; you could not possibly be as sorry as I am.' Ignoring him completely, she set about picking up her clothes.

He caught up with her as she was heading for the door. 'Wait.' His hands grasped one of hers and spun her around to face him.

'What for? A repeat performance—I don't think so,' she shot back, fighting down a reckless impulse to fling herself in his arms and cry her eyes out. She was angry and ashamed, and physically sore, and with her dream of love shattered. But Kelly was a quick learner.

'No.' His mouth compressed into a humourless smile. 'I am not a complete monster, Kelly, though I guess at this minute you will have trouble believing that. Go ahead and get dressed, and then we will talk.' And before she could stop him she was abruptly hauled hard against his lean body and he kissed her again.

The moment his lips touched hers, the familiar longing swept like wildfire through her veins, but just before she capitulated to the wicked temptation of his mouth he pushed her lightly away. His hooded dark eyes were guarded as he looked down at her. 'The bathroom is over there.' He indicated the door with a pointed finger, and he had the gall to pretend to smile with a twist of his lips, but the humour never reached his eyes.

Embarrassed yet again by her traitorous body's response, she blushed scarlet and darted into the bathroom. Five minutes later, washed and dressed and standing before the vanity mirror, she raked her hands through the tangled mass of her hair, trying to restore it to some order. The pins she'd used had vanished in the bed. She bit her bottom lip to stop herself crying. What should have been the most perfect night of her life had turned into the worst.

A rap on the door made her jump. 'Kelly, are you OK?' The caring note in his rich, deep voice was like rubbing salt in an open wound.

Kelly took a deep breath and straightened her slender shoulders, a cynical little smile curving her bruised lips. 'Just coming,' she carolled. No way was she going to let him see how much he had hurt her. But it wasn't easy.

Walking into the bedroom, she was struck anew by the fierce sexual hunger she had felt from the first moment she had laid eyes on him. It wasn't fair. She almost groaned. He was standing by the door, his dark eyes fixed broodingly on his own large hand curved around the handle. The terrible compulsion to stare was almost uncontrollable. His chiselled profile, with the endearing crook in the nose, the high cheekbones and the firm, sensuous mouth, all added up to one staggeringly handsome man. A man whose long, lithe body looked poised for flight. Her stomach clenched, her hunger for him undiminished even now, when he had made it blatantly obvious he no longer wanted her. Probably never had.

Where is your pride, girl? Kelly asked herself, and, straightening her shoulders, her long lashes half-lowered over her too vulnerable eyes, she rubbed damp palms down her slender hips and walked towards him.

'I'll take you home,' Gianni said in a level voice, not looking at her.

They hadn't been more than ten silent minutes in the car when the tension beating on Kelly's nerves began to give her a terrible headache. She glanced sideways at Gianni through the long length of her lashes. His dark features were calmly composed, as though he hadn't a care in the world. But then, he hadn't, unless she was even more naïve than she thought. She was pretty certain he had got some physical satisfaction from the evening. Even if she'd been inadequate in other ways.

'You never answered my question.'

Gianni's disembodied voice seemed to attack her from the darkness. She twisted her head around. 'What question?'

'Are you on the Pill or is there a chance you might be pregnant?' He slanted her a brief glance, one black brow arching enquiringly.

'No, and highly unlikely,' she said flatly, taking a deep, shaky breath and surreptitiously crossing her fingers.

A large hand landed on her thigh, and she flinched. 'I will take care of you, Kelly, if the need arises,' he said. His tone implied that he would rather it didn't.

Furiously she knocked his hand off her leg, colour staining her cheeks, and she blessed the darkness. 'There will be no need. I can take care of myself.'

'As you did tonight?' Gianni grated harshly.

'Just shut up and drive,' Kelly snapped, not prepared to argue.

The car swung alongside the kerb outside the iron gates; clearly choosing not to drive in, Gianni turned in his seat. He looked at her slender body curled into the corner of the passenger seat, as far away from him as she could get. With her face scrubbed free of make-up, and her silver hair hanging loose around her shoulders, she looked so young, and guilt hit him like a punch to the stomach. 'I didn't mean to hurt you tonight.' He had the totally alien desire to protect her.

Tears ached at the backs of Kelly's eyes. 'You didn't,' she managed to say, and, fumbling with her seatbelt, she avoided his knowing gaze.

'I did and I am sorry. But I was surprised. I thought…'

'You thought I was an easy lay—the English tourist; I know the reputation,' she said scathingly, turning her back on him and trying to open the door. She had to get away before she broke down and bawled her eyes out. Her delicately arched brows drew together in fierce concentration. How the hell did the door open? And how the hell had she allowed herself to act so bloody dumb?

'No, no, never that.' Gianni reached out for her with a half-groan. 'You don't understand, Kelly. I was amazed you were innocent, and shock made me shout at you.' He linked confident arms around her tense body and eased her around to face him. 'But I don't want us to end like this.' He smoothed a few strands of pale hair from her creased brow.

Held against his hard, lithe body, with his brilliant gaze riveted to hers, dimly she understood how a bird must feel, mesmerised by the predatory eyes of a great cat.

'You don't?' she asked, hardly daring to hope. His brown eyes were gleaming with what actually looked like remorse. Her skin prickled with sudden heat, and Gianni's hand dropped lower, to tangle in a whole handful of her silken hair and twist it around his fingers, his dark, compelling gaze never leaving hers. Her tongue snaked out to moisten her dry lips.

'No.' His eyes dropped to the lush fullness of her damp lips, and, bending his head, he gently brushed them with his. He touched her and she melted; it was that basic, Kelly realised with a low groan.

Gianni lifted his head and stared down into her wary blue eyes; he knew he had put the suspicion there and hated himself for it. He lifted a finger and pressed it against the pulse that beat madly in her neck. 'This chemistry between us is more than I believed possible between a man and woman. Tonight I was a fool. In the urgency of passion I took what should have been a special gift, like the thief you once called me. I was angrier with myself than you. But the next time I swear will be perfect.'

Kelly heard what he was saying and suddenly she understood. This wonderful, vulnerable man had been angry because he thought he had not pleased her. The love in her heart burst into flame all over again. 'Oh, Gianni, any time I am with you is perfect,' she said impulsively, and she felt as if the weight of the world had been lifted from her shoulders.

His cynical mind thought, Flattery, or fact? He didn't know, but he was going to take the chance—though he would put off telling her who he was just yet. He smiled, a slow, sexy curve of his firm lips, half-humorous and half-cynical. She could no more hide her feelings than fly; her expressive eyes gave her away or she was a great actress, he thought just before he lowered his head to claim her mouth once more.

'And this is Andrea, running after the stray cats at the Coliseum.' Judy Bertoni, her employer, handed Kelly yet another photograph.

They were sitting side by side on the sofa in the salon, sharing a bottle of white wine. Andrea was safely tucked up in bed, and Signor Bertoni was out at the sailing club.

Kelly grinned at Judy. 'You seem to have had a great time in Rome, and you managed to look after Andrea with no bother at all. I feel quite superfluous.'

'The in-laws were impressed, but your help was invaluable.' Judy, a tall, elegant brunette, had been a model before she married, and was not the most hands-on mother in the world.

'I wasn't there,' Kelly reminded her with a grin.

'I know.' Judy smiled a very self-satisfied smirk. 'But

Carlo realised the difference. The weeks we have been here with you to help, he has had a lot more…attention from me, shall we say?' she declared archly. 'In Rome I made sure he noticed the difference, with Andrea occupying most of my time and energy.' She winked at Kelly. 'The result being, when we return to England he is going to employ a full-time nanny. I can't think why I didn't think of doing it before.'

Kelly had to laugh. 'I think your poor husband hasn't got a chance.' When it came to getting what she wanted Judy was a master of the art. Kelly knew for a fact she had pursued Carlo Bertoni quite deliberately, determined to marry him. Judy had confided as much. Carlo Bertoni was a wealthy man and ran the British branch of the family import and export buisness. He was also a rather old-fashioned, traditional Italian male. His mother had never employed a nanny to look after him and he saw no reason why his wife could not look after their child herself.

'Anyway, enough about me,' Judy said, and, refilling the two glasses of wine on the table in front of them, she lifted her glass to her lips and surveyed Kelly through slightly narrowed eyes. 'Marta tells me you have succumbed to the Italian male's charm and found yourself a boyfriend. Come on, spill the beans. Where did you meet? Who is he? What does he do?'

It was a new experience for Kelly, having another woman to talk to, and suddenly she found herself telling Judy all about Gianni. 'I met him here last week. He is gorgeous, tall, dark and handsome, and he works at the harbour and lives in the old town.'

'Oh, no!' Judy exclaimed. 'You've fallen for one of the locals. For heaven's sake, Kelly, you can do much better for yourself than some manual worker.'

Kelly stiffened at Judy's derogatory comment. 'You

don't understand; we are in love,' she defended. For her it was true, and on Friday night when she had finally left Gianni she had been convinced he loved her too. He had arranged to telephone her on Monday and they were to meet next Friday at a small *trattoria* they had visited before.

'Love!' Judy laughed. 'Take my advice, Kelly—if you must have a bit of rough, make sure you are protected.'

'Thanks very much,' Kelly drawled sarcastically, her anger rising at Judy's summary dismissal of Gianni. But in her position as employee she could not really argue with Judy. If Judy had a fault she was a bit of a snob. Biting her lip to stop herself saying something she might regret, Kelly lifted her glass and took a long swallow of wine.

Judy had not even noticed the sarcasm in Kelly's response. 'My pleasure.' She smiled briefly at Kelly, no longer interested, and, glancing at the slim gold Rolex on her wrist, she sighed, picked up the remote control and switched on the television.

So what if Gianni did have calluses on his hands and worked hard for a living? Did that make him any less a man? No, Kelly thought, a dreamy, reminiscent smile curving her full lips, a vivid mental image of his big naked bronzed body filling her mind. She could barely wait until Friday; she missed him so much.

'I wonder where Carlo has got to…he is very late.' Judy's voice impinged on her musings, and at that moment the door opened and in walked Carlo Bertoni.

'Oh, my God! What's happened?' Judy leapt to her feet and dashed to her husband's side.

Kelly's eyes widened like saucers at the picture her employer presented. One arm was in a sling, and a swath of bandages circled his head. His usually tanned face looked grey, and it was obvious he was in some pain.

Within minutes the whole story was revealed. He had been hit by the boom of his yacht, fallen and broken his arm. He had been to the hospital, had an X-ray and five stitches in his head, and his arm put in plaster. He insisted his injuries were not half as bad as the fact he would now miss the big race next week. Then Judy reminded him it was the last night of the open-air opera in Verona tomorrow night and they had VIP seats.

The next day Carlo Bertoni flatly refused to go to the opera. His head was aching and he insisted he would stay at home with Andrea, and Kelly should go in his place. Judy was not pleased but, as she would not miss it for the world because it was a big social occasion, she agreed.

Which was why Kelly was dressed in the pink chiffon dress and, in her matching beaded cardigan, was happily following Judy into the ancient arena at nine that night.

It was huge. Right in the centre of the floor in front of the orchestra pit, where the stage had been erected, was a square area roped off and filled with white chairs. Judy explained as they slid into their seats that these were the VIP seats. The grey chairs rising in row upon row beyond were numbered seats, and then the ancient stone slabs that rose in circle upon circle to the very top of the arena were the un-numbered seats.

With the starlit blackness of the night sky for a roof, the atmosphere was electric as everyone waited for the opera to start. Kelly's head swivelled around in awed wonder at her surroundings; there was hardly a seat left except for a few in front of them. 'This is incredible.' She turned to Judy but her companion was watching the last few people arrive.

'Now *that* is what I call incredible.' Judy shot her a sidelong glance. 'Isn't he the most devastatingly attractive man you have ever seen?'

Following the direction of her employer's gaze, Kelly blinked and jerked upright in her seat.

'Count Gianfranco Maldini, *the* most eligible bachelor in Europe, possibly the world. Will you look at him, Kelly? The man has it all. Style, breeding, handsome as the devil, and filthy rich. He is enough to make a happily married woman drool.'

Kelly was looking, but she could not believe her eyes. The man walking to the seats in front of them was the epitome of sartorial elegance. A perfectly tailored dark suit fitted his broad-shouldered long-bodied frame to perfection, the brilliant white shirt that accompanied it showing exactly the right amount of cuff and the glint of a gold cuff-link beneath the jacket sleeve.

She blinked and blinked again. She shook her head. No, it couldn't be… 'Who did you say it was?' She was totally confused. The man was the spitting image of Gianni, but with subtle differences. This man looked older; his features were the same, but the laughter that sparkled in Gianni's eyes was not evident in this man's cold, arrogant features.

Judy shot her an excited glance. 'Count Gianfranco Maldini. The family estate is in Lombardy, but he has vast holdings all over the place. Carlo knows him and he is hoping to do a deal importing the wine from the Bardolino vineyard the Count owns into England.'

Kelly squeezed her eyes shut, willing the image of the man to go away. She opened her eyes again, and a dreadful fear made the blood drain from her face. The stunningly handsome man not five feet away from her even had the same crook in his nose as her Gianni, but it could not be…

'What did you say his first name was?' Kelly asked, still not prepared to believe it.

'Gianfranco.'

'But isn't that two names?' She was still denying the truth before her very eyes.

'No. Think about it. The pope is called Gianpaulo; Giancarlo, Gianluca—they are all quite popular names. Especially in the kind of aristocratic family Gianfranco Maldini belongs to,' Judy whispered to her in an aside, and then, to Kelly's horror, Judy rose and called something in Italian to the man.

Nausea rose up Kelly's throat like bile. She could not deny the evidence of her own eyes any longer. It was Gianni, her Gianni, but not as she had ever seen him. Tall and sophisticated, and with his unruly curls slicked back from his broad brow, he looked superb. Strikingly handsome, every inch the sophisticated aristocrat his title proved him to be.

The taste of bitter humiliation in her mouth, Kelly tried to huddle down in her seat, her heart squeezing in anguish. He had lied to her, made a complete fool of her, and with each second that passed she died a little more inside.

'And this is Kelly McKenzie, my nanny. Kelly.' Judy's voice rose, and Kelly had no choice but to get to her feet and be introduced to Count Maldini.

'Ah, Kelly.' His dark eyes smiled down at her, and she just knew he was going to say he had met her already.

Pride alone made her jump in and stick out her hand. 'A pleasure to meet you, Count Maldini.' It was bad enough she had made a fool of herself over this man, but no way did she want her stupidity revealed to Judy Bertoni, or anyone else. Her hand was swallowed up in his and he gave her a quizzical look, before lifting her hand and pressing it to his mouth. She felt the electric sensation right down to her toes, and he knew, the devil, and his black eyes were laughing down at her in secret mirth at her charade. 'How do you like our country?' he asked politely.

She wrenched her hand from his. 'The country is nice.' She did not know how she got the words out. She was in shock, but her ordeal was not over, as with impeccable manners he introduced the two women who accompanied him.

His mother, a silver-haired lady who had to be over sixty but looked much younger, gave Kelly one brief glance down her elegant nose and murmured the appropriate response. The other woman was thirty-ish, beautiful and superbly dressed. She had one hand resting on the count's sleeve, and the other she held out to Kelly. Apparently, she was his sister-in-law, Olivia Maldini.

'This must be a great treat for a nanny,' Olivia added to her conventional greeting, her cold dark eyes skimming over Kelly and a patronising smile curving her rather thin lips.

'You could say that,' Kelly snapped back, suddenly seeing red and a few other colours beside. The shock that had kept her frozen for so long was evaporating and in its place was a towering rage. 'I am not really a nanny. I finished university in June and I am just filling in for the summer before I begin my career as a research chemist for the government in October.' Blue eyes flashing angrily, she glanced back up at Gianni—no, not Gianni, she reminded herself, but Count Gianfranco Maldini. The arrogance, the conniving, lying cheek of the man was unbelievable.

'I think it is so important to be truthful about such things straight away, to avoid any misconceptions later. Don't you agree, Count Maldini?' Kelly drawled his name as she asked the question in a voice laced with bitter sarcasm. She was not having these tinpot aristocrats patronising her.

His tanned face flushed dark with embarrassment, or was it rage? For a second she thought she had gone too far. His brown eyes narrowed on her face, hard as jet, but when he spoke he was all suave charm. 'Yes, of course, Kelly, you are right.'

Out of the corner of her eye she saw Judy flash her an angry look before saying something to Olivia in Italian. Probably apologising for her nanny's bad manners, Kelly thought as rage bubbled inside her.

'But in some situations there is no time for the truth to be heard.' Gianfranco's mouth twisted in a wry self-mocking smile at her obvious anger.

What had he expected? He had been so surprised to see Kelly that he had gone along with her obvious wish to pretend she did not know him. A horrendous mistake; he should have admitted straight away he knew her. Hell! Who was he kidding? He should have told her from the outset who he really was, certainly before he had taken her to bed… It was hardly surprising she was furious. But now was not the time or the place to try and explain.

'Excuse us, we have to take our seats now, but perhaps later…' Gianfranco addressed his words to Judy Bertoni '…you and Kelly would like to join us for a late meal?'

Kelly stiffened and, freed from the tension of his dark gaze, she shivered at the thought of spending one more moment in his company. She saw Judy open her mouth and accept, and her worst fear was realised.

There was no way Kelly could eat and drink with this man. The more she looked at him, the more she realised the depths of his deception. The aura of dynamic power and status was glaringly evident. This man was a stranger to her…

She recalled the first day, when he had introduced himself as Gianfranco and she had called him Signor Franco. A laugh and a simple explanation and the last week would never have happened.

Kelly took a deep breath, reminding herself wryly that

she was an adult woman and not a stupid teenager any more. The signs had been there for her to see; the fact that love had blinded her was really her own fault. She lifted her head and discovered to her amazement that rescue had come from the most unexpected source.

'Olivia is right.' Judy was talking to Count Maldini. 'Much as we would have enjoyed joining your party later, I must refuse. My husband is still in great pain. But as he insisted I did not miss the gala tonight, the least I can do is get back to his side as quickly as possible.'

'But of course,' Count Maldini agreed. 'Another time, perhaps.'

Suddenly everyone was making for his or her seat, and Kelly sank back down in her own as the orchestra began to tune up.

'Bitch,' Judy whispered in an aside to Kelly.

'What?' Kelly asked. 'What did I…?'

'No, not you, silly! Olivia Maldini. I told her about Carlo's accident and she immediately implied I should be at home looking after him—her way of making sure I refused the invitation to join their party. Ever since her husband died three years ago…' Judy flashed Kelly an old-fashioned glance '…it has been rumoured she would not be averse to marrying his younger brother. She obviously saw you and me as competition. Mind you, I don't think she will succeed. Gianfranco dates some of…a lot of,' she amended with a knowing grin, 'the most beautiful women in the world. I can't see him settling for one alone, and, though his sister-in-law is OK, she is nothing special.'

With a kind of sick fascination Kelly watched as Gianfranco's party took their seats in the front row. She was numb; she hardly dared breathe because she knew the pain was waiting for her…

Afterwards Kelly did not remember a single scene from the opera *Don Giovanni*.

She heard Judy's voice as if from a distance.

'Hurry, Kelly. We might catch the count on the way out. I want to invite him to dinner. It might help Carlo clinch his business deal with the man.' Judy leapt to her feet.

Kelly had no desire ever to speak to the count again, and in a desperate attempt to delay she deliberately dropped her purse on the floor. Ducking down, she scraped around on the floor, pretending she had lost something, and when she finally straightened up the Maldini party had left and Judy was spitting nails.

Kelly thought her ordeal was over, but no such luck. By the time they got back to the villa Judy had got over her bad temper, and, after discovering her husband was already in bed and asleep, insisted Kelly share a nightcap with her. She proceeded to regale Kelly with every last bit of information she knew about the count.

'Actually, I think I still have the magazine from last year when the count allowed them to do a ten-page spread on his lifestyle. But only on condition they made a large donation to a town on the edge of the River Poe that was almost buried in a landslide.'

It was pure torture for Kelly. She drained her glass of wine, and for the first time in her life wished she could drink a whole bottle and block out the horror of the evening.

But when Judy returned, and spread a well-known Italian magazine on the table and began pointing out the various pictures, it got even worse. Kelly looked at the pictures with sick humiliation almost choking her.

The enormous family home in the heart of the countryside, the New York and the Rome apartments, the ocean-going yacht at Genoa harbour. But what finally broke

Kelly's heart was the picture of what was called a hunting lodge on a hillside above Lake Garda.

She recognised it. The house where he had taken her last Friday—the house he had told her belonged to the company he worked for. As if that was not enough to convince her, the last picture was of Gianni sitting astride his motor bike, apparently talking to a man with a gun bent over his arm—the security guard.

Her whole body clenched in pain, nausea knotting her stomach. The same man who had found them almost naked at the lakeside last week; the same man Gianni had spoken to. While she had thought they were in trouble for trespassing Gianni must have been laughing like a drain at how easily he had fooled her.

'Are you all right?' Judy asked, suddenly noticing Kelly's long silence.

'I feel a bit sick; probably the wine. I think I'll go to bed.' And she ran.

CHAPTER FOUR

SICK at heart, Kelly stripped off her clothes and stepped into the shower. She turned the water on and stood under the soothing spray, her tears mingling with the water. God, what a disaster of a night! A disaster of a week!

She should have known meeting the man of her dreams was too good to be true.

She should have gone with her first impression on seeing Gianni. A man up to no good. She had got that right! He was a lying, deceitful pig.

Kelly sighed. Knowing the truth did not make the pain go away. It hurt, it really hurt, and she had no one to blame but herself. She had allowed herself to succumb to his surface looks and charm, while he had simply been slumming it for a few days. No wonder he had been horrified when he'd discovered she was a virgin and the possibility of pregnancy was a real threat. His anger at the time, and his crack about a paternity suit, made perfect sense now. If or when Count Maldini married it would be to some suitably wealthy well-connected Italian girl, not some unknown orphan like Kelly.

Turning off the shower, she stepped out and took a large towel off the rail, and briskly rubbed herself dry. She was bone tired, her head ached, and all she wanted to do was sleep. She dropped the towel on the floor and walked into the bedroom. She slipped, naked, into bed. But sleep was a long time in coming.

Every time she closed her eyes she saw the image of Gianni... No, not Gianni...Count Gianfranco Maldini, she kept reminding herself, and when she had reminded herself for the hundredth time of his cruel deceit she finally cried herself to sleep.

At seven the following morning a wide-awake, laughing Andrea jumped on Kelly's bed. Bleary-eyed, she surveyed the little boy, and with a wry smile dragged herself out of bed. Experience told her that his parents would not be up for an hour or so yet, and after bathing and dressing Andrea and herself she made her way downstairs to the kitchen.

Fifteen minutes later she sat at the table watching Andrea with an indulgent smile. He was a lovely little boy who, after devouring a bowl of cereal and a glass of orange juice, was intent on tearing a bread roll into the shape of some mythical beast as shown on the cereal packet. His innocent enjoyment of something so simple put her own problems into some kind of perspective.

So she had allowed herself to be sweet-talked into bed by a devious man out for a bit of fun. She was not the first woman in the world to fall for the charms of a sophisticated male on the make, and she would certainly not be the last. Chalk it up to experience and get on with life, she told herself firmly.

Picking up her coffee-cup, she drained it and placed it back on the table. There was about as much chance of Count Gianfranco Maldini ringing her as the Pope marrying, she thought wryly. But in that she was to be proved wrong…

'Right, young man.' She rose to her feet. 'How about…?' But the ringing of the telephone prevented her continuing. 'OK, Andrea, stay there a minute.' Crossing the room to the wall-mounted telephone, she lifted the receiver to her ear.

'*Pronto.*' She gave the conventional greeting.

'Kelly? Kelly, is that you?' There was no mistaking the rich, deep tone of Gianfranco Maldini.

Shock kept her silent for a moment, and her first thought was to hang up, but then anger came to her aid. 'Yes,' she snapped. 'Who is it calling, please, and to whom do you wish to speak?' she asked facetiously.

'Gianfranco, and to you, of course,' his deep voice drawled huskily. 'Look, Kelly, I can understand why you are angry, but please believe me, I meant to tell you—'

'At least you are using your real name,' she cut in bitterly. 'I suppose I should be grateful, but you know, for some strange reason I am not. It might have something to do with the fact I went to bed with a stranger, or maybe just an old-fashioned idea of believing in the truth—something you obviously know nothing about.' Her knuckles gleamed white on the hand that gripped the receiver. She was furious, and amazed he had the nerve to call her.

'Listen to me, Kelly,' Gianfranco demanded harshly; her last crack was an insult he would not accept. No one had ever questioned his honesty before. 'I never had any intention to deceive you. The first day we met I tried to tell you my name and you, in your usual manner, leapt in with "Hello, Signor Franco." You jump to conclusions like a bull at a gate.'

'Oh, I see! So it is my fault. In a whole week you could not get around to telling me you were not a port worker but Count Gianfranco Maldini. I wonder why? Could it possibly be because you were ashamed of mixing with ordinary people, you arrogant snob?' She was on a roll. From the minute last night when she had discovered who her so-called boyfriend really was, she had swung between hurt and humiliation, but now she was just plain angry. 'Suddenly all the little out-of-the-way places you took me make perfect sense. And of course how could I forget your horror that I was not some vastly experienced woman? And your desperate worry I might slap a paternity suit on you.'

'No,' he snapped. 'Now stop right there.' The sheer force of his voice in her ear made Kelly do just that. 'I am trying to be reasonable, but you are not making it easy for me. I apologise for misleading you about my name, but that is all I apologise for. Last night I was quite prepared to acknowledge we were friends, but you jumped in again and made it very obvious you did not want me to. I followed your lead because I thought that was what you wanted.'

He was right, but the 'friend' rankled. 'Maybe so. But it does not alter the fact you deceived me about who you really were.' She had to battle to retain her anger as the sound of his voice alone made her go weak at the knees.

'Maybe, but I am the same Gianni you dated, the same Gianni who wants to see you again on Friday.'

He still wanted to see her; the thought floored her for a moment. 'But you're a count.'

'So now who is being the snob?' Gianfranco drawled mockingly. 'If I don't care, why should you?'

A glimmer of hope flickered in her heart, and for a second she considered the possibility. Then common sense prevailed.

'Kelly? Kelly, are you still there?' Gianfranco asked urgently.

'Yes,' she responded, hardening her heart against him. 'And where are you calling from?' she demanded in a tone laced with sarcasm. 'Genoa—isn't that where you were supposed to be visiting? Yet I could have sworn I saw you in Verona last night.'

'Sarcasm does not become you, Kelly. I know I made a mistake; when I see you again I will explain everything. But I can't talk now. I have a flight to catch to New York, a flight I delayed for a week to be with you. Surely that must count for something?' Gianfranco Maldini could not believe what he was saying. He was virtually pleading with the girl for a date.

'Then don't let me delay you any further.' It was no good prolonging the agony; Judy had told her about his countless girlfriends, and, even if she could fit into his lifestyle, Kelly did not want to. Eventually she wanted marriage and a husband, not to be a rich man's plaything for a few weeks.

Gianfranco cleared his throat. 'Will you still meet me on Friday as we arranged?' And he held his breath as he waited for her answer.

'No,' Kelly said flatly. 'The more I think about it I realise that last Friday was a disaster. Personally, I am going to put it down to experience and forget we ever met; I suggest you do the same.' She glanced across at Andrea; he had put down the bread and was wriggling uncomfortably in his high chair.

'*Dio!* Kelly?' Gianfranco's patience snapped. His ego had taken enough bruising from this woman, and it did not help to be reminded he'd been a failure in bed. 'You be there on Friday, or I will be around at Bertoni's to get you. Understand?' he shouted. He was not used to having his commands disobeyed.

Andrea was watching her with an open mouth and worried brown eyes; he had never heard her angry before, and, though she doubted he understood the words, he could sense something was wrong, and he did not deserve to be upset.

'Yes, OK.' She hung up the telephone. When pigs fly, she thought, moving to lift the young boy from his chair and hugging him tightly to her; she nuzzled his neck while blinking a stray tear from her eye.

Gianfranco slipped the telephone into the inside pocket of his expertly tailored jacket, and strode across the concourse to the boarding gate for his flight. It was a new experience for him to have to persuade a woman to see him, and one he was not sure he liked. His hard mouth twisted in a wry grimace. He'd give it one more try. If Kelly turned up on Friday night, fine. If she didn't he was not pursuing her. His decision made, he handed his boarding pass to the female attendant with a broad smile, and quite unconsciously made the girl's day.

'Who was that on the telephone?' Judy asked as she walked into the kitchen, wearing only a blue satin robe.

'It was for me,' Kelly mumbled as she held Andrea in her arms.

'Ah, the boyfriend,' Judy said, and, moving to where Kelly stood, took Andrea from her. 'And this is my favourite boyfriend.' She kissed her son good morning, then placed him on his feet on the floor.

Kelly smiled; whatever Judy's faults, she did love her son.

'It's no good hanging around with a silly smile on your face, Kelly,' said Judy, totally misinterpreting the reason for the smile. 'Take my advice and drop the local boy. You are a good-looking woman—you should set your sights a whole lot higher. Go after someone like Count Maldini, a real catch. Last night I could see he was interested—yours was the only hand he kissed,' Judy opined with a sigh. 'But then, even if you got him, keeping him would be the problem.' Picking up a cup, she filled it with coffee from the pot and walked out with the comment, 'For Carlo, poor dear; he is feeling very sorry for himself this morning.'

Judy's comment gave Kelly pause for thought. She was intelligent, educated and considered herself as good as any other person on the planet. Gianfranco was a count. So what? Perhaps she had overreacted. He had called this morning, as promised. He did still want to see her and explain—well, according to him anyway. Surely he deserved a hearing, or was she the inverted snob he had intimated?

By the next morning Kelly had reached a decision: she would meet Gianfranco on Friday and hear what he had to say…

On Thursday afternoon Kelly was sitting on a plane winging its way back to England, glad to be going home and back to reality. On Tuesday Carlo Bertoni had declared there was no point staying in Italy any longer, since, as he could not compete in the yacht race, he might as well get back to work in London. Generously he had suggested Kelly stay on, on holiday, until the end of her contract in ten days' time. Marta was staying that long anyway, and Kelly had immediately accepted his offer.

But on Wednesday morning she had been leafing through the pages of the national newspaper and seen a picture of Count Maldini taken at a reception in New York on the Monday evening, with a stunning-looking redhead on his arm. Kelly had been able to fool herself no more; the affair, fling, was over, and there was no point in deluding herself otherwise. It was time she cut loose any connection whatsoever with Count Maldini.

On Thursday evening she said goodbye to the Bertoni family at Heathrow Airport. They were heading for their London townhouse and Kelly was heading for her family home: a small three-bedroom house in a quiet area of Bournemouth.

'Pregnant,' the doctor declared, and Kelly groaned. Her periods had always been irregular, and she had not been sick or dizzy, or had any of the complaints usually connected with pregnancy. She had felt lousy in general, but she had put that down to crying herself to sleep most nights over Gianfranco. It had only been a month ago, when she'd realised she could not fasten her jeans, that she'd been brave enough to check dates. It was only what she had feared for the last four weeks, but to hear Dr Jones confirm it was still a shock.

'You really should have seen me a lot sooner, Kelly. Still, no harm done, you're remarkably fit. I gather there is no father on the horizon?' he prompted gently. He had known the young girl before him all her life, he watched her mother die in childbirth, and her father die of cancer, and now this. 'By the date you gave me, you are thirteen weeks pregnant.'

'Yes, that would be right. Thank you, Dr Jones.' Kelly exited the surgery, clasping a card in her hand for her first ante-natal appointment.

Sitting in the coffee shop of the largest department store in Bournemouth, gazing dazedly at the Christmas decorations, Kelly was sure things could not get worse. But they did.

Judy Bertoni appeared out of nowhere. Apparently she was visiting her parents for the day. Kelly cursed the fact she had taken off her coat and hung it on the stand provided, and spent the next half-hour wondering how she could leave without revealing when she stood up that she had filled out somewhat. The jersey wool tube skirt and matching sweater did nothing to disguise it. Eventually she had no option but to get up, as one of the side-effects of her pregnancy was a constant desire to visit the bathroom.

Eagle-eyed, figure-conscious Judy noticed immediately, and Kelly was subjected to a long speech on the inadvisability of dating a local Italian boy, and 'I told you so'.

Kelly was sorely tempted to blurt out who the father was, but managed to restrain herself. Judy, in her Mother Teresa act, promised she would keep in touch and send her Andrea's cast-offs. Kelly should have been grateful, but she wasn't; she felt sick and fat and fed-up.

She was even fatter and more fed-up when she returned from work at six on a cold Friday night in January. After a refreshing shower, and a meal of chicken and chips, she finally settled down on the sofa, prepared to spend the evening relaxing. With a Mozart tape in her Walkman, she held the earplugs to her stomach. She had read somewhere that music was good for the unborn baby and she hoped it was true.

The doorbell rang.

'Sugar!' she exclaimed, and, hauling herself up off the sofa, moved slowly to the door. It was probably Margaret. Since the house next door had been sold while Kelly had been in Italy, her new neighbour—a middle-aged spinster with an elderly mother who suffered from Alzheimer's and a bachelor brother, Jim, to look after—had taken to calling on Kelly. She hadn't the heart to turn the woman away.

'Just coming,' Kelly called as the doorbell rang again, longer and louder. 'Where's the fire?' she muttered under her breath, and opened the front door.

'Do you usually open the door without first enquiring who it is?' Gianfranco queried with a frown of grim disapproval creasing his broad brow.

In the first second of recognition her blue eyes widened, her heart leaping with joy, but instantly reality intruded. She'd tried to tell herself she was over him, had put him out of her mind and her heart. But seeing him before her, looking as rakishly handsome as ever, with a camel cashmere overcoat worn over a perfectly tailored dark business suit, his black hair rumpled by the winter wind, she knew she was not.

'What's it to you?' she snapped, angry at her own weakness where this man was concerned. At the same time she wished she were wearing something more glamorous.

Gianfranco's dark eyes swept over her face, taking in the tumbled mass of fine blonde hair, the slight blue shadows beneath her magnificent sapphire eyes, the beauty of her face not withstanding her belligerent expression. She did not look delighted to see him, and, lowering his gaze to where her breasts pressed firm against the soft blue wool of her sweater, and lower still to where the garment stretched over the soft mound of her stomach, he knew why. So it was true… He took a deep steadying breath.

'Your protection is everything to me—you are the mother of my baby,' Gianfranco declared firmly as he stepped into the hall and closed the door behind him.

What little colour she had drained from Kelly's face, and her blue eyes widened to their fullest extent as she gazed up in pure shock at the man towering over her. Gianfranco here, in her home, and he knew she was having his baby… 'But…how…?' She swayed, suddenly feeling faint, and could not get the sentence out, a host of different emotions tangling her tongue.

'Come, let's sit down.' Gianfranco grabbed her arm. 'It can't be good for you standing in a cold hall in your condition.' He unerringly led her into the sitting room of her own home.

'Now wait a minute,' she finally managed, shakily finding her voice.

'I think we have waited rather too many minutes—months, in fact,' he teased, his dark eyes roaming pointedly down to her stomach and back to her face as he led her to the sofa and eased her down into it, lowering his long length beside her and taking her hand in one of his.

The closeness of his large male body, the familiar male scent that was uniquely Gianfranco, all conspired to make her heart race. A dull red flush suffused her cheeks. It wasn't fair; he only had to touch her and, even fat and pregnant, she still felt the same instant sensual response, every hair on her body standing on end.

'How did you find me—and how did you know I was pregnant?' Kelly asked the question she should have asked the minute he walked in the door, looking somewhere over his left shoulder, unwilling to meet his knowing brown eyes. The fact he had accepted the baby she was carrying was his, without her having to say a word, had totally stunned her.

Gianfranco was not the sort of man to do anything without a reason, and she could think of no valid reason for his being here. He had made his opinion of unwanted pregnancy abundantly clear the one time they had made love. In her secret dreams she had sometimes thought of him turning up on her doorstep and declaring his undying love. But harsh reality told her he was much more likely to take one look at her, perhaps give her a cheque and definitely run.

'I was at a New Year's Eve party in Rome. Judy Bertoni was there and naturally I asked after you. She took great delight in telling me you had succumbed to the charms of some local man in Desenzano and that you are pregnant,' he told her simply. He saw no need to elaborate on the bare facts.

'You didn't tell her it was you?' Kelly asked hastily. The fewer people who knew what an idiot she had been the better, was her reasoning.

One dark brow arched sardonically. 'I am not a complete

fool, Kelly, I knew I had to check with you first. But it took all my considerable will-power not to ask her for your address,' Gianfranco said with a grim smile. 'Instead I hired a private detective to discover where you lived.' He gave a very Latin shrug of his shoulders. 'And here I am.' He squeezed her hand in his.

Kelly's blue eyes involuntarily followed the movement of his broad shoulders, and swallowed hard. He really was a magnificent male animal, and very much here… Not for her, she tried to tell herself, but her raging hormones thought otherwise.

'You tracked me down?' She latched on to the detective bit, amazed at the nerve of the man. 'Do you do that with all your dates?' she demanded curtly, not sure she liked the idea but helplessly flustered by the sensual warmth of his hand holding hers. Was it only she who felt the electric tension in the air? she wondered, chewing nervously on her bottom lip. Though, on second thoughts, she couldn't help feeling flattered that he had hired a detective to find her, but she was also wary—she didn't trust him an inch.

'So why are you here?' she demanded bravely, tilting her head to look up at him, and the gleam of triumph in his dark eyes sent a shiver down her spine. Suddenly she had a horrible suspicion she knew the answer to her own question, and she immediately voiced her fear. 'If you think I am going to have an abortion, forget it!' she declared, her blue eyes flashing flames. 'This is my child, my responsibility, and you can get lost.'

'*Dio!* Jumping to conclusions as usual.' Gianfranco leapt to his feet and stormed across the small living room. Tearing off his topcoat, he flung it on a chair and flipped open his jacket; he was boiling with rage. He had been ever since, after months of fighting his desire for Kelly, he had succumbed to the temptation to seek out Judy Bertoni and ask after her. With relish Judy had told him Kelly was pregnant by some local Italian youth. Of course, he had known immediately he was the father, and when he had got over the initial shock he had been furious that Kelly had not told him herself.

'How dare you say that to me?' he demanded arrogantly. She saw the naked anger flare in his eyes, and something more she did not recognise. 'To suggest I would wish to kill my own child? What kind of monster do you take me for? What did I ever do to you to give you such a low opinion of me?'

'Pretend to be someone else,' Kelly slipped in snidely.

He stilled in the middle of the floor, his broad shoulders tensing, and said, 'So I am to pay for that one silly mistake for the rest of my life. Is that why you never saw fit to inform me you were having my child?' he asked hardly, his hooded eyes half-closed, masking his expression. 'Is that why you never turned up for our date on the Friday evening?' With each question he moved a step closer. 'Is that why you now accuse me of wanting to murder my child?' Gianfranco asked bitterly, his dark eyes flaring with contempt. 'Pay-back time on your part? My God, I thought better of you than that, Kelly.'

'You actually kept our date?' She was staggered by his revelation, her brief burst of anger draining away as she accepted the thought; it pleased her enormously, and restored some of her battered pride. She had spent the last few months in abject misery because of this man. At the lowest point, when her pregnancy had been confirmed, she had been tempted to call him, but she only had to recall his horror the one time they had made love and he'd discovered she was not protected to know it would be a waste of time. But he was obviously not the complete bastard she had thought him.

Gianfranco focused on her seated figure with a blistering fury that seemed to increase with each word he spoke. 'Kept it? I waited all night and drank myself into oblivion. And where were you? Marta the housekeeper told me the next day. Back home in England after refusing a free holiday. That's how much you cared.'

As the meaning of his outburst hit her Kelly could only stare at him open-mouthed. He actually had cared about her. The notion was as startling as it was seductive.

'Nothing to say? I am not surprised,' Gianfranco drawled with savage derision. 'You used me, got yourself pregnant and came scurrying back to England without the least intention of ever telling me.'

'No. It wasn't like that,' Kelly burst out impulsively. 'I was going to meet you on the Friday, but…' She trailed off, nervously moistening her dry lips with the tip of her tongue.

Gianfranco's black brows arched in surprise. The Kelly he remembered had been bluntly honest, to the point of indiscretion. He drew a steadying breath, banking down his anger, and his eyes narrowing on her lovely face, he took a step towards her. 'But what, Kelly…?' he prompted silkily, and in another stride he had crossed the space dividing them and settled on the sofa next to her. He reached out and caught her by the shoulders, gently urged her back against the soft cushions. 'Tell me…' Anger would get him nowhere with Kelly, she had too much spirit, but a little judicious questioning should do the trick.

Gianfranco's brilliant eyes clashed with hers and her breath caught in her throat, his proximity doing unimaginable things to her nervous system. 'I…I…' Kelly stammered to a halt, embarrassed by what she had almost revealed.

'Go on,' he encouraged, his dark eyes burning into hers with mesmerising effect.

Why not tell him? She was no good at dissembling anyway. 'On the Wednesday I saw a picture of you and your latest girlfriend—a very beautiful redhead—taken two nights before in New York, in the newspaper,' she confessed bluntly. 'There did not seem much point after that.'

Her response stunned him. He drew back slightly, and looked down at her with incredulous eyes for a long moment. 'You were jealous...' he declared, and for the first time in months his firm lips parted over gleaming white teeth in a broad self-satisfied smile.

'I was not,' she denied adamantly, but the scarlet blush that enveloped her face told its own story.

Gianfranco's hand slipped from her shoulder to encircle her waist and pull her towards him, his night-dark eyes never leaving hers for a second. 'No matter,' he murmured in a low-pitched undertone, and covered her lips with his own in a long, slow, sensual kiss that drove every sensible thought from Kelly's mind, and ignited the familiar electrifying sensations in every part of her body.

Dazed and breathless when he finally lifted his head, she could only stare at him in bemusement. 'Why did you do that?' she murmured.

Gianfranco eased her back against the cushions, lifted a large hand, and rested the tip of a finger against the pulse beating madly in her throat. 'To prove you still want me,' he drawled huskily. 'An essential prerequisite in a wife.' Cupping her chin, he added, 'And we are going to be married, Kelly.'

On seeking out Kelly, Gianfranco had told himself he simply wanted to check up on her and make sure she was financially provided for. He was as surprised as Kelly looked to hear the offer of marriage come out of his mouth.

But the more he thought about it, the more sense it made. His mother would be delighted—she was always nagging him to marry, and produce an heir. With Kelly already pregnant there could be no doubt of the girl's fertility, unlike poor Olivia. Yes, it was the right decision.

Kelly stared at him blankly, unable to believe her ears, and, leaning over her, his breath fanning her cheek, he slipped a hand under her legs and suddenly she was stretched out on the sofa.

'Wait.' She tried to object, but the word 'marriage' had shocked her rigid.

Gianfranco lifted his head, a wide, confident smile parting his lips. 'We have both waited long enough, Kelly.' And then he kissed her again.

She wanted to resist, and she did try—she lifted her hands to his chest to push him away, but feeling the firm beat of his heart beneath her fingertips had the opposite effect, and of their own volition her hands snaked up to clasp around his neck. Her lips parted, her tongue duelling with his instinctively in a desperate hunger of passion too long denied.

His hand slipped under her sweater to curve over the full mound of her breast, and she quivered, heat surging through her veins. Pressed against the awesome male body, she forgot everything but the feel, the scent of him. She ached for him.

Gianfranco groaned, raised his head, and with one deft movement pushed her jumper up so her lush, unfettered breasts were open to his gaze. '*Dio*, I love your breasts.' Black eyes glittering, he ran an exploring finger over the pouting rosy tips, and her whole body arched in shivering delight. His dark head lowered and his mouth closed over a rigid peak.

'Gianfranco.' Kelly moaned his name in a pleasure that was almost pain.

His head jerked up, eyes clashing with hers. 'Did I hurt you? The baby, is it safe?'

CHAPTER FIVE

THE baby! It was like a douche of cold water on her overheated flesh. Struggling to sit up, she pushed at his mighty chest. 'Get off me.'

Gianfranco reared back and, lifting her into a sitting position, smoothed her sweater down over her breasts. 'I promised myself I would not jump on you, Kelly, but I only have to look at you to want you,' he said huskily. 'Even with this glorious bump.' One large hand spread out over her stomach, and right at that moment the baby kicked. 'It moved,' he declared, his dark eyes fixed on her stomach in rapt fascination. 'I can't wait till we are married and I can look after you both properly.' He lifted his head. 'I didn't hurt you or the baby?' His gleaming eyes sought hers for reassurance.

'No, no, you didn't,' Kelly said stiltedly. She could not lie to him, but neither was she going to let him walk all over her. It was the sheer conceit of the man that angered Kelly. She hadn't seen him for almost five months, and he strolled back into her life and offered marriage as if he was doing her a favour. 'As for marriage—that will not be necessary,' she told him bluntly.

He did not want her; it was only the child he was interested in. And, getting to her feet, she glanced down at where he sat, the look of puzzled outrage in his dark eyes enough to make her want to laugh. 'I can do without your noble gesture—I am perfectly capable of looking after my own child,' she said sweetly. 'Now, would you like a coffee before you leave?' she offered.

Before she could move, Gianfranco leapt to his feet, his hands grasping her shoulders.

'What the hell are you talking about, Kelly? Noble? I am not noble—I haven't a noble bone in my body.'

'I thought all "counts" were noblemen, or supposed to be,' she prompted mockingly.

He paused, his hard mouth curving in a bitter, cynical smile. 'So that is what is bothering you—the fact I have a title. I should have guessed you would be the opposite of most women of my acquaintance, who love the idea.' His hands tightened on her shoulders, his brown eyes clashing with her blue ones, and her heart gave a curious lurch at the glittering intensity of his gaze.

'I never wanted nor ever expected to have a title—that was my brother's birthright. But three years ago he was killed in a yachting accident and the title was thrust upon me. Do you really think I enjoyed giving up my freewheeling lifestyle working in the financial markets of the world to take on the burden of the family estates as well, to have to work twice as hard with twice as much responsibility?' he spelt out grimly. 'The day I met you was the first time in three years I had taken a weekend off, and the first time I had been back to Desenzano since my brother's death.'

'Why are you telling me all this now?' she asked, intensely aware of his hard male body towering over her, his long fingers kneading her slender shoulders, as if he would force her to listen.

'Because the minute I saw you, so beautiful, so carefree, I decided to forget about everything and give myself a holiday and try to get to know you. So, yes, you are right in a way, I should have told you who I was, but for once I simply wanted to enjoy myself; is that so hard to understand?'

Kelly had never coveted wealth. She enjoyed her life,

and as long as she had enough to get by on she was quite happy, but she could understand great wealth must bring with it great responsibilities. 'Yes, I suppose so.' The thought that he thought she was beautiful was balm to her bruised heart, and slowly she was recovering from the shock of seeing him again. 'But marriage?' That was something else again, she thought, unaware she had voiced that thought out loud.

'Yes, Kelly,' Gianfranco cut in, pulling her closer to the hard heat of his body. 'You will marry me, and have my child. I have not spent the last few months going crazy over a blonde-haired little spitfire to be turned down now.'

He smoothed a possessive hand over her quivering length, lingering on her stomach. 'You are mine, and this baby is mine,' he husked quietly, and smiled.

How did he do that? One minute he was all outraged predatory male and moments later he was smiling tenderly into her guarded blue eyes. 'Yes,' she murmured, thinking, in her confused state, he was asking if the baby was his.

His dark head lowered and he let his tongue trace the fullness of her lips before delving into the moist depths. His hand slid down her back to the base of her spine, moving against her in a way that made her blatantly aware of his arousal.

Kelly tried to remain rigid in his embrace, but her body softened against the hard heat of Gianfranco's massive frame.

'You want me, and I want you; what more is there to say?' He breathed the words against her mouth and softly to her throat and ear, then back once more to her pouting lips. He nudged her lips apart again and dipped into her mouth with his tongue, in a rhythm that made a moan rise in her throat.

'Gianni,' she gasped helplessly, but she retained enough

common sense to know he was deliberately trying to seduce her.

He felt her tremble and loved her reaction. 'You called me Gianni; you have not forgotten.' He groaned with feeling against her mouth, scanning her with glittering eyes filled with hunger and something more. He stared down into her dazed yet wary eyes and he wanted to take her there and then, his body screaming for release. Instead he drew in a steadying breath and eased her to arm's length. 'Perhaps a drink is in order, but not coffee—I need something stronger,' he opined bluntly.

Kelly heard the faint humour in his tone and smiled. He sounded like a man sorely tried. 'I think I can oblige. There is half a bottle of whisky left over from Christmas in the kitchen. Have a seat and I'll get it.'

She badly needed to put some space between them. He was right about her wanting him. She did, always had since the first moment she'd set eyes on him. Gianni or Gianfranco, it didn't matter; he was the man she loved, she acknowledged as she walked into the kitchen on shaking legs. If she was honest with herself, Gianfranco's surprising offer of marriage was more than she had ever hoped for, and it was very tempting. She opened a cupboard and withdrew the bottle of amber nectar.

A few minutes later she walked back into the living room, with a tray bearing a glass of whisky and a glass of milk. A quick glance and she saw Gianfranco was leaning against the mantelpiece, one hand fingering the silver-framed photograph of a couple with their arms around each other. His eyes caught hers before she could look away. 'Your parents?' He indicated the picture. 'I never thought to ask…where are they?'

'Both dead,' she said softly.

'So you are alone in the world,' he declared grimly. In

one lithe stride he was beside her, and, taking the tray from her hands, he placed it on the coffee table. Straightening up, he handed her the glass of milk. 'You should not carry anything in your condition.'

His fingers brushed hers as she took the glass, sending a tingling sensation up her arm. Their eyes met, his dark and knowing, hers guarded. 'I'm not ill, only pregnant,' she said drily. 'I'm still at work,' she tagged on, sinking down into a convenient armchair with a sigh. She was also tired and emotionally confused, but she had no intention of telling Gianfranco. Instead she lifted the glass to her mouth and took a long swallow of the cool creamy liquid.

'You still work!' he exclaimed, and stared at her as if she had gone mad. 'That's it.' Gianfranco drained his glass of whisky in one gulp, banged it down on the table, and turned to frown down at her. He had flown to England angry, not sure what he was going to do about Kelly, but one look at her and he had heard himself asking her to marry him. Thank God he had. It appalled him to realise she was alone in the world, and it also brought home to him how little he really knew about her. Well, all that had to change, he decided in his usual arrogant manner.

'As I remember, you were going to work as a research chemist.' His dark brows drew together in a thunderous frown. 'That is out. There is no way you should be anywhere near a laboratory—you could catch anything, do untold damage to our child.'

Her head tilted back, her blue eyes lifting to his, and what she saw made her suck in her breath—he was deadly serious. 'But…'

'No buts. You will resign tomorrow—in fact, I will do it for you.'

'Now wait just a minute…'

'No. On this I will not budge. As my wife, you are not working in a laboratory.'

'Gianfranco, really, it is the twenty-first century—women work all through their pregnancy at all sorts of jobs. Some go back three months after the child is born.'

'Not you,' he declared adamantly.

She could argue, she reasoned, but somehow she didn't want to. There was something very seductive about having a man take charge.

'You are not going to argue?' One dark brow arched in puzzlement as she watched and she almost giggled. He was standing over her, his great body taut with tension.

'Do you want me to?' she asked softly. Incredible as it seemed, she was beginning to think that perhaps there was some hope for them. She loved him, she was carrying his child, and he wanted to marry her. Common sense told her at least to listen.

'No. Oh, no. Kelly.' To her astonishment, he dropped to his knees at her feet.

He caught her hand and turned it over in his much larger one. 'I know our relationship got off to a rocky start,' he said, picking his words with care. 'I know this is not the ideal situation to find ourselves in. But know this, Kelly.' His rough, deep voice was thick with some overwhelming emotion. 'I really do want to marry you, child or no child, the sooner the better.'

Kelly trembled as Gianfranco lifted her hand to his lips and pressed a tender kiss into her palm, before raising his head, his gaze roaming over her beautiful face. There was no mistaking the sincerity, the simmering passion in the deep brown eyes that finally met hers.

'Kelly, my love, give me a second chance.' He took a deep, rasping breath. 'I don't want to rush you into anything you don't want, but marry me soon,' he pleaded huskily. 'You know it makes sense.'

Kelly wasn't aware she was giving him a second chance, she thought muzzily, but, as his arms drifted around her again and pulled her gently into the warmth of his embrace, she didn't resist. She could not. His dark head lowered and his lips found hers. This was where the last hour had been leading; this was what she had been afraid of. She was incapable of controlling her own response. Why deny it, she asked herself with a flash of insight, when she wanted him so much? Her senses were swimming with pleasure, her mouth clinging to his as he held her tightly against him, his tongue darting between her lips, exploring her mouth with an urgent passion.

'*Dio*, you feel so good. You don't know what you do to me, *cara*.' His deep voice shook as he eased her slightly away from him. 'Say yes, Kelly.'

For months she had been telling herself she would be fine as a single parent. But was she being fair to her unborn child? Kelly asked herself, studying Gianfranco's handsome face with brilliant blue eyes. Now she had a choice; he was offering marriage, and two parents must be better than one. It was no contest because, dear heaven, she loved him.

Instead of the 'yes' that trembled on her lips Kelly heard herself ask, 'Who was the redhead?'

'Natalie. The wife of an American cousin of mine. Her husband was in the Far East on business and I deputised for him at the charity dinner,' he explained huskily. 'Only at the dinner, I swear.'

For a long moment she stared into his incredible eyes, and she believed him. 'In that case…' She reached her arms around his neck, urging him back to her, 'Yes, oh, yes.' Her long lashes fluttered down over her brilliant blue eyes, her fingers tangling in the silky black hair of his head, her lips blindly seeking his again.

She never saw the flare of triumph in his night-dark eyes as he gathered her close and kissed her long and slow, and when she finally opened her eyes she gazed up at him, totally enslaved all over again.

'You have made me the happiest man alive.'

'Happiest man…' she murmured, floating in a sensuous bubble. 'Are you sure you want to marry me?' She had to ask. It was like a dream, and she wanted to pinch herself to make sure it was true.

'I have never wanted anything more in my life, except perhaps tonight I want to make love to you, as I should have done the first time. Long and slow, very slow.'

'Sounds good,' she sighed, and tightened her hands behind his head.

'No, not here—the bedroom.' And, lifting her in his arms, he carried her out of the room, up the stairs, and without hesitation walked into the first bedroom he came to. One glance at the double bed and Gianfranco wanted to lay her down on it. But he forced himself to lower Kelly slowly to her feet.

As if waking from a dream, Kelly stood in the middle of the floor and looked up. Gianfranco was towering over her, his arms linked loosely around her waist. His eyes, dark with desire, roamed over her small frame, but when his hands reached for the bottom of her sweater she froze.

Suddenly she was terribly conscious of her altered physical state. 'No,' Kelly whispered and grasped his hands with hers. 'I'm not the same.' She looked up into his handsome face and placed a restraining hand on his chest. 'I'm fat—my waist has gone,' she said, scarlet with embarrassment.

Gianfranco wanted to laugh, she looked so beautiful, so woebegone, but he had more sense than to do so. 'You are not fat, Kelly, you are luscious and swollen with my child. I have never seen you more beautiful.' And, lifting her hand from his chest, he led her to the bed. Then, squeezing her hand, he added, 'But if you are nervous you can undress me first.' His dark eyes held hers as he quickly removed his shoes and socks, and then, straightening, more slowly removed his tie, undid the first two buttons of his shirt. 'Help me, Kelly,' he husked.

Intrigued, she forgot her own embarrassment and, sliding her small hands over his chest, she quickly unbuttoned the rest of his shirt. He slipped it from his shoulders and Kelly slid her hands back up over the tanned hair-roughened chest with tactile delight. 'You feel hot,' Kelly murmured, lifting fascinated eyes to his. 'And so hard.'

Gianfranco almost groaned out loud. She had got that right; he was so hard he thought he'd burst. But even if it killed him he was going to make it right for her this time, he vowed. He smiled gently. 'Now the trousers,' he prompted.

Her head dipped, her slender fingers making short work of the waist fastening, but she hesitated a second before pulling down the zip, her knuckles stroking the rigid length of him through the fine fabric of his shorts.

There was something very exciting, empowering, about undressing a man, Kelly thought, her heart racing as she gently eased his trousers down over his hips, then, dropping to her knees, she slid them down his long legs. Intent upon her task, she never saw the grimace of agony on his face as her long hair brushed against his naked thighs and the hard length of his arousal, barely covered by black silk.

Stooping, Gianfranco lifted her to her feet. 'Enough,' he said huskily as he bent to her mouth. 'I can't wait much longer.'

As his mouth covered hers his hand slipped under her

sweater and lifted it, his hands gliding up over her breasts, caressing her with expert tenderness.

Kelly shivered, her whole body flushing with heat, and lifted her arms, but before she could put them around him he had whipped her jumper over her head, and claimed her mouth once more.

She forgot about her thickened waistline, forgot everything, and mindlessly kissed him back.

He lifted his head and pulled her arms from around him. Stepping back, he whipped off his shorts and slid his hands down the elastic waist of her leggings, easing them down her hips.

'No panties, Kelly?' He grinned, but his eyes darkened to black as he looked at her. 'I didn't know how beautiful a woman could be until now,' he husked softly, blatantly scrutinising her high firm breasts with their rosy tips so hard, so tempting, the soft swell of her stomach, and lower to the long shapely legs and the cluster of pale curls at the apex of her thighs.

'Kelly, you are the most utterly feminine woman I have ever seen,' he declared, his breathing heavy. He lifted a finger and slowly stroked over the smooth skin of her shoulder, then lower in a line across the soft curve of her breasts.

Helplessly she swayed towards him, her own eyes raking over his bronzed torso, the symmetry of muscle and sinew, the savage splendour of his powerful aroused body. She murmured his name and reached out to touch him, with a look in her sapphire eyes as old as Eve.

He groaned with sheer impatience and lifted her in his arms again, sinking to the bed with her.

The full contact of his naked body with hers made Kelly dizzy with desire. The blood drummed in her ears, and blindly she reached for him. Gianfranco reared up over her, filling her vision, and bent his head to her breast.

She felt the warm, moist pressure of his mouth taking the rigid tip inside and she moaned softly, her body arching towards the sensual pleasure of his mouth. Her hands clung to his wide shoulders, her fingers digging into his flesh, helpless captive to the erotic expertise of his tongue and teeth.

His hand moved to tenderly caress the soft mound of her belly, and all the while his mouth and other hand teased her breasts, his thumb scraping over the rigid tip, driving her crazy, her body writhing in an explicit demand for more. 'Gianfranco,' she pleaded.

He lifted his head, his black eyes glittering with passion. 'Slowly, slowly,' he rasped, and lowered his head to brush her lips with his.

Kelly eagerly opened her mouth for him as he eased his hand from her stomach down to the soft curls guarding her feminine core, making her body tremble. His fingers delved into the soft velvet folds to find the moist heat, and stroked and touched until she groaned out loud.

He lifted his head to look into her passion-glazed eyes. 'You want me,' he breathed. 'And I want you.'

Kelly bit into the flesh of his chest, wild with need; she didn't understand the urge, but her mouth found a small male nipple and licked and kissed it, her nails digging into his flesh harder and harder as his long fingers continued to mercilessly explore her body. Her heart hammered and she writhed against him. She felt him shudder and groan, and, made brave by the passion riding her, slid a hand down to his powerful body until she reached the rigid length of him and closed around him.

'No,' Gianfranco rasped, and, catching her hand, he pulled it from his body. 'Not yet; I don't want to hurt you.'

And, rolling onto his back, he lifted her over him, his night-black eyes dilated with passion. 'Trust me,' he grated as he slowly surged up into the sweet, hot heart of her femininity.

Her brilliant sapphire eyes widened, the pupils expanding until they almost eclipsed the blue. A whimper of sound escaped her throat as he drew her towards him, his mouth lifting to capture a taut nipple. He suckled her tender flesh with an avid enjoyment that drove her wild with desire as his strong hands held her waist, keeping her exactly where he wanted her. Her head fell back, her hands flat on his broad chest, fingers digging into his flesh as slowly, with subtle movements of his hands and hips, he rocked her higher and higher until she was drowning in the unimaginable wonder of pure sensation. He was hard and hot, and drove her to the edge of ecstasy—more pleasure than she had ever imagined existed. Her nails scratched across his chest and she cried out his name, as he swiftly reversed their positions. For a second he stared down at her, hunger and determination warring in the dark, taut features.

'This time, Kelly, this time for you,' he said hoarsely, and then moved again.

He filled her completely, and Kelly was lost in an all-encompassing passion, a primeval need, that drove her mindlessly onto another plane where time was suspended and her shuddering body reached and found the little death, the pitch of human passion, in a fierce, convulsive climax. Her blue eyes flew wide open in shocked wonder at the awesome joy of fulfilment. His harsh groan of satisfaction as he spilled his seed inside her mingled with her keening cry of his name.

Her hands clung to his broad shoulders, then softly stroked the sweat-damp skin. 'I thought the first time was wonderful, but…' She breathed unevenly, looking up into his night-black eyes.

'Shhh.' Gianfranco slipped onto his side. 'I know.' And, pressing soft little kisses to her face and hair, he held her tenderly against him.

'I never knew…' she whispered, breaking the silence, rubbing her head against a strong tanned shoulder like a satisfied kitten.

Gianfranco looked into her dazed blue eyes. 'Now you know why I was so angry the first time,' he said huskily, with all the confidence of a man who knew he had satisfied his lady.

Tension snaked through her. Sadly she remembered the aftermath last time. 'Because I might get pregnant,' she muttered with a slight frown. 'But that hardly applies now.'

With a deep throaty chuckle, Gianfranco planted a swift kiss on her small nose. 'No, my sweet. It wasn't so much the fact you were innocent that made me angry, but because, though I was loath to admit it, I never gave you the satisfaction you should have had,' he declared ruefully. 'I lost control. You were too innocent to know the difference, but I did. It was quite a blow to my male ego, so I took it out on you, and for that I apologise.'

'Oh, oh, I see.' A dawning realisation lit her wide blue eyes as they met his. Gianfranco, her macho lover, feeling vulnerable as the next man about his performance in bed? The thought made her grin.

'It wasn't funny at the time.' He nipped teasingly at the small lobe of her ear. 'And I promise you it will never happen again. I am going to spend the rest of my life making love to you to prove it.' He found her lips and kissed her long and lingeringly, then trailed kisses in an erotic path down her throat, her breasts, and to the soft swell of her stomach.

Kelly glanced down to where his dark head lay against her stomach and she wanted to believe a miracle had happened and he loved her. 'You don't have to marry me,' she murmured reluctantly, not wanting to burst the miraculous bubble she seemed to be floating in, but knowing she had to give him the choice.

Gianfranco rubbed his cheek against her belly, and, caressing the smooth mound, he pressed worshipful kisses on her silken skin. 'Our son,' he said, and, rearing up on one elbow, he let his other large hand gently, almost reverently, massage her stomach. 'And I do have to marry you, because I never want to be apart from you again.'

Kelly looked long and hard into his dark eyes, wanting to believe him. But was it her or a son he wanted? she asked herself. 'It might be a girl.'

'Girl, boy. I don't care as long as I have you.' Then he started to make love to her again, with a gentle seductive tenderness, an expertise that banished all her fears, and finally convinced her he loved her as he completely overwhelmed her all over again.

CHAPTER SIX

THEY were married four days later on the Friday, and Kelly, walking out of the registrar's office with Gianfranco's arm around her shoulders, was still reeling from the speed of it all.

'Wait.' Margaret, who had agreed with her brother Jim to be their witness, stopped them on the steps. 'You have to have a photograph,' she said, and raised her camera to her eye. 'Say cheese.'

'I'd rather say sex,' Gianfranco whispered in Kelly's ear, and brought a beaming smile to her face.

'You are insatiable,' Kelly chuckled a moment later, her blue eyes laughing up at him. The past few days they had made love morning, noon and night. In between, Gianfranco had organised everything. Kelly had resigned from her job, and her family home was up for sale with a local estate agent, Gianfranco insisting her home was going to be with him from now on.

The only thing Kelly had done herself was shop; she had bought a trousseau of sorts, given the limitations of her figure: lacy underwear and a couple of satin nightgowns, a few smart-casual clothes and one cocktail dress, plus the outfit she was wearing.

It was a winter-white cashmere dress, long-sleeved, with a softly curved bow-neck that revealed a hint of cleavage. The fine wool skimmed her figure, and flared ever so slightly from her knees almost to her feet. Elegant and ideal for a January day, it moulded her stomach, but Kelly didn't mind. If famous film stars could reveal their bumps in the nude, she told herself, her small tummy was perfectly acceptable. Apart from her posy of yellow rosebuds, her only adornment was the diamond crucifix around her slender throat.

'You look beautiful,' Gianfranco told her as he helped her into the waiting car. 'My wife,' and he kissed her with a very self-satisfied grin on his handsome face.

Seated in the VIP lounge at the airport, Kelly glanced across at her very new husband. He was standing by the business desk, sending messages to heaven knew where, while they waited for their flight to be called for Rome. He made her heart leap with love. He looked so devastatingly handsome in a perfectly tailored dark navy three-piece suit, and brilliant white silk shirt. A lock of black hair fell forward over his broad brow, and she watched with some amusement as he gesticulated with one hand while talking on the telephone. In that moment it hit her how very Latin he was.

The briefest of frowns marred her smooth brow as for the first time she wondered how she would get on living in what was for her a foreign country, with Gianfranco and his family.

Kelly stood on the balcony later that day and gaped in awe at the view before her. The whole of Rome appeared spread out below. Two strong arms wrapped around her non-existent waist, and a dark head bent and a warm mouth nuzzled her ear. 'You like the view, *cara*?'

Like it? She loved it! She'd unpacked her suitcase while Gianfranco had made a few urgent business calls, then he'd given her a swift tour of the penthouse—the sitting room was comfortable but elegant, decorated in blue and gold, the furniture was a selection of tasteful antiques, while the master bedroom was a symphony in cream and dark rose and the other three bedrooms were just as elegant.

She turned slowly in the arms that held her, and beamed up into Gianfranco's darkly handsome face. 'The view is magnificent—the apartment is magnificent.' Reaching a slender finger to his face, she added, 'And you are magnificent.' As she traced the outline of his sensuous lips with the pad of one finger, her blue eyes meshed with his. 'Can we stay here forever?'

A long kiss later Gianfranco answered. 'Not for ever, but for the next three days certainly. Then we must go to my country estate, and I will have to get back to work.'

'Do you think your family will like me?' Kelly voiced her fear. 'Maybe you should have asked them to the wedding?' Gianfranco bent his head, his lips brushing hers again, and she savoured the sweetness with the tip of her tongue as he grinned down into her luminous blue eyes.

'They will love you, and there wasn't time to ask them to the wedding. Anyway, you have already met Mother and Olivia, and they know why we married. Mother is arranging a reception for you in two weeks' time to introduce you to everyone.' Something about what he said disturbed her, but before she had time to think he added, 'But right now I want to start the honeymoon.' Bending down, he scooped her bodily into his arms, with an easy strength that made her lace her arms around his neck and nuzzle her lips against the pulse that beat in the strong column of his throat as he carried her through to the bedroom.

'Do you have any idea how much I want you?' Gianfranco asked roughly as he lowered her to her feet and speedily divested her of her clothes. 'How much I ache for you?' And his own clothes were removed.

Kelly's heart raced at the sight of him. He was all-powerful, virile male, and the very air in the room seemed charged with an electric current of sensualism.

Gianfranco's dark eyes roamed possessively over her naked form, the high, firm breasts, then lower to the growing swell of her stomach, and lower still to the soft curve of her hips and thighs.

Kelly proudly exulted in his scrutiny; this was her husband. Her own gaze swept over his wide shoulders, the mat of soft, dark hair on his broad chest descending in a fine line to brush out and cradle his sex. She heard the harsh intake of his breath and the sudden rise and fall of his chest, and tilted back her head to look up at him.

Gianfranco's deep, dark eyes seemed to pierce her soul as he reached for her. 'Kelly, my wife,' he growled. 'At last.' He hauled her to him with a savage urgency that surprised her.

Her hands found his shoulders as his tongue plundered the tender interior of her mouth. He kissed her deep and long, his hard body burning against her, until her head swam and she could hardly breathe. Then he lifted her to the bed.

'Gianfranco.' Kelly surfaced long enough from the heady magic of his kiss to say his name.

'Who else?' he growled sexily. 'You are mine now.' He muttered something huskily in Italian before his mouth dipped down to capture one taut nipple and suckle her tender flesh with intense erotic delight that drove her wild with wanting.

In the long passion-filled hours that followed they fed off each other's hunger to the point of exhaustion. Kelly thought Gianfranco had taught her all about love in the past few days, but he still surprised her.

'You make me insatiable,' Gianfranco rasped on a shuddering sigh as he reluctantly withdrew from the sleek heart of her and drew her gently into the hard curve of his body. 'I must remember you are pregnant, and control myself.'

Kelly smiled. She had lost count of the times he had driven them both to the brink and over. 'A bit late now, my love,' she murmured sleepily, resting her head on the side of his chest, her long lashes falling down over her sapphire eyes. 'But it is our wedding night.' She whispered the words against his sweat-slicked skin, her body sated and exhausted.

A sound jerked her out of a deep sleep and, rolling over on the bed, she reached for Gianfranco and found only space. Hauling herself up into a sitting position, she blinked and looked around. Their holiday was obviously over.

The past three days had been the most marvellous of her life. Gianfranco had shown her Rome, the Colisseum, the Trevi fountain, where she'd thrown the obligatory coin, all the obvious tourist attractions, and a few not so obvious. There was the tiny church tucked away in a narrow street, with an altar screen of unbelievable beauty. A small restaurant with plastic tablecloths, serving the most mouth-watering food in Italy, according to her husband.

A sigh of sheer contentment was followed by her stomach's rumbling. She was eating for two and they had missed dinner again last night. Slipping out of bed, she padded to the bathroom and after a brisk shower she walked back into the bedroom, wearing only a large fluffy towel tucked around her body toga-style.

'Good morning, *cara*,' Gianfranco drawled huskily, placing a loaded tray containing coffee and a selection of pastries down on the bedside table. He walked towards her, his eyes bright with amusement at her scantily covered, rumpled state. 'Sorry to rush you, but I want to make it home by midday if possible.' He pressed a swift kiss on her lush lips.

'Monday morning and the honeymoon is over.' Kelly sighed dramatically, her blue eyes sparkling up at him; he looked devastatingly attractive in blue jeans and a black Armani sweater.

'Don't worry,' Gianfranco instructed, 'I will take you on a proper honeymoon—anywhere you want. The Maldives, the Caribbean. Once our child is born and we can be alone.' His deep voice dropped sexily and, lifting his hand, he brushed her hair behind one ear. The touch of his warm fingers and the sensual promise in his dark eyes made her heart skip a beat. 'I promise,' he mouthed against her slightly parted lips, and kissed her again. 'Now eat and pack and dress.' With a tender pat to her stomach, he spun on his heel and left the room.

Refreshed by the coffee and food, in five minutes she was dressed in a pair of pale grey trousers, in fine wool blend, and a crew-neck blue sweater. On her feet she wore comfortable black loafers, and she had draped a dove-grey leather jacket over the suitcase. She gave her hair a quick brush, leaving it to fall long and straight from a centre parting, and she was ready.

'Ready?' Gianfranco demanded sauntering back into the room and looping a long arm around her waist.

'I guess so.' Kelly's eyes were nervous as she glanced up at him. 'I hope your mother likes me…'

'You worry too much,' he teased, and kissed her again, and when she was suitably breathless he lifted his head. 'I adore you, and my mother likes whoever I like,' he drawled with unconscious arrogance, and, bending, he picked up the suitcase. 'Come on.'

If he thought he was reassuring Kelly he was wrong. Common sense told her no woman was going to be delighted to have missed her only son's wedding and then have him turn up with a pregnant wife. Acceptance was the best she could hope for, she reasoned, and the first seed of doubt took root in her heart. Had she done the right thing in marrying Gianfranco? She loved him, but would love be enough?

Kelly looked out of the window of the Ferrari with some trepidation as Gianfranco brought the car to a halt in a huge paved courtyard outside the impressive entrance portico of his family home. They had stopped on the way for lunch, but now they had arrived there was no ducking the inevitable any longer; she was about to meet his mother as his wife. She glanced back at her husband, but he was already out of the car and a second later had opened the car door for her.

'Welcome to Il Casa Maldini.' He gestured at the huge building with a wave of one hand, and, grasping her arm, helped her out of the low-slung sports car. 'A Ferrari was obviously not designed for a pregnant lady,' he said, grinning down at her as he swept an arm around her shoulders. 'From now on we will use the Mercedes.'

With some astonishment Kelly realised 'Il Casa Maldini' was actually engraved in the stone lintel above the great door. 'Some house,' she murmured. She tipped her head back and stared up at the building. Built in an open-ended rectangle, three storeys high, it was enormous. The ochre stuccoed walls gleamed golden in the pale winter sunshine.

'*Sì*, my family has owned the land around here for countless generations. Maldini is a very old and very much respected name,' he stated as he led her up the steps to the massive double doors, now magically opened by a small white-headed man.

In a flurry of introductions Kelly discovered the man's name was Aldo, his wife Maria was the cook; there were six more servants whose names she barely registered, and finally a young girl of about eighteen, Anna, who smiled shyly when Gianfranco introduced her to Kelly as her personal maid.

His mother appeared from a room at one side of the massive oak-panelled hall, and welcomed her son with a kiss on each cheek. Her greeting to Kelly was less demonstrative.

'I am sorry I missed the wedding, but it was so unexpected, so quick.' And her dark eyes, so uncannily like her son's, dropped down to Kelly's stomach and then quickly back to her face as she added, 'Welcome, Kelly; I know you *inglese* shake hands.' She held out a perfectly manicured hand.

'Thank you,' Kelly murmured. Hot colour scorching her cheeks, she took the hand offered her and hoped she had made the right noises, feeling intimidated by the woman, the line of servants and the overwhelming grandeur of the place.

Five minutes later, seated on a rather hard satin-backed sofa, Kelly looked around her in barely concealed awe. The furniture was all antique, and the magnificent marble fireplace was a masterpiece. But it was the ceiling that made her gasp, being exquisitely painted and depicting some kind of pastoral scene, with men and women lying around in various stages of undress, draped in vines and flowers.

'Kelly? What would you like?'

Kelly tore her gaze away from the stunning frescoes and glanced across at Gianfranco. He was standing by the fireplace, a thumb hooked in the hip-hugging band of his jeans, his other hand curved around a crystal glass half-full of what looked like whisky. Aldo the butler stood a few paces away from him.

'Alcohol is out for you, but coffee, or fresh juice? Aldo is waiting.'

'Oh, I'll have a cup of tea, please.' Kelly said the first thing that came into her head. She had not realised they were waiting for her.

'You are so English,' Gianfranco's mother said with a little laugh. 'I think you will find our ways quite strange.'

Aldo left after a quick command from Gianfranco, and then he turned to smile down at his mother. 'Rubbish, Mamma. Kelly will soon learn. With you to teach her, how could she not?' And the two of them shared a look of mutual understanding.

Watching, Kelly felt vaguely left out for a second, and not at all sure what it was she was supposed to learn from her very grand-looking, elegant mother-in-law.

Aldo returned and served the tea, while Gianfranco and his mother carried on a conversation in Italian, which effectively excluded Kelly. She knew some Italian, and had for the past few months been trying to learn more with the help of tapes, but they spoke too fast for Kelly to pick up more than a few words.

Suddenly dark eyes were turned on Kelly. 'Excuse us, Kelly, but my son and I have so much to catch up on, and I forget you do not speak our language.'

'That's perfectly all right,' Kelly said quietly, returning her teacup to the tray. 'I understand…' she hesitated '…Signora Maldini.' She had no idea how to address her new mother-in-law.

'Oh, please, as we are all going to live together, you must call me Carmela.'

Kelly smiled. 'Why, thank you, Carmela.'

'My pleasure, and now if you have finished your tea,

perhaps you would like Anna to show you the main part of the house, and then to your suite.' A bell was rung and in minutes Anna appeared at the door.

She was being sent to her room! Kelly almost laughed out loud. 'No, really—' she began to object, when Carmela cut in.

'In your delicate condition I am sure you will appreciate a rest in the afternoon. We dine at nine.'

Kelly glanced expectantly up at Gianfranco, sure he would object to what sounded to Kelly like a dismissal and offer to give her a guided tour himself. But instead he strolled across to where she sat and, reaching for her hand, urged her to her feet.

'Mamma is right. You go along with Anna. I have a few calls to make.' His lips brushed hers in a fleeting caress and, turning her towards the door, he patted her bottom. 'I'll see you soon.'

Hiding her disappointment, Kelly followed Anna as she dutifully pointed out the many reception rooms. Then she led Kelly up the grand staircase and along various corridors, pointing out Carmela's suite and Olivia's next to it. Kelly was slightly surprised at the mention of Olivia; she had not realised the woman lived here as well. The upper floor was the servants' quarters.

Gianfranco's suite was in the west wing of the house, and was more like an apartment, but without a kitchen. One huge bedroom and a large dressing room, two bathrooms, a comfortable sitting room and another slightly smaller bedroom. Standing in the middle of the sitting room, Kelly looked around, her mood lifting as she surveyed the fire burning brightly in the fireplace. It felt warm and welcoming. She sighed with relief and dismissed the maid.

One wall was lined with shelves and books. Old trophies were scattered around and, reading the inscriptions, Kelly realised they were for sailing. A large leather sofa and two armchairs were placed around the fireplace, and in one corner stood a writing table, in another a huge state-of-the-art television...

The main bedroom was equally inviting, with a large oak four-poster double bed, Kelly thought as she strolled into the dressing room on her way to the bathroom.

The dressing room was lined with cupboards on two sides, various chests of drawers and an ornate dressing table; all the furniture was large, but with the high ceilings everything was in proportion.

Kelly opened a wardrobe door and smiled. Anna had unpacked for her, and her clothes were lined alongside some of Gianfranco's. It was a comforting sight.

Two hours later, showered and changed into a soft blue wool skirt and matching blouse in blue and cream, Kelly curled up in a leather armchair and began to wonder where her husband had got to.

Getting up from the chair, she restlessly walked across to one of the elegant arched windows and looked out over the courtyard, the sweeping drive lined by Cypress trees, a beautifully tended Italian-style garden and, in the distance, the terracotta roofs of a village, all surrounded by mile upon mile of undulating cultivated land. She picked out row upon row of vines to one side, and vast olive groves.

A deep heartfelt sigh escaped her and she pressed her head against the cool glass of the window-pane. It was stupid, but true: she had not the nerve to go looking for her husband. The house was huge and her first impression on entering had been of gloom—the great hall, hung with ancient oil paintings of severe-looking men and women, a massive central staircase that ended with a galleried landing with numerous corridors off it.

Taking a deep breath, she straightened her shoulders.

Kelly, my girl, you are a married, pregnant adult woman, not a stupid adolescent, she lectured herself sternly. There was nothing stopping her going to look for her husband, and she turned on her heel. She was halfway across the room when the door opened and Gianfranco walked in.

'Sorry I was so long.' He slanted her a brief smile. 'But with everything that has happened I have neglected my work of late.'

'Sorry if I am an inconvenience,' nerves made her snap resentfully.

Collapsing on the sofa, Gianfranco held out a hand to her. 'Come here, my sensuous little wife,' he said softly, catching the flash of uncertainty she could not hide. 'No need to feel neglected, but I do have to work.'

Seated in the curve of his arm, Kelly listened as he explained.

'Apart from when I have to go to New York, I usually spend four days here over the weekend, when I attend to estate matters. The rest of the time I spend in my office in Rome. Obviously now I am a married man I will have to rethink my working practice, as I have no intention of leaving you alone more than I can help. I can easily work from here, and curtail my visits to Rome somewhat.'

'Why bother? I could stay in Rome with you.' She flashed him a brilliant smile; the thought of escaping his family for half of every week held great appeal.

'No, don't be ridiculous.' He clasped her shoulders and turned her around to face him. 'You need someone with you at all times in your condition.' His lips turned up in a self-satisfied smile. 'Me, and when I am not around Mamma and Olivia. The situation is ideal.'

Her mouth dropped open. He had to be kidding. But

before she could protest he had planted a swift kiss on her lips and got to his feet.

'I need a shower, *carissima*, and then...' his dark eyes gleamed wickedly '...we can both have a rest before dinner.'

CHAPTER SEVEN

IT WAS Saturday night and the guests were due to arrive in twenty minutes.

'What do you think, Anna?' she asked the young girl.

'Bellissima.' Anna grinned. 'Very elegant.'

'Thank you.' Kelly smiled back. The one good thing to come out of her first two weeks at the Casa Maldini was Anna. She was friendly, could speak a little English, and was eager to help. In fact, she had just spent half an hour doing Kelly's hair in an elaborate twist on the crown of her head with a few loose tendrils to frame her face. She watched the girl depart, then nervously she glanced once more at her reflection in the mirror. She so wanted to make a good impression on Gianfranco's friends.

The past two weeks had not been easy. She had expected some difficulty in adjusting to her husband's lifestyle, but she had never expected to feel so lonely. Aldo woke them in the morning at seven with coffee. Ten minutes later Gianfranco, washed and dressed, left her lying in bed while he started work, and if she was lucky she saw him at lunch. But most days it was eight in the evening before he reappeared.

Only once had he taken her out. With supreme efficiency he had whisked her into Verona and opened a bank account for her. Then he had registered her with his doctor and waited while she had a scan. On returning to the house he had dismissed her with a brief smile and told her he would see her later. By 'later' he meant over a very formal dinner with his mother and Olivia, or in bed.

Her lips quirked in the briefest of smiles; at least in bed she had his full attention, but it was the only place, she wryly conceded.

She had made a disturbing discovery about her husband. 'Count Gianfranco Maldini' the businessman was a totally different male animal from the Gianni she had fallen in love with. He was a workaholic, and he was spoilt rotten. His mother and Olivia waited on him hand and foot, as did all the staff, as if he was the Master of the Universe, and he took their adoration as his due. Their attitude to Kelly was not so friendly, though she had tried telling herself she must be mistaken when she thought she understood Olivia's sly comments in Italian. She had tried to convince herself she was being paranoid, but yesterday was a case in point.

Gianfranco had informed her in the morning that his mother and Olivia were going to take her shopping. When Kelly had asked him to go with her instead he had pleaded pressure of work, and then added, 'Mamma knows the right places to shop for a woman in your condition, whereas I haven't a clue.'

Sensitivity was obviously not his strong point. Kelly knew damn fine what he had meant. Probably the only clothes he had ever bought for women were of the designer variety from exclusive boutiques. Not maternity wear.

She'd been seething with resentment by the time she had returned from the shopping trip. Carmela and Olivia had overridden anything she had suggested with the comment that they knew best the acceptable way for pregnant women to dress in Italian society. Kelly had felt about two inches tall and shut up. Consequently she'd returned to the house with three of the most enormous dresses she'd ever clapped eyes on. However hard she tried, she could not convince herself Carmela and Olivia were looking after her best interests—in fact, quite the reverse.

She had said as much to Gianfranco, and he had gone all cold on her. He had told her she was jumping to ridiculous conclusions over a few misunderstood words, and then suggested it was her hormones playing up because of her pregnancy.

Walking out of the bedroom, Kelly knew she was pinning all her hopes on tonight; she wanted to fit in and make friends, but not at the loss of her pride and self-esteem. Which was why she was wearing the dress she had bought herself in England.

Taking a deep breath, she walked into the salon. Gianfranco had come down earlier. Olivia, looking stunning in a midnight-blue strapless and backless dress that clung to her every curve, was standing so close to him that they were almost touching.

Seeing her husband looking so incredibly handsome in a formal black dinner suit, smiling down at Olivia, gave Kelly a nasty jolt somewhere in the region of her heart. Straightening her shoulders, she walked into the middle of the room. 'Good evening.'

It was like watching a tableau unfold. Carmela was the first to notice Kelly, and when she did her perfectly plucked eyebrows rose in surprise.

Then Olivia laughed. 'Surely you're not wearing that?' she said, eyeing Kelly as if she had crawled out from under a rock.

Stiffening defensively, Kelly said, 'Yes, I am.' It was a perfectly plain silk-jersey black dress. Tiny diamanté straps supported a bodice that was cut in a straight line across her breasts. The material, cut on the bias, clung slightly from under her bust to just above her knees.

Kelly ignored the babble of Italian that ensued and glanced across at Gianfranco, waiting for him to smile to give her some support.

Gianfranco's dark eyes made a swift analytical survey of her stiffly held figure as he walked across to her. 'You look very nice, Kelly.' In fact, he thought she looked delectable, but he could see his mother's point of view.

'Damned with faint praise,' Kelly said drily as Gianfranco stopped and stared down at her from beneath hooded lids, his expression unreadable.

'No, really, you know you always look beautiful,' he said soothingly. 'But Mamma thought you would have worn one of the gowns she bought for you. She is of the opinion they are much more suitable for a wife during her confinement, and on matters of taste Mamma does know what is best. You would do well to take notice of her.'

Confinement! The old-fashioned term made Kelly bristle with indignation. Dear heaven, her arrogant husband and his sainted mother had got that right! she thought. She was beginning to feel more and more as if she was in jail. Well, to hell with the pair of them, tonight she was going to enjoy herself, if it was the last thing she did.

'I'll make your apologies, should it be necessary, while you change,' Gianfranco continued smoothly. 'But hurry.'

'No.'

One ebony brow arched. 'No! You refuse?'

She almost laughed, he looked so astounded. 'Got it in one.'

He caught her arm. 'Kelly, you're behaving foolishly. Now go upstairs and change,' he commanded, his dark eyes revealing his irritation.

Kelly glared up at him. 'I would look foolish if I wore any of the dresses I got yesterday. I'm five and a half months pregnant, not nine,' she snorted, nervous tension heightening her already rising temper. 'They make me look like an elephant. You should—you should see them.'

Gianfranco smiled when she began to splutter—a very

masculine grin. 'I see.' He let go of her arm. 'Female vanity I can understand,' he drawled mockingly.

She wanted to hit him; he was so damn condescending. But she never got the chance as Aldo announced the first guests had arrived. Carefully holding her temper under tight control, Kelly braced herself to meet a host of strangers.

It was nowhere near as bad as she had feared. Gianfranco's friends were not nearly as intimidating as his mother and sister-in-law, a mixture of local people and business acquaintances, and when Judy and Carlo Bertoni arrived Kelly could not hide her delight.

The buffet meal was exquisite, the conversation a mixture of English and Italian. Carmela sparkled and was the perfect hostess, and with Olivia quickly had a group of people hanging onto her every word.

Kelly, finding herself alone for a moment, began to relax. Gianfranco was at the other side of the room, deep in discussion with a group of men in what was obviously a male-only conversation.

Suddenly beside Kelly, Judy chuckled. 'Aren't you the dark horse?'

Kelly glanced at her and blushed.

Judy's eyes lit with amusement. 'Your local lad turned out to be Count Gianfranco Maldini—what a story! Come on, tell all. How did it happen?'

Kelly told her, ending with, 'In a way I have you to thank, because apparently when you told him at New Year that I was pregnant he came to look for me, and the rest, as they say, is history,' she quipped.

'That's great!' Judy asserted with a grin. 'But let me give you some advice; your Gianfranco has had plenty of women in his time, and he treated them all with a casualness you wouldn't believe. He is not the type for deep emotional commitment. But you're carrying his child, and

Italians love children, so make sure you make the most of it, and don't let him out of your sight.'

'Thanks, Judy.' Kelly forced a smile. She needed reminding of her husband's past women like a hole in the head, but that was Judy. 'But we are marr…' She never finished the sentence, as someone bumped into her and sent a shower of liquid down the front of her dress.

'Oh, I'm so sorry.' Olivia appeared in front of Kelly. 'I didn't see you there, and now your dress is ruined. How clumsy of me.' Kelly glanced up and the malevolence in the dark eyes that met hers froze her to the spot. 'Now you will *have* to change.'

Kelly couldn't believe the pettiness of it… But, overcome with embarrassment, as the dampness had made the fabric stick to her stomach, she did not want to make a scene. 'Yes,' she agreed.

With a hard glance at Olivia, Judy said, 'I'll come with you.'

Before they could move Gianfranco materialised at her side. His dark eyes swept down over her small body and the tell-tale damp patch over her stomach. 'What happened?' Everyone around them seemed to go silent.

'Nothing, really—an accident. Don't make a fuss.' She turned a deep, embarrassed shade of red.

Olivia laid a hand on his arm and he turned towards her as she said something in rapid Italian. The people around them laughed. Gianfranco grinned and, glancing back at Kelly, placed a hand in the small of her back. 'Hurry along, then.'

Kelly nodded without comprehending what had been said, and, with Judy at her side, exited the room.

'That bitch did that deliberately,' Judy remarked as they walked up the stairs. 'You're going to have to watch her.'

'No, really, it was an accident,' Kelly lied, not believing it for a second. 'These things happen.'

'That is not what she just told your husband,' Judy revealed bluntly. 'She joked it was the extra weight you were carrying—the Maldini heir—that made you stumble. Why do you think they all laughed?'

'No, I don't believe you,' Kelly said staunchly, defending Gianfranco and at the same time feeling incredibly hurt.

'Then I suggest you learn Italian—quick,' Judy declared drily.

Ignoring her, Kelly stripped off the dress, and after a brief visit to the bathroom to sponge down her stomach returned to the bedroom.

'Is this your bedroom?' Judy asked, glancing around and wandering into the sitting room, and finally the dressing room, where she flung open the wardrobe doors.

'Yes, of course.' Kelly followed her in and eyed her meagre supply of clothes with a jaundiced eye.

'You're in worse trouble than I thought,' Judy commented. 'This isn't the master suite of Casa Maldini. You do know that?' Judy lifted an enquiring eyebrow in Kelly's direction.

'No,' Kelly said with a dry smile. 'But I do know my own bedroom suite.'

'Maybe, but remember the magazine article I showed you, the luxurious master suite is in the other wing.'

'That's Olivia's,' Kelly muttered, pulling one of the new dresses from the wardrobe. The least offensive was a white muslin concoction sprigged with pink roses.

'Ah! So the black widow is firmly entrenched. I'm sorry to say this, Kelly, but you'd better get a grip. You are the top female in this house now, and it's time you started acting like it, or Olivia is going to walk all over you.'

'Really, Judy, you're being melodramatic.' She liked

Judy, but she knew her attitude towards men was manipulative; she only had to think of how she had used Kelly last summer to get her husband to agree to a full-time nanny.

Judy shook her head and sighed. 'Listen up, Kelly. There have been rumours about Olivia and Gianfranco for ages now, but it is also common knowledge Olivia can't have children. She was married for ten years to his brother and tried everything. If you are not very careful she will take over not just the master suite, but your husband and your child if you let her.'

'You have a vivid imagination,' Kelly muttered, lifting the dress prior to putting it over her head, but Judy's words had struck a chord.

'Oh, my God! You're never going to wear that!' Judy tore it from her hand. 'Where is your style, woman?'

Kelly sighed. 'Carmela and Olivia took me shopping and assured me this is what the best-dressed Italian mum-to-be wears.'

'Over my dead body,' Judy asserted and, rifling through the wardrobe, withdrew the winter-white cashmere dress that she'd worn for her wedding. 'Here, wear that—at least it has some style—and for heaven's sake think about what I have told you. You are far too trusting for your own good.'

The sound of music floated into the grand hall as the two girls made their way back downstairs. The dancing had started. Kelly glanced across the room just as Gianfranco took Olivia into his arms and started to dance.

Carlo Bertoni appeared and slid an arm around Judy. 'Where have you been? I missed you,' he declared, and as Kelly watched Judy smiled up into her husband's eyes.

'Helping the lady of the house change.'

'And very lovely you look.' Carlo smiled at Kelly. 'Gianfranco is a very lucky man.'

Kelly forced a smile. 'Thank you, Carlo.' But, watching Gianfranco dancing, with Olivia's arms now wrapped around his neck, she began to wonder how lucky she was herself. Somehow seeing the two so intimately together lent credence to Judy's outrageous suggestions. She felt sick to her stomach and was hit by a wave of such bitter jealousy she had to close her eyes for a moment.

Opening them again, she glanced around the room. It wasn't just Olivia who was ogling her husband, she noted. Gianfranco, with his great height and superbly muscled body, moved with a rhythm, a lithe, sexy elegance, which, combined with his dark good looks, attracted the appreciative eyes of almost every female present.

Gianfranco loved her, she told herself firmly. They were married, for heaven's sake. But a fluttering in her stomach reminded her she was pregnant and why he had married her. Then Gianfranco caught sight of her, his glorious eyes widening in delight, and she was reassured by the brilliant smile that he winged her way. She was worrying over nothing.

Kelly was wearing the dress she had married him in, and for a moment Gianfranco was stunned anew by how beautiful she looked. His wife, with her pale hair swept up on top of her head, her slender body ripening softly with his child. Yes, he had made the right decision marrying her, he congratulated himself, his chest swelling with pride. She was every inch a lady and, contrary to what he had been led to believe by married men of his acquaintance, marriage had made little difference to his life at all—except he had a warm and willing woman in his bed every night. Married life was good. His friends adored Kelly, the evening was a great success, and he wished the whole lot would leave so he could take her to bed.

The music stopped and he disengaged himself from his courtesy dance with his sister-in-law. He was stopped from claiming Kelly by Olivia's hand on his arm. He listened with barely concealed impatience to what she had to say, but when his mother joined in his attention was caught. Old loyalties vied with new, and slowly his dark brows drew together in a frown.

Kelly saw the frown, and she watched as he worked his way through the crowd towards her. Gianfranco reached for Kelly with a strong arm and pulled her to his side. 'I see you've changed,' he said, bending his dark head towards her, and under cover of apparently kissing her neck, said softly, 'Beautiful though you look, would it have been too much of a hardship to wear one of the gowns Mamma chose for you?'

'Yes,' she declared mutinously. She had already had this argument earlier, and she was not about to start trying to defend her choice again.

'Dance with me,' Gianfranco demanded. She stilled, and the large hand at her spine pulled her closer. 'Smile,' he suggested silkily, glittering dark eyes absorbing the defiance in her beautiful face. 'Or people might suspect that we are arguing.'

'Heaven forbid anyone would dare argue with you, Gianfranco,' she drawled sarcastically. And was punished by being kissed in a brief, hard kiss. Her nostrils flared on the disturbingly familiar scent of him, her body instantly melting in the circle of his arms. 'People are watching,' she said, her face flushing scarlet.

'So what? I am master in my own home,' he murmured against her ear as he guided her gently around the floor. 'You would do well to remember that. I am not used to the women in my life bending my ear about clothes,' he declared with all the aristocratic arrogance of his illustrious ancestors. 'It has got to stop—understand?'

Involuntarily Kelly flinched and missed a step, stung by the implied threat in his statement…

'Olivia was right, you are rather clumsy tonight,' he remarked.

Judy had not been lying! In that second Kelly wanted to thump him; her blue eyes flashed fire as they met his. 'And you are a blind chauvinist pig!' she whispered tightly.

Her sapphire eyes were magnificent when anger or passion aroused her, but he did not want to argue with her. 'Don't get upset, Kelly.' His gleaming dark eyes held hers. 'I will forgive you. It's probably your hormones playing up.'

Kelly pulled free just as the music stopped, but before she could speak Carmela tapped Gianfranco on the arm. 'The guests will soon be leaving.'

Half an hour later the last of the guests had left. Carmela declared the evening a great success and suggested they all have a nightcap. Kelly refused, said goodnight and made straight for the stairs.

Inside she was a seething mass of conflicting emotions. She loved Gianfranco, but he, by his own words, had admitted he had been laughing at her with Olivia. She couldn't believe he was so insensitive to her feelings. But then, she did not know him that well, as she was fast discovering.

Once in the bedroom, she quickly undressed, and in the bathroom she washed, then brushed out her hair, before slipping on a blue satin nightgown. She grimaced slightly—it was getting a little snug—and walked back into the bedroom.

After an instant's hesitation at seeing Gianfranco, she continued towards the bed.

'Rather a hasty exit, Kelly,' he opined hardly. 'It wouldn't have hurt you to share a nightcap with Mamma.'

'I thought I'd leave you to it, then you could all have a good laugh at me,' she snapped.

In the process of divesting himself of his clothes he stopped and faced her, his dinner suit discarded and his fingers lingering on the last button of his shirt.

'What exactly do you mean by that?' He shrugged off his shirt and stood before her in just black silk boxers. His dark eyes narrowed intently on her pale face. 'You have been in a strange mood for the past hour.'

'Maybe because I don't like being told what to wear, or being ordered to change.'

Gianfranco stilled, his broad shoulders tensing. 'Maybe you should learn some courtesy to my mother, when she has very generously tried to help you,' he opined bluntly.

'Maybe you should learn some courtesy to me, your *wife*,' she snarled, the events of the evening finally getting on top of her. 'Like when your sister-in-law tipped her drink all over me and apologised. Yet, according to Judy, when you appeared she told you it was my clumsiness and you all had a jolly good laugh.'

A dark stain of red ran along his high cheekbones. At least he had the grace to blush, which was something, Kelly thought bitterly. Thoroughly fed-up, she did not want to argue with him, she wanted him to hold her in his arms and reassure her of his love, and instead he was staring at her with eyes as cold as ice.

'Everyone laughed; as the host, I smiled in agreement with my guests, the correct thing to do,' he said with chilling politeness. 'But you are being ridiculous, Kelly. I have known Olivia a lot longer than you and she would not lie.'

'No? You're inferring that I would?' Kelly shot back at him in outrage.

'Yes—no.' For once her indomitable husband had to struggle for words. 'You were probably mistaken, a woman in your condition.'

'If you mention my condition once more, so help me I will flatten you,' she screeched tempestuously.

His jaw clenched. 'Contain yourself, Kelly, such temper cannot be good for you or the baby.'

Too angry to bother guarding her tongue, Kelly flared, 'And you supporting Olivia over your wife is? The woman sleeps in the master suite and her husband has been dead over three years. But then maybe she is waiting for the new master to take his place, or perhaps you already have,' she snarled, shaking with anger.

Gianfranco went rigid, tension emanating from him in waves. Hooded black eyes surveyed her with a look of such simmering rage that she involuntarily stepped back, afraid of a physical attack. Her anger vanished. She knew she had gone too far. What on earth had possessed her to throw Judy's coarse rumours in his face?

'You do well to retreat, Kelly. If you were not carrying my child I would make you pay for such a slanderous slur on your husband and a woman who has done you no harm but welcomed you into the family home.'

Kelly had never seen Gianfranco so angry; his eyes were flat and cold, and somehow that frightened her. He caught her shoulders and she trembled. His tanned near-naked body had the familiar devastating effect on Kelly. He was so close she had trouble breathing. 'Sorry,' she murmured, completely subjugated by his towering presence.

Gianfranco saw the fear in her deep blue eyes and checked himself. She in turn infuriated and enchanted him, and if he could get his hands on whoever it was putting such stupid ideas in her head he would strangle them. 'Tell me, who has been filling your head with such rubbish?' he demanded, staring down at her, noting the panicked bounding of her heart and the rise and fall of her breasts against the soft satin covering them.

'No one.' Kelly lowered her eyes and stared at his broad chest. 'It probably is just my hormones playing up,' she offered as an excuse, and perhaps it was, she told herself, filled with shame at what she had implied. She had sounded like the worst kind of jealous wife. But she was not going to betray Judy. 'When Anna showed me around I knew Olivia...' She trailed off.

Gianfranco breathed a sigh of relief and pulled her into his arms. Hormones he could understand. He brushed his lips across her smooth brow in a tender gesture. 'Perhaps I should have explained earlier, but you have to understand Olivia was devastated by the death of her husband Alfredo—my brother. We all were. But Olivia had a nervous breakdown and was ill for over a year, and, although she appears very confident and in control, she is still very fragile. She is family, so naturally Mamma and I look after her.'

Kelly was feeling worse by the minute. 'Oh, how terrible for her.' Her soft heart was touched.

'Yes, *cara*,' he murmured softly. 'In a way you have everything that was once hers.'

Her body was shivering in the protective circle of his strong arms, but not with cold. She loved him; she would do anything for him. She could not bear him to be angry with her, and yet she couldn't help it. 'But not you.' The words just popped out.

He chuckled, a deep, husky sound, and moulded her against him. 'No, never me, but I'm flattered you're jealous, *cara*.' One lean, strong hand cupped her chin, his dark eyes intent on her lovely face. 'But you are now married to the present count, and not only that, you are pregnant with probably the next one. Something that Olivia would have killed for when Alfredo was alive but it was not to be. So try to make allowances for her, hmm?'

She nodded her head, and his mouth, hot and urgent, covered her own as he kissed her with a long, lingering sexuality.

Kelly tried to make allowances, she really did… But it wasn't easy.

Olivia's hurtful comments whenever Gianfranco was not around, her hints that they had been lovers, were like water torture, slowly draining all Kelly's confidence and self-esteem. She tried to talk to Gianfranco but he dismissed her fears, sometimes with a laugh, occasionally with cold disdain, which hurt her even more, but usually with a kiss. But sex was no longer enough for Kelly. She needed more, she needed her husband's support, and when it was not forthcoming she grew more miserable and withdrawn by the day.

Kelly gave up mentioning Olivia to her husband, and with no one to turn to she struggled vainly against her doubts and fear. Gianfranco told her he adored her, made love to her, but he never made any attempt to find out how her mind worked. He treated her like a treasured pet. Sometimes when a sense of hopelessness overwhelmed her she wandered into the little-used rooms of the great house and gave in to her growing sense of isolation and misery, crying herself sick. It said it all that nobody even missed her…

When Gianfranco mentioned two weeks later that he was leaving for America the next day, Kelly wanted to object. She looked at him across the width of their private sitting room. He was handsome, powerful, autocratic, but she realised bitterly, there was no point. He did what he wanted when he wanted; he was not asking her approval, simply telling her, and she simply agreed. In a brief moment of clarity her melancholy lifted enough for her to wonder where the cartwheeling, kick-boxing, bright young career-minded woman of last summer had gone. But Gianfranco's smile as he took her in his arms and kissed her made the image fade.

Within hours of Gianfranco departing, Carmela was called away to stay with a sick friend in Verona, and Kelly was left with only Olivia for company.

At dinner that night Olivia showed her true colours. She lashed into Kelly, telling her that she was gold-digging little slut and Gianfranco cared nothing for her, only the child. When Kelly tried to respond Olivia actually threw a glass of wine over her.

Running from the room, Kelly seriously wondered if the woman was mentally stable at all. She had seen madness in her eyes. Perhaps all her hateful comments and innuendoes were the work of a twisted mind. Paradoxically it made Kelly feel much better. Gianfranco was her husband, and Olivia could not hurt Kelly unless she let her. The easiest way was to avoid Olivia altogether. With that thought in mind, Kelly informed Aldo she would be eating in her suite until the master returned.

Gianfranco phoned the next morning, and after assuring himself Kelly was fine he asked to speak to his mother. Kelly told him she had gone to visit a sick friend. She knew he assumed she meant for a few hours, but didn't elaborate. She was so pleased to hear the sound of his voice she wanted nothing to spoil their rapport.

Kelly heaved a sigh of relief as she watched Olivia drive away the next afternoon to visit Rome. Alone in the house, without Olivia's hateful presence, Kelly thought she might get to like it, but, as a woman who had always been active, she found being waited on hand and foot slightly irksome.

Making a determined effort to get over the misery that was blighting her pregnancy and could not be good for the baby, Kelly took to going for long walks exploring the surrounding countryside. One day she stopped off at the local bar in the nearest village for a refreshing glass of lemonade before returning to the Casa Maldini. Gradually her confidence returned. She even found the nerve to drive the Mercedes that Gianfranco had put at her disposal, and travelled further afield to go shopping. Usually Anna accompanied her.

Ten days later her mother-in-law returned, full of apologies for her absence, and Olivia turned up a couple of hours later.

The next day Gianfranco arrived. Kelly watched him slide out from behind the wheel of his sports car. He was dressed casually in a black leather jacket, black roll-neck sweater, and wickedly skin-tight jeans. With his hair falling over his brow she was vividly reminded of Gianni and the fun they had had with the motorbike, and her heart turned over with love. She looked down at herself, and a regretful sigh escaped her; nothing could hide the fact she was over six months pregnant. But she had dressed with care in black trousers and a bright red and black tunic, and she knew she looked good.

Kelly glanced up and Gianfranco's dark eyes met hers, and in unison they smiled. He stepped forward and crushed her in his arms, kissing her with a hungry passion that wiped all the doubt and fear from her mind.

Over the next two days they made love often. For Kelly a kind of radiant hope began to break through the suspicion and misery of the last few weeks. Gianfranco spent most of the day closeted in his study, but his nights were all hers.

The third night, Kelly dressed in black jersey silk harem pants, with a matching top lavishly covered in multicoloured embroidery. She looked great and felt even better. Full of confidence, she hummed a tune as she descended the stairs into the hall.

Gianfranco always dressed first, and then went downstairs for his usual whisky and soda before dinner, but tonight he had delayed long enough to make love to her in the shower, which was the reason for her good humour.

Olivia was standing in the hall looking her usual immaculate self in a black dress.

'Hi, Olivia,' Kelly said with a polite smile.

'Smile while you have the chance—you won't for much longer,' Olivia sneered, and swept into the dining room in front of Kelly.

A bit of Kelly's renewed confidence slipped as she walked into the room.

It slipped a lot further over dinner. The conversation was stilted, and Gianfranco sat for the most part in a brooding silence. When Kelly said anything he replied in monosyllables, and she was heartily glad when the meal was over. She made her excuses and was the first to leave the table. There was something about this house, she thought fancifully as she walked out into the gloomy hall, that reeked of dark deeds and hidden passions.

'Wait, Kelly.' Gianfranco grasped her arm. 'Come into the study a minute; we need to talk.'

'You've got that right,' she said with feeling. 'What the hell was all that about?' she demanded, following him into the study.

Gianfranco stopped by the desk and swung around to face her. He looked at Kelly, with her blonde hair falling smooth as silk to her shoulders and her blue eyes fixed on him, looking as innocent as sin! He wanted her as he had never wanted any other woman, but she had to realise as his wife she had certain standards to maintain. He was a very busy man, with an estate and a financial empire to run. He expected his home life to proceed like clockwork, and he didn't have time to oversee it himself. He should have had this conversation with Kelly weeks ago, but in the time they spent together she knocked every sensible thought out of his head and all he could think of was making love to her. She drove him crazy, probably always would, but it was time he laid down some ground rules.

'So talk,' Kelly said, glancing across at her husband, looking magnificently male and moody. 'I don't know why you're being so brooding.' She gave a little laugh.

His eyes narrowed, not a glimmer of a smile softening his saturnine features. 'Kelly, as my wife you have a certain position to uphold in the community, and there are certain things that are not acceptable.'

Her smooth brow pleated in a frown; he had to be joking. 'Like picking my nose?' she joked, hoping to lighten the atmosphere. But she failed…

CHAPTER EIGHT

IGNORING her attempt at humour, Gianfranco said, 'It has been brought to my attention that in my absence you were seen in the village on your own in the local bar.'

'So? I was tired and I stopped for a glass of lemonade.' She didn't see his point.

'Kelly, that is not suitable behaviour for my wife, nor is speeding around the countryside in a car with one of the servants. Could you imagine my mother or Olivia ever doing such a thing? They were horrified when they found out,' he told her, a grim smile parting his firm lips. 'I can't be here all the time, and when I am away I would be obliged if you would try and listen to their advice. Olivia assures me she did try to tell you what was expected of the lady of the house, and warned you more than once about your behaviour. You ignored her.'

His comment was like a red rag to a bull. Now she knew what Olivia had meant earlier about wiping the smile off her face. 'That is amazing, considering your mother wasn't here almost the whole time you were away. As for Olivia, apart from calling me a tramp the first night you left, she shot off to Rome the next day. In fact, if it hadn't been for Anna I wouldn't have spoken to a soul until your mother came back the day before you.'

He folded his arms across his broad chest. 'Rubbish.' His disdainful smile had been replaced by a stern, fixed stare. 'I told them to look after you.'

Kelly stared at him. 'You arrogant, conceited, pompous oaf!' she said, her hands on her hips. 'If you could hear yourself.' She shook her head, her blonde hair flying around her face. 'You sound like you're lecturing a child.'

'Not a child, Kelly, but you.' He gave her a cold smile. 'And you do have a tendency to act as a child.'

'Sorry,' she shot back sarcastically, 'but you have the tendency to act like God.'

His hands fell to his sides and he leant back against the desk and stuffed them in his pockets. 'And you have a tendency to, I wouldn't say lie, exactly, but exaggerate,' he drawled cynically. 'I called you every day and you never once mentioned you were alone. Odd, wouldn't you say?' One dark brow arched sardonically.

She looked at him; he was standing with his hands in his pockets, tightening the fine wool of his trousers across his thighs. He was a virile, sexy man and she loved him, but she did not have to listen to this.

'Nowhere near as odd as having a husband who does not believe a word I say,' she opined bitterly, and, spinning on her heel, she left, with tears blinding her eyes. She'd had such hopes for their reunion, but nothing had changed.

Midnight and Kelly was lying wide-awake in bed, tensely waiting for Gianfranco. She heard the sound of the shower running, then silence. The bedroom door opened and closed. Dry mouthed, her stomach swirling with a mixture of desire and dismay, Kelly watched him through the thick screen of her lashes as he walked towards the bed. He was so splendidly male; his naked olive-skinned body gleamed in the rays of moonlight shining through the window. He was a wonderful lover, but however much she tried to ignore the fact she knew in her heart it was no longer enough. A marriage needed more than sex—like sharing each other's hopes, and fears, trust. She opened her mouth to say as much when he slipped into bed beside her, only to have it covered with a tender kiss.

'Sorry, Kelly.' He gathered her in his arms. 'Mamma told me you were right; forgive me.' Quickly divesting her of her nightgown, he gathered her gently in his arms.

Held close against his naked length, she sighed and forgave him. He made love to her with an aching tenderness that brought tears to her eyes. It was only afterwards that doubt reared its ugly head again. Gianfranco believed his mother, believed Olivia, but his wife was another matter entirely. And the thought hurt so much that sleep was a long time coming.

'Buon giorno, cara.'

Kelly's eyes fluttered open. Gianfranco was standing by the bed, wearing a grey three-piece suit. He looked exactly what he was, an incredibly handsome, dynamic businessman, but more importantly her husband, and she stretched and smiled up at him.

'Sorry to wake you, sweetheart, but I am leaving shortly for Rome. It looks as if I will probably have to stay a night or two, and I couldn't leave without kissing my wife goodbye.' He sent her a slow, teasing smile that made her heart beat faster in her chest. 'Miss me and be good. I'll call tonight.' Swooping down, he pressed a long, hard kiss on her softly parted lips.

Dazed by his kiss, she didn't get the chance to object before he had left.

Nothing had really changed, she thought sadly as she wandered aimlessly through the great hall the next morning.

Aldo called her to the telephone. It was Judy Bertoni. Glad to hear a familiar voice, Kelly jumped at the chance when Judy suggested she drive over to Desenzano for lunch and a bit of shopping. Apparently she had opened the house by the lake early, as her father-in-law was ill and the family were staying in Italy to be near him.

Kelly told Carmela where she was going, and, by the time she arrived in Desenzano two hours later, her melancholy mood had lifted a little. Judy greeted her, and seeing the garden where she'd first met Gianfranco, when she'd thought he was a thief, brought a smile to her face.

Driving back towards the Casa Maldini at seven o'clock that night, Kelly was in a much better frame of mind. The trunk of the Mercedes was stuffed full of things for the baby, and a few for herself. She had hardly used the allowance Gianfranco had given her. She only hoped he wasn't mad at how much she had spent today, with Judy's encouragement.

The next thing she saw was the headlights of a car coming straight for her. She swerved violently, and stopped. The seatbelt cut into her stomach like a knife, but prevented her from knocking herself out against the windscreen. With her heart pounding she looked around—the other car had gone. Shaking with shock, she felt her brow. Not much of a bump, she consoled herself, but it was some minutes before she stopped trembling enough to drive on.

By the time she reached the Casa Maldini, she felt ill. Getting out of the car, she instructed Aldo to bring in her purchases and went straight upstairs. A visit to the bathroom confirmed her worst fear: she was bleeding.

Carefully she walked back into the bedroom, and Anna was just entering with some packages. Kelly managed to tell her she needed the doctor, and in seconds Carmela was there and helping her undress and get into bed.

The next few hours were a nightmare. Dr Credo arrived, and after a thorough investigation decided Kelly should stay where she was. The baby appeared to be safe, but he was not taking any chances. Bedrest for at least the next week, and he would check every morning.

* * *

'*Idiota,* must you always be such an impulsive fool?' Gianfranco's voice woke her from a shallow sleep.

She opened her eyes and looked up to see him standing by the bed. He was wearing a dark suit, a white silk shirt open at the throat, a tie hanging loose around his neck. His black hair was rumpled, and his dark eyes were shooting sparks.

'You're back,' she said inanely.

'Back? Of course I'm back. I left a room full of people in the middle of some crucial negotiations and hired a helicopter. What do you expect when I am told you drive the car almost in a ditch and nearly kill yourself and the baby? Are you mad or just plain stupid? What on earth possessed you to drive to Desenzano after Olivia told you not to? Do you have a death wish or something?' Staccato-voiced, like a machine-gun firing, he let rip with the questions.

'And hello to you, too,' Kelly murmured, closing her eyes against the tears that threatened to fall. Olivia again! Why wasn't she surprised? But this time she was not about to argue; she needed all her strength for her baby. She was finally accepting that Gianfranco had about as much sensitivity as a rhinoceros—he was raving at her like a lunatic when she could have done with some tender loving care.

'Damn it, look at me when I am talking to you.'

Kelly, clutching the coverlet with two hands over her chest, opened eyes awash with tears and looked up.

Gianfranco stilled, his face turning grey beneath the tan. What in God's name was he doing yelling at her? She looked shocked and she was crying. He had never seen Kelly cry and it broke his heart. 'Kelly,' he began in a voice that shook.

'What on earth is going on in here?' Carmela walked into the bedroom. 'Really, Gianfranco, you're shouting so loud the servants can hear you.' With a furious glance at her son she sat down on the side of the bed and, brushing Kelly's hair from her brow with an elegant beringed hand, added, 'Take no notice of him, child, he doesn't know what he is saying.'

Kelly was so stunned by her mother-in-law's intervention that she couldn't say a word.

'You go to sleep, as the doctor ordered, and don't worry—you and the baby are going to be fine.' Then, turning blistering eyes back to her son, she got to her feet and pushed his arm. 'As for you, go and get a drink and calm down.'

Gianfranco hesitated for a second, his night-black eyes seeking Kelly's, but she avoided his gaze, and, spinning on his heel, he left the room.

Kelly's whole attitude changed overnight. The shock of the accident and the realisation that, but for the grace of God, it could have been much worse and she might have lost the baby filled her mind to the exclusion of everything else. When Gianfranco walked in the next morning she listened to his apology for yelling; she even half-believed him when he said it had been because he was so terrified of losing her it had made him angry. But she refused to get excited. The doctor had said no excitement, no stress, and plenty of bedrest.

When he took her in his arms and kissed her she responded as usual, but with a slight indefinable restraint. When he told her the doctor had said no sex until after the baby was born she accepted it, and when he suggested he sleep in the other bedroom, so as not to disturb her, she accepted that as well.

A kind of lethargy enfolded her, all she wanted to do was rest and take care of her child. Gianfranco was kindness itself. He took her out to dinner with friends, and he was solicitous of her welfare. That was when she saw him.

His business kept him in Rome, and a trip to Australia to check out a vineyard there took up most of his time. Olivia's sly comments no longer bothered her—her baby was more important than the petty jealousies of a widowed sister-in-law, Kelly told herself.

When she called Gianfranco in Rome one night, and Olivia answered the telephone, Kelly listened as Gianfranco explained without being asked that Olivia was there to shop, so naturally she was staying in the family apartment. Kelly responded with, 'Yes, of course.' Her only interest was her baby.

It was Easter weekend that finally broke her out of her lethargy. The sun was shining, spring had arrived and, eight months pregnant, Kelly finally slipped on the white and rose muslin dress Carmela had bought her. A wry smile curved her lips when she caught sight of her reflection in the mirror. It seemed an age ago when she had complained about it, but now it actually looked quite good, because she filled it.

'*Cara*. Are you ready?' Gianfranco walked into the bedroom, and stopped.

Kelly was standing by the mirror, smiling, and he didn't think he had ever seen her looking more beautiful. She was wearing a white and pink loose-fitting dress with a wide floppy collar, with her long silver-gilt hair falling way past her shoulders. She reminded him of a Gainsborough painting, and he had to stuff his hand in his pocket to control the instant tightening in his groin. He hadn't dared sleep with her because he did not trust himself not to make love to her. Instead he was working like the devil, so when the time came he would be able to take a long break with his wife and child. Only one more month, and then another few weeks and she would be his again.

Telling himself to get his mind above his waist, he

walked across and took her arm. Kelly smiled up at him, and he dropped a brief kiss on her lips—the most he dared to allow himself. 'Come on, I'll take you down to dinner.'

With Gianfranco's arm around her Kelly relaxed into the hard warmth of his body, feeling once more the familiar rush of happiness his touch evoked.

When he stroked her stomach with his free hand, and bent his dark head towards her and said huskily, 'Not long now; I can hardly wait,' she actually trembled slightly, and felt loved.

Dinner was pleasant. Carmela even complimented Kelly on her appearance. Given that she had chosen the dress, it was a bit of a back-handed compliment, but it raised Kelly's spirits anyway. It was over coffee the bomb dropped…

Carmela started it. 'All of Rome society attends. We always go as a family, and stay the night. It is the biggest charity gala of the year. Probably because after the restrictions of Lent are over everyone wants to celebrate.'

'Sounds good.' Kelly grinned; she felt better than she had in months. 'I can't wait.'

She listened as Gianfranco explained he had to attend it, as it was expected of him, and all the reasons why Kelly could not. It was too far to travel in her condition—they couldn't take any chances with the baby. They would only be gone the one night, and Anna and all the staff had strict instructions to look after her.

He had to be joking! Kelly thought. Next weekend, of all weekends! It was her birthday on the Saturday!

Olivia smiled at Gianfranco. 'If Kelly is worried about being on her own, I don't mind missing the gala and staying with her.'

'That's very generous of you,' Gianfranco said with a

beaming smile for Olivia. 'But not necessary—is it, Kelly?' he asked, his dark eyes capturing Kelly's.

'No. I'll be perfectly all right with Anna.' At least Anna genuinely seemed to like her. She was no longer sure of *any* of her dinner companions…

It suddenly hit her that for the past few months she had been married to Gianfranco her lifestyle had changed dramatically; with a few exceptions she had agreed to everything he wanted, so unsure was she of her position as his wife. He, on the other hand, had made no compromise whatsoever in his lifestyle. His trips abroad, his frequent stays in Rome… In a flash of blinding clarity she saw it all, and did not like what she had become. Bit by bit, her confidence in herself as a woman had been chipped away. Without a murmur she'd accepted separate bedrooms, because he said it would be better for her. How often in the night had she awakened, alone in the huge bed, full of fear at the enormity of giving birth? She would have liked the comfort and protection of Gianfranco's arms around her. It didn't have to be sex…

She recalled how insatiable he had been when they were first married. He was a very virile man with a great sex drive. What had Judy said? *'He is not the type for deep emotional commitment…don't let him out of your sight.'* Perhaps she should have listened…

Kelly sat up straighter in the hard-backed dining chair; seated at Gianfranco's right, she flicked a look at his chiselled profile—darkly masculine and supremely confident. He also looked tired. Perhaps he had been unfaithful. How would she know, stuck in the country? All her doubts suddenly resurfaced in her head.

'You're sure?' Gianfranco said quickly, his black eyes narrowing on her pale face with an intensity that seemed to want to read her mind.

Kelly forced a smile to her stiff lips. 'Positive.' She placed her hand over his on the table. 'Now, if you will excuse me.' She squeezed his hand before letting go. 'I'm rather tired.' Pushing back her chair, she flinched as Gianfranco leapt immediately to his feet and took her arm, helping her up.

She needed breathing space, time to marshal her thoughts, but Gianfranco insisted on taking her to her room and helping her undress. She saw the desire flare in his dark eyes as he lifted her nightgown over her head and smoothed it down over her shoulders, his large hand lingering tenderly on her stomach.

Over the past few weeks she had deliberately suppressed the memories of what it felt like to be in his arms, wild with passion, her whole being centred on him, drowning in desire. Now, at the worst possible moment, heat flooded through her, and she trembled. She wanted to be angry with him, but she couldn't. He would remember her birthday, Kelly told herself; even he could not be that insensitive. She was worrying over nothing.

'I know, I know, Kelly,' Gianfranco murmured, and took her in his arms and kissed her long and gently, his dark eyes narrowed intently on her face. 'But it won't be for much longer.' A rueful smile twisted his firm lips, and, taking her hand, he pressed it hard against his aroused flesh. 'It is a lot worse for me, I can assure you.' He groaned. 'But as soon as we can I am going to take you away for a long holiday.'

He wanted her and he loved her—he must do, because she couldn't bear it if he didn't. 'There is no need for us both to suffer,' she whispered, her slender fingers deftly unfastening his trousers.

'No. No. It's not fair. I can do nothing for you; the doctor was quite explicit.'

Kelly simply smiled, her heart racing, and very soon Gianfranco was saying, 'Yes. Yes.'

Kelly slept soundly that night, totally reassured Gianfranco did love her, and she went on thinking it until she watched the Mercedes vanish out of sight early the next Saturday morning.

Tears filled her eyes as she made her way back upstairs to her bedroom and, curling up in a ball on the bed, she let them fall. Today was her birthday, and she had been so sure Gianfranco would remember, stay with her. In her mind it had become a crucial test of his commitment. She had been wrong…

The house was full of servants and yet she had never felt so totally and utterly alone in her whole life. She cried, great racking sobs that shook her whole body; she wept until she had no tears left. It was a nagging pain in her lower back some time later that finally forced her to sit up on the bed. Kelly rubbed her tear-swollen eyes; wallowing in self-pity was no good, for her or the baby.

At ten o'clock the same night Kelly could delay no longer. The pains had started mid-afternoon but she had rested and eaten dinner and tried to pretend it wasn't happening. It was too soon…

Aldo drove her to the hospital in Verona, and Anna accompanied her. Kelly was grateful for her help. Anna held her hand and reassured her when the pain was almost unbearable, and at five to one in the morning Kelly gave birth to a healthy baby girl with a striking mop of ginger hair. In the euphoria of holding her baby in her arms, she could forgive for a moment the fact Gianfranco had not been with her when she needed him. And in the next hour she forgot about everything as the doctor and nurse fussed over her.

The sound of hushed voices wakened Kelly, and her eyes fluttered open. Groggily she glanced around. She was in a private room, and then immediately she remembered, her gaze flying to the side of the bed and the crib.

Gianfranco, tall, dark and incredibly handsome, was at the foot of the crib, still dressed in the formal dinner suit he had obviously worn for the charity gala. His chiselled features looked oddly severe. His mother was standing beside him, but his whole concentration was fixed on the baby.

He was here at last, Kelly thought, her heart swelling with love and pride, and was about to speak to let him know she was awake.

'It's ginger.' He glanced at his mother, an expression of complete amazement on his handsome face, and then back to the baby.

Kelly heard him, and something in her rebelled. 'She is a girl, not an it,' she murmured, hauling herself up into a sitting position.

'Kelly, Kelly, *mia cara*.' Gianfranco dashed to her side, and his dark eyes, blazing with emotion, caught and held hers.

'Kelly, she is beautiful; a perfect little girl. Thank you, thank you. I can't begin to tell you how sorry I am I wasn't here.' Sitting down on the side of the bed, he cupped her face in his strong hands and scattered dozens of frantic kisses on her eyes, her brow, her nose, and finally he covered her mouth.

A slight cough broke them apart. Carmela said, 'Congratulations, Kelly! She is perfect, and now I think I should leave you three alone to get used to being a family.' And to Kelly's surprise she actually bent down and kissed her cheek before departing.

'You don't mind she is not a boy?' Kelly asked Gianfranco as he got up and went back to the crib, staring at his child as if he had never seen a baby before.

He turned his dark eyes gleaming with pride. 'Of course not, *cara.*' His firm lips turned back against brilliant white teeth in the most magnificent smile Kelly had ever seen. 'The next one will probably be a boy.' His comment gave Kelly pause for thought, but then the doctor arrived.

'So how is the new mother now?' Dr Credo asked jovially, standing by the bed. Taking Kelly's wrist in his hand, he took her pulse.

'Fine.' She smiled up at him while the nurse deftly slipped another pillow behind her back.

'Good. You gave us a bit of a scare earlier. Three weeks early—well, one week early really, as two weeks either side of the given date is acceptable. But I am happy to say the baby is perfect. You, on the other hand, are going to have to take care. You haemorrhaged a little after the birth, so we are going to keep you here for a week.' Letting go of her wrist, he turned and took Gianfranco's arm and led him to the far side of the room, talking softly.

Kelly heard the raised voice of her husband and glanced across at him. He was standing, broad shoulders taut, his hands curled into fists at his sides, his face grey beneath the tan, the strong features rigid with some intolerable emotion. His dark gaze moved back to her face, his eyes widening as though he had suddenly realised some great truth. He was a father, and the thought crossed her mind that he did not look particularly ecstatic, more shell-shocked, but she didn't care, as the nurse handed her her baby.

She gazed down in awe at the beautiful, tiny face, the shock of bright red hair, and she was filled with an overwhelming love. She hugged the child to her breast, and pressed the lightest of kisses to the baby's cheek. 'Anna,' she whispered. Then, with the assistance of the nurse, the baby was suckling at her breast.

When the doctor and nurse left, Gianfranco slowly returned to the bedside, his dark eyes narrowing intently. A lump rose in his throat; his lids came down over tear-filled dark eyes, hiding his thoughts.

'Look, Gianfranco, she's feeding,' Kelly murmured, wanting to share the magic moment. 'Isn't she gorgeous?'

He lifted his lashes, making no attempt to hide the moisture in his eyes. 'Yes, you both are,' he said huskily, and, sinking down on the bed beside Kelly, he reached out a finger and gently traced the curve of the baby's cheek, the curve of Kelly's breast.

He watched mother and child, and silently thanked God for their safety. No thanks to him, he thought, for once in his life completely humbled. The information Dr Credo had revealed to him had shocked him to his soul. He had never known Kelly's mother had died in childbirth, but then he had never asked, he castigated himself. Dr Credo had said she did not like talking about it. Apparently he had contacted her own doctor in England for her notes, and that was how he knew. He had assured Gianfranco it was not genetic. But it didn't make Gianfranco feel any better.

'Do you want to hold her?' Kelly asked, pulling the soft cotton of her gown back over her luscious breast. She lifted her head, her eyes, glowing like sapphires, brimming with happiness, seeking his. She chuckled at the flicker of fear she saw in the dark depths that met hers.

'Come on, she won't bite,' she said simply. Nothing could spoil her delight in her child, and she watched as Gianfranco very carefully took the child from her arms.

They looked good together: the broad-shouldered dark-haired father cuddling the infant in his strong arms, a totally besotted look on his handsome face as he stared down at the baby.

'She has my father's hair, but she definitely has your eyes,' Kelly bubbled on. 'I thought we might call her Anna

Louise. You picked Alfredo for a boy and said I could choose if it was a girl. So what do you think? Anna after Anna, who has been a good friend to me, and was such a help last night, and Louise after my mother.'

'Anna Louise is perfect,' Gianfranco said quietly. He could hardly object to his child being named after a servant when the said servant was the only friend Kelly had made in their brief marriage. He had been partying the night away when Kelly had needed him. In all his thirty-one years he had never felt so inadequate—a new experience for him. But he made a silent vow that from now on his first priority was his wife and child.

The nurse entered and took the infant from Gianfranco and placed her in the crib.

'Rest, Signora Maldini,' she said, and, turning back to Kelly, gently eased out a pillow to allow Kelly to lie back down in the bed.

'Yes,' Kelly sighed. 'I am rather tired.' Her long lashes fluttered down. She smiled as she felt the soft brush of Gianfranco's mouth against her own. 'Nice,' she murmured, and slept.

When Kelly awoke three hours later the first of the flowers were delivered, and by evening the nurse complained they were running out of vases. From Gianfranco came dozens of red roses; the card read simply *'Thank you, my love'* and his name. From the staff, from friends…half from people Kelly didn't know. But the headily scented blooms that filled the air completely eclipsed the faint hospital smell.

It was the best week of her life. Gianfranco visited morning and night, and he presented her with an exquisite diamond bracelet. For our daughter, he had said, and kissed her. He brought Anna with him one morning, which delighted Kelly, and on another Olivia, which did not. When

Gianfranco was talking to the nurse Olivia got her dig in. 'You couldn't even do this right—we wanted a boy.'

Kelly ignored her; she was so happy. Judy Bertoni arrived, and let drop she was pregnant again, and the two girls arranged, with Gianfranco's tacit agreement, to spend a few days' shopping when the baby was a bit older.

Apart from the doctor, all the staff spoke only Italian, and much to Kelly's satisfaction her own Italian had improved dramatically, thanks to her tapes.

The following Saturday it was mid-morning when Gianfranco strolled in. Casually dressed in beige trousers and shirt, with a lambswool sweater draped across his broad shoulders, he looked sensational.

'Ready to go, Kelly?' Gianfranco asked in a deep, husky drawl.

'Yes.' She rose to her feet; something warm quivered deep down inside her as her eyes collided with deep dark brown. 'Though I don't know about this dress,' she said, suddenly nervous. It was one Judy had brought in for her, a mint-green wild-silk sheath buttoned down the front from the slightly scooped neck to the hem. Good for feeding, Judy had said. But to Kelly it seemed a little short and a lot clingy under Gianfranco's discerning gaze.

In one lithe stride he was beside her and, wrapping an arm around her waist, he smiled down into her exquisite face. 'You look perfect,' he murmured, and kissed her.

Excitement lanced through her nerve-endings, and sent her pulse-rate racing. Kelly was shocked, fighting against a tide of fierce physical awareness. She had just had a baby; somehow she had thought it would make a difference but it didn't.

'Come on, the car, the baby carriage—everything awaits you, Kelly, and I have a surprise for you.' Gianfranco slashed her a gleaming smile and kissed her again.

'But first the nurse has to carry the baby off the premises and I have to sign you out.'

They stopped at the reception desk, and Kelly waited impatiently while Gianfranco completed the paperwork. She glanced across, as he seemed to be taking a long time. When he came back to her his smile had gone and he looked oddly sombre.

'Something wrong?' she asked, fearful that she might not be able to leave yet.

A muscle jerked beside his unsmiling mouth. 'No, nothing at all.'

But, by the time the car drew up outside the Casa Maldini, though Kelly had tried to hang on to her optimism, she'd failed. They had hardly spoken a word, and it was a tight-mouthed, austere Gianfranco who helped her into the house with baby Anna.

Their reception committee was waiting. Carmela, Olivia and the staff—everyone fussed over the baby. Until Gianfranco took the carrycot holding the baby in one hand and Kelly by the arm with the other. 'I'll take you upstairs.'

A few minutes later Kelly was standing in the middle of a nursery, with every conceivable object a baby could possibly want or need. Gianfranco, with amazing efficiency, had placed the sleeping child in the delicate crib provided, and, straightening up, he gestured with one elegant hand to one of two doors set in one wall. 'Through there is a connecting bedroom with *en suite* bathroom for the nanny, and another bathroom.'

'It is beautiful.' She gazed around at the walls, skilfully painted with a nursery-rhyme scene of a rolling landscape with all kinds of field animals. When her eyes finally reached the figure in the mural she realised it was Little Miss Muffet. She bit back an exclamation at the sight of the enormous spider! She was lost for words…

'While you thought the guest rooms were being decorated this nursery suite was being devised, and it connects with ours. It was Olivia's idea to keep it a surprise.'

The spider should have told her Olivia had had a hand in it, she thought cynically. 'Yes, it is a lovely surprise.' Tearing her eyes from his, she moved to the cot and smiled down at her sleeping baby. 'We will be fine here, won't we, darling?' she murmured.

Straightening up, she glanced back at Gianfranco. 'I think I'll check out the rest later; I could do with a lie-down.' She tried to smile brightly, but it didn't quite come off as she crossed to the door that connected with her old room.

Long, elegant fingers wrapped around her arm and stopped her. 'Wait, Kelly; Mamma has arranged some interviews this afternoon to choose a nanny—obviously you will want to take part,' he said, scrutinising her with dark, impassive eyes.

'No,' she said tightly. 'Let's get one thing clear right now: I am not having my baby looked after by a nanny for quite some time—if ever.' On this point she was adamant. 'Is that clear enough for you?'

'Yes, clear enough. I get the message. I can't do anything right in your eyes.' Gianfranco suddenly exploded. 'Why didn't you tell me it was your birthday last Saturday?' His abrupt change of subject made Kelly's head spin. 'I would never have known except when I signed you out at the hospital the nurse suggested if you had given birth an hour earlier you and Anna would have shared the same birthday. Have you any idea how low that makes me feel?'

'Not half as low as I felt,' Kelly responded with muted sarcasm.

'I don't need to be reminded of that.' Dark hooded eyes met hers. 'Do you imagine for one second I would have left you alone on your birthday, or that I don't regret missing the birth of our child?'

'If you say so,' she agreed. Their baby was sleeping not three feet away and she did not want to argue. She heard his hissed intake of breath and put a hand on his arm. 'I'm sorry but I assumed you knew it was my birthday when you applied for our marriage licence. And you took my passport.' She justified her reasoning, but, seeing the grim expression in his eyes, she changed tack. 'I know you are a Leo, born on the third of August,' she tried to placate him. 'But perhaps it is a male-female thing—Venus, Mars. Let's not fight about it.'

'You're right; I should have known. I'll make it up to you.' He reached out, his strong hands clasping her tense shoulders, drawing her closer. He dropped a kiss on her upturned face, his dark eyes burning into hers. 'I don't deserve you.'

Her heartbeat thudded and she drew in a quick, excited breath, a wealth of emotions welling up within her. She loved her husband, the father of her child; what else mattered? Kelly lifted her hands and circled his neck, pushing her fingers slowly into his thick, luxuriant hair, and she had an almost unbearable longing to be held in his arms again, to feel the long length of his hard body pressed against her without the inconvenience of her once swollen stomach. 'No, you don't, but you've got me,' she teased.

He didn't laugh, but bent his head and let his tongue dart between her parted lips in an erotic invasion that turned her bones to water, and made her tremble. 'Ah, Kelly,' Gianfranco husked in his accented drawl. 'You don't know what you do to me.'

She knew what she would like to do to him, she thought breathlessly, the hardness of his aroused body setting her imagination in overdrive.

'Oops, sorry.' Olivia giggled. 'I couldn't wait to find out what Kelly thinks of the nursery.'

Gianfranco's arms fell from around Kelly. 'She loves it. Don't you, *cara*?'

The phrase 'dropped like a hot brick' sprang to mind... Kelly moved stiffly back and, glancing at Olivia, said, 'Yes, it's great.'

Anna started to cry. Saved by the baby. 'If you will excuse me, Anna needs feeding.' Crossing to the cot, she lifted Anna in her arms.

'You really should get her on a bottle as soon as possible,' Olivia offered. 'Then anyone could feed her.'

Ignoring the other woman's comment, Kelly settled down on the nursing chair, and in minutes Anna was suckling greedily at her breast.

Gianfranco surveyed the mother and child, his black eyes fixed on Kelly's breast. Astonishingly he felt a stab of something very like jealousy towards his daughter. He wanted to be where Anna was, and his body warned him to get out fast. 'I must go,' he said shortly.

Kelly glanced up, but he was already exiting the room. Now that she was left with the baby and only her thoughts, the events of the last half-hour ran through her mind, and warning bells rang loud in her head. What kind of woman had she become? Placating Gianfranco at any cost! Actually apologising to him for his forgetting her birthday! Afraid to speak her mind except on the simplest of topics, in case she offended him or his family. What kind of weak example of womanhood was that to set her precious daughter?

Four weeks later, restless and unable to sleep, Kelly slid out of bed. She glanced briefly at the connecting door to the room Gianfranco occupied and for a moment was tempted to go to him. But he had decreed no sleeping together until she got the all-clear from the doctor at six weeks. He had given her a diamond necklace to match the bracelet as a belated birthday present, also a car for her personal use, and he was good with Anna—when he was around. But he was not around much.

Love was a fearsome emotion, she thought with a sudden shiver. Except for the love of her child—*that* was totally different. She would do anything for Anna, and with that thought in mind she walked along to the nursery. Her breast milk was drying up, and the nurse had suggested supplementing Anna with formula, but the baby did not seem to like it much. Quietly she opened the nursery door, and shock held her rigid for a second.

Olivia had Anna in her arms and was feeding her with a bottle of formula. 'What the hell do you think you are doing?'

Olivia looked at Kelly. 'Practising for when you are gone.'

Snatching the baby from Olivia's arms, Kelly was shaking with anger. Now she knew why Anna was not feeding well from her. 'Get out, and keep away from my child,' she snapped.

'Your child?' Olivia sneered. 'Haven't you realised yet? Gianfranco is going to dump you as soon as you stop breast-feeding and we are going to be a family. Why do you think your so-called marriage was only a civil ceremony in England? He does not even need to divorce you to marry me in church, you stupid cow.' And Olivia walked out.

Kelly tried to tell herself it was the ravings of a slightly unhinged woman. But deep inside she didn't really believe it. She had put up with a lot to stay with Gianfranco, but when it came to her daughter she would fight like a tigress.

CHAPTER NINE

Three years later.

ST AIDEN'S COVE in Cornwall was virtually deserted, although it was early summer. Kelly stood beside the outcrop of rocks on the tiny beach and watched her daughter methodically shovelling sand into a small red bucket; nothing would stop Annalou's determination to build a sandcastle, and Kelly was vividly reminded of Gianfranco. Annalou had her father's eyes, and also his confidence. Nothing seemed to bother her.

Unfortunately the same could not be said for her mother, Kelly conceded wryly. It had been a June day, much like this, when she had made her escape from the Casa Maldini.

In the end it had been quite simple, she recalled, her mind going back to that traumatic time. She had told Gianfranco what Olivia had done, and he had told her she was overreacting. They had argued, but for once Kelly had refused to give in.

The night before she was to go to the doctor for her final check Gianfranco had walked into her bedroom. She could see him now in her mind's eye, looking breathtakingly handsome, wearing only a robe, his long tanned legs slightly splayed as he had stared down at where she lay in the big bed. 'Tomorrow you see the doctor—I am right?'

His dark eyes, smouldering with a brooding intensity, had caught and held hers, and she had felt every nerve in her body leap to quivering life. As if compelled to, he had sat down on the side of the bed and taken her in his arms. The warm, musky male fragrance had been dizzyingly familiar as he'd covered her mouth with his and kissed her with a hungry, urgent passion.

'Bella mia,' he had groaned against her mouth, his supple fingers stroking her breast, his other hand lifting to sweep the soft fall of her hair down her back, his night-black eyes skimming her upturned face, the softly parted lips. 'Hurry back tomorrow. I am dying of frustration.' He'd kissed her again.

Fool that she was, two kisses had been all it took to convince her that her fears were groundless and Gianfranco loved her. They were a family, and the future looked rosy. But his parting comment—'Remember to ask the doctor to give you the Pill—it is the safest birth control'—had dented her euphoria somewhat.

But nothing like the shock she had got the next day. She had returned from the doctor's, excitement bubbling inside her, and headed straight for Gianfranco's study, unable to wait to give him the good news.

Even now it still hurt, Kelly thought bitterly. The door had been partially open, and she had seen them together. Gianfranco and Olivia in each other's arms. Judy's warning, Olivia's actions—all had made perfect sense. But it was what her husband and Olivia had said that had horrified her, had prompted her decision to leave immediately.

'I can assure you, Olivia, Kelly and I will certainly not be having any more children.'

'So why wait? Get rid of her now, Gianfranco. I can take care of Anna Louise; I love her.'

No way was Olivia getting her hands on Kelly's child.

Kelly had acted her socks off. Her sad face had been genuine when she'd told Gianfranco later that the doctor had said another week, but not for the reason he had thought. With a little persuasion Gianfranco had agreed Kelly and the baby could visit Judy Bertoni for a few days, while he took the opportunity to clear up some business in New York.

Ironically Gianfranco had provided her means of escape. He had given her a state-of-the-art mobile phone, with instructions to call him any time, so that way he would not disturb her when she was busy with Anna Louise. Raiding his study, she had looked for her passport and by a bizarre stroke of luck she had seen the new one Gianfranco had obtained for her with the baby listed on it. He had said he would take her on holiday, but she couldn't believe the nerve of the man. Obviously the holiday was to have been her pay-off! Well, he was in for a rude awakening, she had vowed.

The next day she had been on a plane to England, and by the evening she had emptied her bank account—the money from the sale of her house a welcome bonus. She'd made a point of telephoning Gianfranco several times, so as not to arouse suspicion. The final call she had made the next morning, when she'd left the hotel where she had spent the night. She told him she had left the car at Rome Airport and she had left him. Olivia was welcome to him, but not her baby.

He had still been yelling down the telephone when she'd switched it off and thrown it into the road. A black cab had put paid to it.

Remembering her honorary Uncle Tom from her childhood, she had headed for his home in Cornwall, and he had welcomed her and Anna Louise with open arms. After he had heard her story, he had insisted she stay with him in his cottage overlooking the bay. He had introduced her to his neighbours as Kelly Hope, his recently widowed niece, and her baby, and told Kelly all she had to do to stay hidden was to stay off any government computer—Inland Revenue, health and education systems etc.

With the money from her house in Tom's bank account, it had been no problem. Ellen Jones, whose father was a friend of Tom's, ran a small gymnastics club in the nearby town of Newquay, and she had given Kelly a part-time job helping out at the club, and she paid her cash.

For three years Kelly's life had worked fine. She glanced back at Annalou. She was gritting her little teeth, her whole attention concentrated on making the 'biggest sand castle ever' for Uncle Tom.

Kelly's eyes squeezed shut in a spasm of pain. They had buried Tom yesterday. It was Tom who had shortened Anna Louise to Annalou. Yet they would never, ever see him again. She would never hear that deep Cornish burr in his tone as he comforted and cajoled her. Their lives would have to change...

Gianfranco hesitated, to control the pounding of the blood in his veins. It was Kelly, more beautiful than ever, her luscious body honed to perfection; even the cheap black dress she was wearing could not hide that. The neckline was low enough to reveal the upper curve of her breasts, and short enough to reveal her shapely legs. Her silver-blonde hair was longer, untamed, falling almost to her waist. He had given her everything, and she had betrayed him...

Silently he moved forward.

'So this is where you are hiding, Kelly?'

After three years Kelly recognised the deep, accented voice instantly. Her eyes flew open, shock lancing through her. She stared; she couldn't help it. He was standing not a foot away. An all-powerful male. His tanned face had a few more lines, but they only added to his dark, devastating good looks. He was dressed in perfectly tailored black trousers and a black roll-neck sweater. With his great height and broad-shouldered, virile body, that simply oozed sex appeal, he looked like some avenging angel—or devil—she realised as his eyes, black as night, roamed over her with unconcealed contempt. Goosebumps erupted all over her body and she reeled back against the rock as though blasted by the banked-down violence in his eyes.

'You,' she murmured—it was as if by thinking about him earlier she had conjured him up. Quickly she tore her gaze away from his and sought Annalou, who was sitting in the sand, her brown eyes turned quizzically up at the man.

'Big man,' Annalou said. 'Do you want to make a sandcastle?'

Gianfranco glanced down, and immediately dropped to his haunches with lithe grace. 'Anna, isn't it?' he said softly. And as Kelly watched the transformation on his hard, sculptured face was miraculous. He smiled at the child. 'I love to make sandcastles, Anna.' He reached out a none too steady hand to touch the fiery red hair surrounding the angelic-looking face. Two sets of identical deep brown eyes met and fused with each other. It was instant attraction.

Kelly saw Annalou grin, and she had to swallow the lump in her throat that threatened to choke her.

'My name is Anna Louise Hope, but everyone calls me Annalou,' she corrected him seriously.

Gianfranco shot a glance at Kelly that would have blistered paint. But the face he turned back to the child was gentle. 'Then I shall call you Annalou,' he said with a smile. 'And you can call me Daddy.'

Go straight for the jugular, why don't you? Kelly was struck dumb by Gianfranco's blunt admission.

Annalou looked up at Gianfranco with wide excited eyes.

'You my daddy?' she began…then, glancing up at Kelly, 'Mummy?' she said. Only one word, suddenly unsure for the first time in her young life.

Narrowed black eyes lifted to Kelly. Gianfranco was watching her like a great black panther waiting to pounce. He scanned her ashen face and horrified eyes. 'Tell her, Kelly,' he drawled silkily.

Kelly could hardly string two coherent thoughts together, let alone a sentence, she was shivering in so much shock. Annalou hadn't noticed the absence of a daddy in her life until she had started playschool after Easter. Kelly had told her he lived far away, and left it at that. Looking down at the man and the child, at the triumph on the face of the former, she realised with a sinking heart she had nowhere to go… She was trapped.

Bending her knees, she dropped in the sand beside Annalou. 'Yes, sweetheart.' She instinctively curved a protective arm around her shoulders. 'This—' She saw the derision in Gianfranco's eyes, and stammered helplessly. 'He—I mean, this man is your daddy.'

Annalou wriggled from under Kelly's arm and threw herself at Gianfranco. 'You really are my daddy.' And with childish logic added, 'Uncle Tom had to go to heaven, so he has sent you.'

Gianfranco closed his arms around Annalou, and held her hard to his broad chest. 'Something like that.' Gianfranco slashed a look of utter hatred over the top of the child's head at Kelly, and, leaping smoothly to his feet with Annalou still in his arms, he added, 'But, unlike your Uncle Tom, I am going to stay with you forever.' He made his promise softly, with a kiss on the child's smooth cheek that Annalou happily returned.

Lifting his proud head, his narrowed eyes studied Kelly's stricken white face with a kind of grim satisfaction. 'Isn't that so, Mummy?' He demanded her compliance, the derision in the deep, dark drawl obvious to Kelly, but lost on the child.

Kelly staggered unsteadily to her feet; she had turned even paler as the full horror of what he had said sank in. She had escaped Gianfranco once, but he would never make the same mistake again. At least not where his child was concerned. As for her… She was probably just as dispensable now as she had been three years ago.

'Mummy?' Annalou's small face was turned towards her, her expression expectant, waiting for her mother's confirmation of the wonderful news.

Suddenly, Kelly was overwhelmed with the most horrible feeling of guilt, mixed with a deep-rooted fear for the future. But she could do nothing but agree…

Hours later, the sandcastle built and marvelled over, Kelly had been unable to avoid taking Gianfranco back to her home. Tom had left her the house in his will, along with his money—which was actually what was left of hers! He had lived on his pension, and it had stopped at his death. Kelly had been worrying over what she was going to do, but now that worry was replaced with a much greater fear. Annalou was too young to notice, but Gianfranco had made it obvious by each look and gesture in Kelly's direction that he was biding his time until they were alone, and then all hell would break loose.

'Read a story, Daddy,' Annalou said, now bathed and safely tucked up in bed. She turned away from where Kelly stood to Gianfranco, at the opposite side of the bed. 'Please.'

Kelly felt a swift stab of jealousy at how quickly her daughter had fallen under Gianfranco's spell. But then she glanced across at him, his black hair dishevelled, his dark eyes smiling down at the little girl. Kelly doubted any female from three to ninety-three could resist his seemingly effortless charm. He was lounging on the bed, one arm around Annalou, the other holding the book, one long leg stretched out on top of the coverlet, his other foot on the floor. The fabric pulled taut across his muscled thighs was enough to make any woman groan, and to Kelly's dismay she was no exception…

Her hands turned into tight fists at her sides. She had to get out of here; the tension that had simmered between Gianfranco and her all afternoon was driving her mad and her nerves were at screaming pitch. 'Goodnight, sweetheart.' She leant over and pressed a kiss to the downy cheek, making sure to avoid any contact with Gianfranco, and, straightening up, she added, 'I'll leave Daddy to tuck you in.'

She almost ran out of the bedroom and stumbled back down the stairs. Walking into the kitchen, she eyed the table, a grim smile curving her lips. They had eaten beans on toast for dinner—hardly Gianfranco's style, but Annalou's favourite. Quickly she set about cleaning up. She washed the dishes, wiped down the benches—anything to keep busy so she did not have to think. But she could not control her thoughts so easily. Finally, with nothing left to do, she wandered back into the living area and across to the picture window that filled almost the whole wall. She stood still as a statue and gazed out over the sand and sea.

She had been so happy—perhaps not happy, she amended, but certainly content here. It had been an old barn, converted quite simply with the front door at one end opening into one large living area, and a kitchen, utility room and rear door at the back. A staircase up the side of the wall led to a galleried landing with two bedrooms and a bathroom. It stood on its own on the outskirts of the small fishing village, and had originally been rented out as a holiday home. Tom had stayed here once and then bought it.

Tom; if only he were here now, she thought as she squeezed back a stray tear. He would know what to do. He would know how to handle Gianfranco. Still, straightening her shoulders, she drew in a deep breath. She had matured a lot in the last three years; she was no longer the naïve pregnant girl who had jumped at Gianfranco's offer of marriage, flattered that he had hired a detective to find her.

'Quite a spectacular hiding place,' a deep husky voice drawled mockingly behind her, and she jumped as if she had been shot, as she had not heard him come downstairs.

Spinning around, she faced him. 'How did you find me?' Kelly went straight onto the attack. 'Detectives again,' she sneered.

Gianfranco studied her with half-closed eyes. 'Your friend Tom wrote and told me.'

Of all the things he could have said, that was the most hurtful; every vestige of colour drained from Kelly's face as she looked up at him with wide, pain-filled eyes. 'No. No, I don't believe you.' Tom would never have betrayed her trust.

He shrugged his broad shoulders. 'Please yourself.' Strolling across the room, he sank down on the leather sofa, his long legs stretched out before him in nonchalant ease. 'It is immaterial now. Though I must congratulate you on doing a very good job. At first I thought it might be post-natal depression, and I checked with Dr Credo. But no… You had left his surgery one hundred per cent fit and happy, with six months' supply of contraception pills in your hand,' he said drily.

Colour flared in Kelly's cheeks, her lie revealed. She threw Gianfranco a sharp look, deeply disturbed at his tone, but she could read nothing from his coldly remote expression.

'You are a great actress. I take my hat off to you,' he said with cutting cynicism. 'I spent a fortune hiring the best detectives known, and they could find no trace of you after you left a London hotel. You have remarkably little family—a second cousin on your father's side in Bristol, I believe, was as near as they got. Your mother was brought up in an orphanage. You were incredibly lucky—or it was great planning?—to have met Tom, my dear wife.' His mouth twisted chillingly. 'Or you would never have got away with it.'

Uneasily Kelly listened and frowned. Gianfranco was right in every detail about her escape, and her family, so why would he lie about Tom telling him where she was? Horrified, she knew Gianfranco was telling the truth. Suddenly her legs felt wobbly, and she moved to sit down in the nearest armchair. She couldn't take it in. Tom had betrayed her. Kelly glanced warily across at Gianfranco. 'When did he write to you?' she asked quietly.

'Ten days ago, from his hospital bed apparently. But I only received the letter last night. He knew he was going to die, so he wrote to inform me that, although he loved you as his own, he could no longer take care of you.' He said it so dispassionately that Kelly was lulled into a false sense of security. In a way she could understand Tom's reasoning, even though she wished with all her heart he had not done it.

'He also said it was time I took care of my own.' One dark brow arched sardonically. '"Chance would be a fine thing," I believe, is the English expression.'

Lounging back on the sofa, Gianfranco was an incredibly attractive vision of relaxed masculinity. To her horror, despite being in the midst of fear, Kelly felt the familiar flood of sensual awareness heat her whole body. He was still the same insensitive, arrogant devil, she reminded herself firmly. 'Yes, well, now you have the chance. You made sure of that when you blurted out you were Annalou's father,' she declared bitterly. 'You could have traumatised the child,' she added for good measure.

In a blur of movement Gianfranco lunged off the sofa and hauled her to her feet by her upper arms. The transformation was incredible; his face was so taut with rage that Kelly feared for her safety.

'You dare say that to me, you bitch! You, who deprived her of her father for three years.' His night-black eyes, leaping with violence, bored into hers. 'Deprived me of my child. Replaced me with your lover, Tom.'

'No. No,' Kelly cried, stunned by his reasoning. 'Let go of me.' She tried to shrug his hands off, terrified at the fury in his tone. 'It wasn't like that.'

She tried again to pull free, but his hands tightened on her arms. 'Yes, it was, my beautiful, traitorous wife. Don't take me for a fool—this house has just two bedrooms,' he said through clenched teeth, and hauled her closer into his hard body.

'There are two beds; I share with Annalou.'

'For appearances' sake, I don't doubt,' he snarled. 'And tonight I share with Anna Louise. *Dio*, you even deprived my child of her family name, and I—I, her father—had to hear her tell me she is always called Annalou.' He focused on her with a dark, blistering anger that heightened the tension to breaking point. 'I saw you today on the beach and I wanted to kill you. Three years of hell you have put me through. But you are not worth losing my freedom for. Instead I am going to make sure you suffer as I have,' he hissed with lethal intent.

The fear and tension that had held her since the moment

he had walked back into her life finally snapped and Kelly exploded. 'Make *me* suffer! You did that from the day you married me. You never wanted me, all you ever wanted was my child. You never even tried to get in touch with me until you discovered I was pregnant. And even—'

'You stood me up,' Gianfranco cut in ruthlessly. 'I do not run after any woman.'

Kelly sucked in air convulsively. He was the same arrogant, conceited jerk he had always been. 'Exactly,' she ground out mockingly. 'As I said, it was only my baby you wanted. Amazing the lengths you would go to, even marrying me for that manic Olivia you love so much. You kept me in that great mausoleum of a house like a damned broodmare; you never believed a word I said, but Olivia or your mother could do no wrong.'

One hand slid upwards to curve around her jaw, and as he tilted her head back his glittering eyes bored down into hers. 'You dare to blame *me*?' he raked back scathingly. 'I gave you everything a woman could want, and you repaid me by running off with my child.'

'You gave me everything but your support.' Everything but your love, she almost added, but stopped herself in time.

'You had that, and if you had demanded more I would have given it. But, no, shall I tell you why you ran?' He emitted a harsh, cynical laugh. 'Because in your usual childish fashion you listened to rumour and innuendo and jumped to a whole lot of false conclusions. I told you I had never loved Olivia as anything but a sister in poor health and needing help, but you chose not to believe me.' His fingers tightened almost cruelly on her chin and she tried to jerk her head away.

'Look at me,' he demanded savagely, and she did, suddenly aware of the brush of his thighs against her own, the close proximity of his large body. 'I might have made mistakes as a husband, but I never deserved what you inflicted on me, the loss of my child.'

Maybe not, Kelly conceded—she had felt guilt over the years, but above all she knew he was lying. She had seen him with Olivia in his arms, and heard him.

He looked at her, and subtly the atmosphere changed. He was smiling, his hard eyes glinting with a devilish light as he said silkily, 'But you know what really gets me? I have tortured myself for three years, wondering if you were all right, staring at the one photograph of my daughter on her first birthday that you deigned to send me. Posted in London with no way to trace it.' He traced his fingers smoothly over her cheek while his other hand closed firmly around her waist. 'Clever, very clever. Then I discover you have a lover—''Uncle'' Tom,' he spat, in a voice laced with bitter contempt.

'No.' She saw it too late in his darkening eyes. Felt it in the hard length of his body pressed against her. 'No, Gianfranco,' she cried, but his mouth took hers and she was shamed by the incredible hunger that shook her to the depths of her being. *No*, her mind cried as her lips helplessly parted to his savage invasion.

Held against the hard length of his body, she tried to struggle, but the total contact was like an electric shock to her system, awakening a dormant awareness she could no longer control.

'Three years you owe me,' he grated as his mouth moved down her throat, then her shoulder.

'No.' Kelly shuddered as his hand slipped inside the bodice of her dress to cup her breast, and at his touch desire swept through her, leaping from nerve-end to nerve-end with a speed that shocked her as it seduced her. The scent of him filled her nostrils, and the taste of him—ah! The familiar taste of him as once more his mouth covered hers was like a drug to her sensually deprived body.

She knew she should stop him, but at that moment his fingers rolled across her rigid nipples and she was swamped in a wave of heat. Instead her arms slipped around his neck. He lowered her to the floor, his lips against her throat, her shoulder, his long body stretched out half over her, his knee between her thighs.

Gianfranco stared down at her; her dress was around her waist, and a scrap of white lace was the only barrier to the heated centre of her. He slipped the dress down her arms and bent his head, his mouth suckling on a rigid nipple.

Kelly shut her eyes, a low moan of dismay and desire equally mixed escaping her. She felt his hand slide up her thigh, his long fingers slip beneath the lace barrier and wrench it from her body. His hand curved around the blonde curls at the apex of her thighs, his long fingers intimately exploring the velvet flesh. She was hot and damp and she shook with a need, a want so agonisingly painful that she cried out his name. And from that moment on she was lost in her own fevered response to the awesome passion he evoked in her body, which had been celibate for far too long.

Rearing up, Gianfranco touched the tip of his tongue to the tip of each breast as he deftly unfastened his trousers. Then he slid his hands under her and lifted her up to accept the fierce thrust of his manhood, burying himself deep in the hot, tight heart of her femininity.

There was nothing tender or gentle about their coupling. More a wild white-water ride, two bodies grinding, drowning in a savage, primitive hunger, hand and mouth, tooth and nail, they caressed and clung until Kelly's body convulsed first, in an agony of exquisite pleasure, and Gianfranco followed, his great body shaking with the force of his release. For a long moment he lay with his face buried in the soft curve of her throat and shoulder, then with a violent curse in Italian he rolled off her.

Kelly understood the curse he had uttered, and heard the slight sound of his clothes being readjusted, the zing of a zip. She shivered. Not with cold but with shame.

Leaping to his feet, Gianfranco ran a hand through his rumpled hair. Damn it, that was not supposed to have happened. He stared down at her, his black eyes raking over her flushed face and the abandoned position of her slender body, and he grimaced. But she was so hot and willing she couldn't help herself. Once she had been all his. *Dio*, how many more men had tasted her sweetness? he wondered grimly.

Kelly saw her briefs lying on the floor and silently groaned, shame keeping her from looking at Gianfranco.

'You could earn a fortune as a porn star. Straighten yourself up, for God's sake,' Gianfranco said bluntly, his voice as hard and cold as ice.

Ashen-faced, Kelly pulled up the bodice of her dress, pulled down the skirt, picked up the torn briefs and, ignoring him, walked into the kitchen and shoved them in the bin.

Zombie-like, she crossed to the bench, filled the kettle at the tap, and switched it on. She took a cup from the shelf and spooned instant coffee into the cup. With her hands propped on the bench and her head bent she waited for the kettle to boil. And all the while her mind was screaming. What have I done? She couldn't believe she had surrendered to Gianfranco so quickly, so uninhibitedly. Three years, she silently groaned, and as far as her traitorous body was concerned it could have been yesterday. Nothing had changed.

Yes, yes, it had, Kelly amended and, straightening up,

she lifted the kettle and poured the water into the cup. She had changed…she was a much stronger woman; bringing a child up on her own had taught her a lot. She lifted the cup of black coffee to her lips with a slightly trembling hand, and after the first mouthful she felt marginally better. At least she had wiped the taste of Gianfranco from her mouth. If only she could wipe him from her life so easily, she thought bitterly.

'Good idea. Make one for me,' Gianfranco commanded.

Kelly spun around at the sound of his voice, about to tell him to make it himself, but caution stopped her. She had a much bigger argument to win than who should make the coffee. He was sitting on one of the three seats at the small breakfast table, his dark head turned towards her, his hooded gaze completely unreadable.

She cleared her suddenly dry throat. 'Black with one sugar, is it?'

Gianfranco raised an eyebrow. 'You remembered.'

'Some things are hard to forget,' she muttered, turning back to the bench and taking another cup from the shelf. And she wasn't talking about the coffee. One look at him looking so cool and composed, while she was still reeling from the shock of having just made love—No, not love, sex—annoyed her immensely.

'Yes, it is gratifying to know I can still make you burn, and cry out *my name*,' he emphasised in his deep, husky drawl. 'It makes the future so much easier; a celibate marriage never appealed to me.'

Kelly realised in stricken apprehension that Gianfranco had read her mind. She could not speak; her tongue was glued to the dry roof of her mouth as she fought to remain calm. She poured water into the cup with her heart hammering in her chest. No way was she resuming married life with Gianfranco, as his words implied.

'From what I have seen, Annalou seems to be a happy, well-balanced little girl.'

Kelly inwardly sighed with relief at the change of subject, but her relief was short-lived. She turned to look at him, and the gleam of mocking triumph in his black eyes sent a shiver down her spine. 'Yes, she is,' Kelly said curtly, and moved to place the cup of coffee on the table in front of him. 'And she is very happy here. She has lots of friends.' If she could convince him to give her a divorce, Kelly thought, nervously chewing her lip, she wouldn't mind his having some custody rights.

'This place looks like a holiday home. I understand you now own it.' He lifted the cup to his mouth and swallowed the hot coffee, then he added smoothly, 'I suppose Annalou can still spend the odd holiday here and keep in touch with her friends.'

'Odd holiday!' Kelly exclaimed. 'We live here.'

'Not any more—we are leaving for Italy in the morning.'

It was no more than she had expected from the moment she had set eyes on him on the beach, but it was still a terrible shock. Kelly staggered back to lean against the kitchen bench, not trusting her legs to support her. 'No, Annalou and I are staying here.' She had to stay in control, be convincing, but she was trembling inside. 'But I am prepared to be reasonable. You and I can get a quickie divorce, and we can share custody. You can visit whenever you like.'

'Have you finished?' he demanded with eyes as cold as the Arctic wastes, and for a moment her mind went blank. 'Good. Because I am taking my daughter back to Italy. Any visiting to be done will be at my discretion.'

'You can't do that. I won't let you.' Kelly burst into speech, trying to sound firm, but nothing could disguise the slight tremor in her voice. The full enormity of what he had said hit her like a punch to the stomach. She felt sick with fear, and she knew she was fighting for her daughter's well-being, never mind her own. 'There is no way I will allow Annalou anywhere near Olivia without me.'

'So, come with her.'

'No.' She instinctively denied the possibility. 'And you can't take Annalou without my permission.' She said it, but didn't really believe it. She knew very well that Gianfranco was a man who got exactly what he wanted. Kelly doubted anyone had thwarted him in his life except herself. If she was honest she was slightly amazed she had got away from him for so long. It was there in the proud tilt of his head, the dark, mocking eyes watching her like an insect under the microscope.

'With you in jail I will have no problem.'

'Jail!' What on earth was he talking about?

Gianfranco set his cup down and the clash when it hit the saucer indicated he was nowhere near as calm as he appeared. He stood up, his mouth curving in a cruel smile. 'I had Kelly Hope checked out the minute I read the letter. A man was waiting at Exeter Airport when I arrived today with the details. You are a respected widow with a child, who for the past three years has been working for an Ellen Jones who owns a gym. Correct?'

At the mention of her job, Kelly suddenly saw where he was leading. 'My private life, where I work, is no concern of yours,' she snapped back.

'Perhaps not, but I wonder what the Inland Revenue will make of you working—the black economy, I believe is the British term for it, or cash in hand?' He chuckled without humour. 'Tax evasion is a serious offence, punishable by a term of imprisonment in some cases.'

Stunned, Kelly could only stare at him. He met her gaze with sardonic challenge as he continued. 'I would not worry too much—it would be your first offence.' He gave a very Latin shrug of his broad shoulders. 'Of course, poor Ellen Jones will also be in trouble. Then there is the kindly doctor, a friend of Tom's, who, without any formal identification from you, has privately taken care of your health, immunised my daughter. He also will suffer.'

Kelly jerked upright and took a step towards him, rigid with fury, her eyes flashing blue flames. 'You are despicable!' she cried. 'You would hurt innocent people, my friends, just to get back at me?' She shook her head in utter disbelief. Jail was no idle threat.

'I don't have to,' he injected as she stared at him in outrage and shock. 'It is your decision, Kelly. You can come with Annalou and me to Italy, or stay here and face the consequences.' He looked at her with triumphant amusement in the black depths of his eyes. 'Either way, I get my daughter.'

CHAPTER TEN

IT HAD been no choice at all, Kelly thought, staring down at her sleeping daughter for a long moment before lifting her head and eyeing the huge painted spider still on the wall with distaste.

Even if she'd faced up to the Inland Revenue, though she had done wrong, she doubted she would have ended up in jail. She had never earned enough money to pay tax anyway. At least that was what Tom had told her. But it would have meant betraying Ellen and probably the doctor. The deciding factor, the one thing Kelly had not been able to countenance, had been to allow Annalou to visit Italy without her, and be subject to Olivia's poisonous presence.

Kelly turned quickly as Gianfranco's voice broke into her musings.

'She is a beautiful child.' He was standing at the opposite side of the bed, his huge body stooped to press a kiss on Annalou's cheek, and the sheer size and strength of him, along with his state of undress, sent her pulse-rate rocketing.

He was wearing a navy-blue towelling robe, loosely belted at the waist and ending mid-thigh, his toned olive skin and mat of black body hair exposed between the low lapels of the garment. Kelly flushed at where her thoughts were leading and looked away, tension in every line of her slim body.

Despising her weakness at reacting so instantly to his unexpected appearance, she was curt in her response. 'Yes, she is, and I want her to stay that way, without any influence from your sister-in-law.' She masked her frustration and fear by prompting coldly, 'I suppose Olivia will be joining us for dinner?'

They had arrived at the Casa Maldini at four. Much to Kelly's surprise, her mother-in-law, Carmela, had welcomed her with open arms, and apologised for not being more of a friend to her the last time she had lived at the house. And Anna was still here, engaged and getting married in August.

Annalou had loved the house immediately, unlike her mother not in the least intimidated by the vast building and the servants. By the time Kelly, with the help of Anna, had put the little girl to bed, Annalou in her usual determined fashion had secured a promise she could be a bridesmaid at the wedding. The only person Kelly had not seen yet was Olivia.

Strolling around the bottom of the bed, Gianfranco stopped beside Kelly and glanced down at her with dark, enigmatic eyes. 'Olivia will not be joining us for dinner, or any other meal. She does not live here any more.'

'What? But you said last night—' And she stopped. He had neither confirmed nor denied Olivia's presence; he had simply said, 'So, come with her.' Kelly searched his face but she could read nothing from his bland expression. 'You let me think…'

One dark brow arched sardonically. 'What you wanted to think, *cara*.' He drawled the endearment. 'I wanted my wife and daughter back in my home, and I used any and every means at my disposal. In my book marriage is for life. Remember that and we will get along fine.'

'Olivia left? When?' Kelly still had trouble believing it, though she had no trouble believing the rest of her indomitable husband's statement. He was a ruthless devil when it came to getting his own way.

'A few weeks after you. She is now married to a banker and living in Switzerland.'

Was he broken-hearted at losing Olivia? Lowering her head to hide her astonishment at his revelation, she surreptitiously glanced up at him from beneath the screen of thick lashes. He didn't look it. In fact, Kelly suddenly noted that his dark eyes were blatantly roaming over her slender body in studied masculine appraisal. She had already bathed and dressed for dinner in a violet satin slip dress with spaghetti straps supporting the bodice, and to her shame she felt her breasts harden against the soft fabric in tingling arousal. She dropped her gaze, but that was worse. Last night he had taken her without even removing his clothes, but tonight, with his robe gaping open, she realised she had never seen so much prime male naked flesh in three long years…which did nothing for her temperature, or her temper.

'Oh, for God's sake, go and put some clothes on!' she exclaimed, brushing past him and heading for the door. 'Dinner is at nine.' Damn! She sounded like his mother, and his husky chuckle did nothing to calm her quivering nerves.

Kelly barely touched the food, even though she had hardly eaten anything all day. She'd phoned Ellen to ask her to keep an eye on the house. Then they'd flown from Exeter by private plane to Verona, and the final leg had been the car journey to the Casa Maldini. Everything had happened so fast, she couldn't think straight; she felt positively light-headed.

A brief glance at Gianfranco seated at the head of the table and Kelly turned an apologetic smile to Carmela and stood up. 'It has been a long day, and I am rather tired, so if you will excuse me I think I will go to bed.'

'Of course,' Carmela responded, 'I understand.'

'You have had a traumatic week. You need a rest,' Gianfranco said smoothly. 'Sleep well.'

He'd got that right, she thought as she stifled a yawn. Tom's death, the funeral five days later, and Gianfranco the next day—it suddenly hit her she had barely slept or eaten for a week. The fact Gianfranco had recognised it was surprising; he wasn't known for his sensitivity.

'Goodnight,' she said firmly, but she could not meet his dark watchful eyes, and she speedily crossed the room with more haste than grace.

Kelly glanced around the bedroom, it was the same room she had occupied before, and Anna had laid her cotton nightie out on the massive four-poster bed. She wondered if Gianfranco still occupied the bedroom next door, and immediately dismissed the thought. Contemplating Gianfranco in bed, any bed, did nothing for her peace of mind.

Picking up her nightie, she walked into the adjoining bathroom. In minutes she had had a shower, and, after drying herself quickly with a large bath towel, she slipped the nightie over her head. A brief glance in the mirror and she grimaced. The white nightie was a simple mass of gathered cotton falling from a round neckline to her feet—with her hair brushed loose and her face free of make-up, the only point of colour was the purple rings under her eyes. She looked like a ghost.

Shrugging her shoulders, Kelly returned to the bedroom, and then on to the nursery. She stood for a few minutes staring down at her sleeping daughter, and then made a silent prayer that Annalou would be happy here. For herself she didn't care. Annalou was everything.

Had she done the right thing? A resigned sigh escaped her. Deep in her heart Kelly knew she had never really had a choice. Gianfranco turning up yesterday had only precipitated matters, as if she was honest Kelly had already decided to get in touch with Gianfranco after Annalou had asked about her father at Easter. Tom's illness and the need to look after him had given her an excuse to delay, but with Tom's death she'd had no more excuses. Which was probably why she imagined she had conjured Gianfranco up yesterday on the beach, she thought wryly.

Sighing, she touched a finger to her daughter's cheek. Had she jumped to conclusions three years ago, as Gianfranco had said? If not, did it matter that Gianfranco had loved Olivia? Olivia was no longer in the equation.

For years she'd tried not to think about her husband because it had hurt too much, but now she faced the facts. Last night had taught her she was still as deeply attracted to him as ever. Only now she did not call it love. She was older and wiser, and for the first time since meeting Gianfranco again Kelly considered the possibility of trying to make the marriage work.

She didn't trust him, but then again he didn't trust her, so they were equal on that score. But they did have a child together, and she did not doubt his love for Annalou; in the short twenty-four hours the bond between father and daughter was obvious for all to see. If Kelly wanted to keep her daughter and give her the happy home life she deserved—and she did—then maybe the best way of achieving that was to reconcile with Gianfranco. Quietly closing the door behind her, Kelly walked back to the bedroom. She was too bone-deep tired to make a decision now, and, crawling into bed, she curled up in a foetal position, yawned widely and within seconds exhaustion claimed her.

Kelly's lashes fluttered against her cheeks and her head fell onto the pillow, the supporting warmth removed. She frowned; she could hear voices and instinctively curled her legs across smooth flesh, unwilling to wake up yet. She snuggled deeper, against a hard male thigh—aroused male! Her eyes flew open and she jerked up. 'What the hell!' she exclaimed, her head spinning: the other side of the bed was occupied.

'Buongiorno, signora.' Anna was in the process of placing a tray with coffee and two cups on the bedside table.

Gianfranco was in her bed, lounging back against the pillows, looking incredibly sexy and, if Kelly wasn't mistaken, stark naked. She tore her eyes away from Gianfranco and back to Anna, and quickly moved to the edge of the bed. 'Thank you for the coffee, but where is Annalou?' she demanded.

'Run along, Anna,' Gianfranco instructed. 'I will explain.'

He had a hell of a lot of explaining to do. Like why was he in her bed? Kelly thought furiously, her blue eyes flashing back to his.

'Relax. I am informed our daughter is washed and dressed, and at this moment in the kitchen having breakfast. She's apparently completely besotted with the household cat,' he drawled. His deep voice, husky with sleep, was like a caress across her skin, and his slumbrous dark eyes were holding her own.

Her whole body flushed with heat, she swallowed convulsively, and tore her eyes away from his as she recalled the feel of his hard thighs only moments ago. Dynamic and all male, he projected a raw virility that was almost frightening in its intensity. Her gaze lingered over the black hair on his broad chest angling down to where the fine sheet covered his thighs. Surely he had not looked so good years ago.

She gulped and said the first thing that came into her

head. 'Why did Anna bring your coffee—it always used to be Aldo?'

A cynical smile quirked the corners of his firm lips. 'It occurred to me I was perhaps a little insensitive three years ago when you were a new bride, and sharing a bed with a man for the first time, to have another man wake you up in the morning. I was used to Aldo but I remember you used to blush and huddle under the bedclothes.'

'You're right, I did.' For a moment she was touched that he had recognised her embarrassment, even if it was three years too late.

'Of course it hardly matters now,' Gianfranco drawled, reclining back against the pillows. 'But I had already arranged it before I left for England and discovered the life you had been leading.'

Kelly recognised the sarcasm, and any softening she had felt towards him vanished in a puff of smoke. 'It was a hell of a lot better than the one I had here,' she gibed, and slid off the bed before turning to challenge him. 'And now perhaps you can explain what you think you are doing in my bed.'

'*Our* bed, Kelly.'

'That's rich coming from you. You couldn't get out of it fast enough when we were married,' she shot back with some sarcasm of her own. It still rankled, even after three years.

'As I recall, you never objected—the safety of our unborn baby was your top priority.' He looked at her quizzically, as if she had just given him the answer he had been looking for. 'I did not know you cared.'

'I didn't.' She shook her head, her long hair flying around her shoulders in tumbling disarray. 'I don't.' He was far too astute and she was mortified at what she had almost given away. 'I'll pour the coffee before it gets cold,' she mumbled, and made a production of filling the two cups while fighting to regain her self-control. Taking a deep breath, Kelly turned back to face him and held out the cup and saucer.

He took it from her hand and drank, replacing the cup on the bedside table; then, leaning back, he watched her with an impassive expression that made Kelly very nervous, and when he spoke in a voice lacking all emotion she almost spilled her own coffee.

'The last time you were here we spent a few weeks sharing a bed, and then the doctor said no sex. I slept in a separate bedroom because I wanted you with a hunger, a passion I could not control.'

Kelly sucked in a breath, her startled gaze flying to his, and she saw the heat in the glittering black depths of his eyes he did not try to hide, and felt reciprocal warmth ignite low in her belly.

'Yes, Kelly. I was a danger to our unborn child because I did not trust myself not to make love to you. You only had to touch me, smile, and everything else faded into oblivion against the irresistible urge to have you.'

Her mouth fell open in amazement. As excuses went it was a Lulu, but she wasn't sure she believed him. She bit her lip. 'Yes, well,' she muttered, and, lifting her coffee-cup, she drained it. The conversation was becoming far too personal, and she didn't want to go there…

He stretched out, the long, powerful length of him at ease, but his hooded eyes were watchful on her. 'You know it's true,' he drawled. 'You proved it on one memorable occasion when you gave me the relief I craved, but afterwards I felt guilty, less of a man because I could not do the same for you at the time. But now there are no such restrictions and, if the other night is anything to go by, you are desperate. You obviously want me as badly as I want you.'

Kelly clenched her teeth and slammed her cup down on the table. She would not rise to his bait, she vowed, and counted to ten under her breath.

'No denial. Very sensible,' Gianfranco prompted, and at that she did swing back to face him.

'I suppose you are now going to try and tell me you loved me all along and not Olivia?' she sneered.

His mouth twisted in a mockery of a smile. 'No, I am not. You never trusted me before. Why should now be any different? As for love—it does not come into it.' His expression hardened. 'The first time we made love or had sex…whatever, you drove me crazy, and you still do. This time we will share a bed, and we will enjoy each other until such time as the passion fades. It will be fun with no consequences.'

He laughed without humour, his dark eyes sardonically appraising her stiffly held figure in the childish white nightgown, her long hair falling down her back in a tumbling mass. 'You may look like an innocent but we both know you are an experienced lady now. How many have there been besides Tom?'

Kelly's hands clenched into fists, anger rising like a tidal wave. 'Why, you…'

'No, don't answer that.' He held up a large hand. 'We will not talk of the past—it is enough Tom is dead,' he reminded her brutally. 'And you and I are very much alive.'

Her eyes met his and she flinched at the implacable intent she saw in them. 'You can't be serious.'

'Never more so, *mia cara*.' Gianfranco's mocking voice echoed in the tense silence. He swung his long legs off the bed and stood up, totally unconcerned at his nudity.

It wasn't fair, Kelly thought helplessly, that the sight of

his naked body could arouse her, and she was shamed at her weakness. She didn't hesitate. She ran for the bathroom and locked the door behind her, her heart pounding like a jackhammer in her breast.

It was half an hour later before she ventured out of the bathroom; showered and wearing a white towelling robe, she peered anxiously around the bedroom, but it was empty. In a matter of minutes Kelly was dressed in a blue cotton summer dress, and with sandals on her feet went looking for her daughter.

The sight that met her eyes as she descended the stairs brought a reluctant smile to her lips. Gianfranco was on all fours and Annalou was straddling his back, her tiny hands knotted in his hair, yelling, 'Faster, faster, Daddy.'

As Kelly reached the bottom step Gianfranco stopped at her feet and lifted his head. 'Get her off me before she tears every hair from my head. I'm begging you on my knees.'

He quite literally was, and Kelly laughed and lifted Annalou off her father's back and onto her feet. 'What's all this about?' She tried to sound serious but the light in her eyes gave her away.

'Daddy said he would buy me a pony, and I was practising. He is going to take me riding some time.'

It was obvious Annalou was completely at ease with her daddy and her new home. Kelly bent down and gave her a quick hug, and, straightening up, wistfully wished she could feel as comfortable in Gianfranco's presence. He had risen to his feet, and, casually dressed in cream cotton trousers and a white shirt, he took her breath away.

'I promised to take Annalou out for the day to buy her a pony.'

'What? A pony?' Kelly said, pulling her thoughts back from the wayward track they were heading. 'To ride, you mean?'

Gianfranco's grin slashed across his face. 'Yes, a pony and yes, to ride,' he said blandly. 'You had better come with us, to make sure you approve of the purchase. I thought we could make a day of it and have lunch in Verona. Perhaps buy some summer clothes for you both.'

'Please, Mummy, yes.' Annalou pulled at her skirt.

Kelly cast a fulminating look at Gianfranco. So their clothes were not good enough and he was going to spoil the child rotten. But her voice was steady as she said, 'If you can spare the time that would be nice.' She wasn't going to argue in front of Annalou.

Taking Kelly by the arm, he said softly, 'I have a lot of time to make up, and we both know why.'

His lean, elegant fingers, lightly restraining her arm, heated her skin. The threat inherent in his comment silenced Kelly. A narrowed glance up into his darkly handsome face told her she had no choice, and, grasping Annalou with her free hand, she allowed herself to be ushered out of the house.

He took them to stables on the outskirts of Verona. And to Kelly's amazement the owner actually had a tiny Shetland pony. Annalou was delighted, but took a fit of the sulks when her father explained the pony could not go with them, but had to be transported later by horsebox. The little girl soon brightened when they arrived in Verona. After buying a host of toys and clothes, Gianfranco suggested a drive to Lake Garda and the hunting lodge, with its small private beach.

Kelly's mouth went dry as he took off his shirt and sat down beside her, his eyes fixed on Annalou paddling around in the shallows. Kelly looked away from his bronzed torso rippling with muscle and swallowed hard. It brought back the disturbing memory of the last time she'd been here with Gianni, when she'd been innocent and in love. Sure she'd been loved in return, she had felt free to touch him, caress him.

Suddenly she was blinded by tears, and was thankful for the sunglasses that hid her eyes. Kelly blinked and stared sightlessly out over the lake, hating to admit it, but knowing it was true: whether he was commoner or count, betrayer or betrayed by her desertion, she still felt the same. She ached for him with the same agony of need, the same hunger, and the same love…

They had been married and lived together for six short months and slept together for little more than one. Perhaps this time it would be better—at least there was no Olivia…

Alarmed at where her thoughts were leading her—straight back into his bed—she said quickly, 'Time to go; it's getting late, and Annalou has had enough excitement for one day.'

Gianfranco nodded his head, and she saw the amusement lurking in his dark eyes. As though he had read her mind and understood exactly how she felt.

'Too many memories, *cara*.' Rising to his feet, he slanted her a heavy-lidded look. 'But now we make new ones.' And, striding across to Annalou, he picked her up in his arms. Kelly had the unenviable feeling she wished it was her.

It had been a lovely day, Kelly agreed with Annalou as she tucked her into bed. But, going down for dinner half an hour later, she was a bundle of nerves. She sat through the meal, making polite conversation with her husband and her mother-in-law, but underneath her emotions were in turmoil.

She heaved a sigh of relief when after the coffee stage Gianfranco said he had some paperwork to attend to and left.

Kelly's relief turned to panic a couple of hours later when, walking out of the bathroom wrapped in only a bath towel, she stopped dead. Gianfranco was standing by the bed wearing a towelling robe. A bottle of champagne stood on the nearby table with two glasses.

'A toast to our reunion,' he drawled mockingly, and as she watched he opened the champagne and filled the two glasses, and then walked towards her with a glass in each hand. He held one out to her.

Her heart thumped erratically; it was a moment of truth, Kelly knew. If she took the glass and said nothing she was agreeing to resume being his wife in every sense. She lifted her head, her wary blue eyes scanning his harshly set features, and fleetingly the thought crossed Kelly's mind that he was not quite as confident as he appeared. Quickly she dismissed the idea as wishful thinking. The decision was hers to take…true. But realistically she knew Gianfranco would have his way whatever…

She took it. 'Thank you, I could use a drink.' The slight quiver in her voice revealed her apprehension.

His brilliant dark eyes roamed over her with explicit sexual hunger, and then met and held hers. Suddenly the atmosphere crackled with electric tension.

Kelly felt her body heat as he raised the glass to his mouth. 'To my wife, the mother of my child; our marriage starts here.' And he drank it down in one gulp.

With a hand that trembled, Kelly lifted her glass to her lips and took one long swallow. Then spluttered and lowered her head as the bubbles went down the wrong way.

Gianfranco took the glass from her hand and moved to put them both on the bedside table. Then he turned back to face Kelly. 'Come here,' he commanded tautly.

She lifted her head. Her watering eyes collided with his smouldering dark gaze, and instantly she was swamped by her intense awareness of him. His sinfully sensuous mouth, the proud tilt of his dark head, his lithe, powerful physique poised and waiting…

Mesmerised by his male beauty, Kelly took a step forward and another… She felt her face flush, heaviness in her breasts, her nipples hardening. She hesitated and swallowed hard, before slowly moving forward again. He wasn't going to make this easy for her…

'You look nervous,' he drawled softly. His hands reached out to her tense shoulders and drew her closer, his dark eyes black and knowing on her lovely face. 'Yet there is no need; you are an experienced woman,' Gianfranco said thickly, one hand curving around her throat and tilting her head back.

If only he knew he was the only man who had ever touched her, Kelly thought, but didn't tell him. She had to keep some defence, even if false, she thought as she trembled with need as all her senses heightened to fever pitch.

His hand slid down over her breastbone, caught the towel, and with one deft movement she was standing naked before him. Tiny flames glinted in the black eyes that slowly ravished her shapely body with a long look, before his head bent and his mouth brushed surprisingly gently over hers until he felt her willing response, then his tongue delved sensually into the moist interior of her mouth.

'Exquisite,' Gianfranco groaned against her lips, and tipped her back onto the bed. For a moment eyes as dark as jet raked over her, then he shrugged off his robe.

It was what Kelly had been waiting for. Naked and powerful, he was sheer masculine perfection. Her blue eyes greedily surveyed his great body, the harsh glare of the artificial light gleamed on muscle and sinew, and she ached for him with a hunger so deep that she could not wait. She reached out her hand.

'Soon, *cara*.' He smiled in purely masculine promise as he came down to her and immediately ravished her mouth with his again.

Not another word was spoken over the next few hours. It was an erotic banquet of the senses.

Kelly had never experienced such an intensity of sensations as Gianfranco extorted from her, nor felt the incredible need to do the same to him. Finally, when he was buried deep inside her for the third time, her heart pounding, lost to everything but the explosive excitement she craved, she gazed wildly at him. She saw the skin pulled taut across his cheekbones and the savage satisfaction as he watched her shuddering on the painfully exquisite edge of release. Then with every thrusting stroke he drove her quivering body to a climax so intense she cried out in ecstasy, mindless to everything but the wonder of his total possession.

Wrapped in his arms, exhausted but fulfilled, she should have stayed silent, but she didn't…

CHAPTER ELEVEN

GIANFRANCO rolled off the bed and headed for the bathroom again. Kelly groaned; her body aching but satiated, she lay on her back and waited for his return. Her dreamy blue eyes followed him as he walked back, lithe and naked, to sit down on the side of the wildly rumpled bed.

'You will run out of those before long,' she teased. It was a new experience for Kelly to have him wear a condom, though he had quickly taught her how to put them on. 'I don't know why you bother.' She lifted her hand and stroked gently up his chest, her heart full of love.

'Because, Kelly,' Gianfranco's dark eyes gleamed down with grim amusement into her own, 'much as I want you, I am taking no chances with my health. The Pill protects only against pregnancy, not sexually transmitted diseases. I don't know where you or Tom have been in the past three years,' he drawled hardly.

As the import of his words sank in, Kelly stared at him, incapable of tearing her gaze away from his handsome but suddenly cynical features. Her hand fell from his chest, her fingers curling into fists at her sides. The last few hours meant nothing to him, nothing at all. She had been in danger of fooling herself yet again.

She lowered her lashes to hide the pain and fury in her eyes, and choked back the surge of anger constricting her throat. She wasn't on the Pill—the supercilious swine had just assumed she was, and on top of that he thought she might be diseased. If ever the veil of love was torn from a woman's eyes, it was in that moment for Kelly.

She could explain, maybe even convince him, but she was damned if she would. With a superhuman effort of will Kelly forced a smile to her love-swollen lips. 'Whatever you say.' Forcing a wide yawn, she turned away from him and pulled the coverlet over her shoulder. She felt the mattress depress as he lay down beside her, and she made no resistance when he wrapped an arm around her and pulled her into the warmth of his body. What was the point? She loved him, wanted him, but some small part of her heart froze. That night set the pattern for the weeks ahead.

The next morning Gianfranco introduced her to the nanny he'd employed to help her look after their daughter, a large widow in her forties, Signora Mussi. He also made it plain the woman was a guard against any repeat of Kelly's desire to run away with Annalou. The rest of the staff had the same instructions. Kelly didn't bother to object because she knew it would be useless, and in any case she intended to stay with her daughter whatever the cost.

In the weeks that followed Kelly's life fell into a routine. She spent all day with Annalou, in the evenings and weekends Gianfranco joined them, and the nights... The nights were spent with her husband.

Kelly had studied chemistry, but nothing had prepared her for the sexual chemistry between them. Every night in the huge four-poster bed they came together with a hunger, a need that knew no bounds. Gianfranco taught her every subtle erotic nuance the human body was capable of and then some! And she was a willing learner. They tormented and teased and pleasured each other, and afterwards fell into a sleep of utter exhaustion in each other's arms.

Before, when they had been together, Kelly had been pregnant the whole time. Their lovemaking had been wonderful, but now she realised just how restrained Gianfranco had been. Three years later he had no such inhibitions; he delighted in her body with a fervour that bordered on obsession. Sometimes in the early morning she would wake to find him watching her with an intensity that was scary. He could spend hours caressing every inch of her body. But it was the same for her. She gloried in the freedom to explore his hard masculine frame, until finally they would find yet more ways to please each other.

At first Kelly was hopeful the passion they shared would bring them closer together, but as the weeks moved into months she had to accept it would not.

In day-to-day life they were Mummy and Daddy, for Annalou. They obeyed the social niceties on the few occasions they appeared as a couple, at business dinners or events at the Casa Maldini. But the rest of the time they were like two strangers. Gianfranco was as much a workaholic as ever, but without travelling abroad. Kelly busied herself with Annalou and making friends with the staff and, much to her surprise, Carmela. Lunches and shopping trips were quite frequent occurrences and went some way to combating Kelly's sense of loneliness.

It was a glorious, hot, sunny day on the twenty-third of August, Anna's wedding-day. Annalou was standing in the entrance to the small village church, a picture in a froth of pale blue silk with cream roses embroidered around the Peter Pan collar, and the crinoline skirt caught up in scallops around the bottom with cream satin bows.

'Now do as the chief bridesmaid tells you and stand still and behave yourself,' Kelly told her quietly. 'Your daddy and I must take our seats.'

'Yes, Mummy.'

Sitting in the front pew, Kelly glanced around the church. She recognised most of the faces: they were all people who worked for her husband. She cast a sidelong glance at

Gianfranco beside her. The expertly tailored silver-grey silk suit he wore fitted his impressive frame to perfection, but could not hide the raw animal magnetism of the man. She studied his dark, devastatingly handsome face, and surprisingly discerned tiredness around his eyes and mouth that gave a harshness to his features. He glanced back at her as though sensing her surveillance, one perfect ebony brow arching quizzically.

Kelly shook her head and stared straight ahead. So he looked a bit haggard—not surprising, the way he worked—and played. The last two nights they had made love with a desperation on Kelly's part she was not proud of. Still, they did not have the kind of relationship that allowed her to show concern for him. Anyway, she had enough problems of her own. The biggest one having arisen two days ago—when she had collected Annalou's dress from Verona she had also visited Dr Credo, and discovered she was pregnant again. At first she had been delighted, until she'd remembered Gianfranco's telling Olivia he wanted no more children.

The bride was beautiful, the service, the photos, the reception…everything was perfect, but Kelly went through the whole thing worried sick.

'It was the bestest wedding ever,' Annalou said later that evening, standing in the nursery, washed and ready for bed, having finally been persuaded to take off her bridesmaid's dress. 'Anna was beautiful; my wedding will be like that. Was yours, Mummy?'

Kelly chuckled. 'Something like that,' and, glancing across at Gianfranco, she was surprised to see what looked like a flicker of pain in his dark eyes. He had just been laughing and telling Annalou she was a little princess.

'Into bed.' Kelly watched as Annalou climbed on the

bed, and then, bending over her, she tucked her in and kissed her.

'You looked lovely as well, Mummy,' Annalou murmured sleepily. Kelly swallowed the lump in her throat, touched by her child's words.

'Thank you, sweetheart. Now go to sleep.' Straightening up, she smoothed her hands down her hips, straightening the skirt of her dress. It was a designer gown in heavy silk, French navy trimmed with cream, with a low-cut square neck that revealed the slight curve of her breasts, and short sleeves. It followed the line of her shapely body to perfection. But not for much longer, she thought wryly.

'I don't think I told you how beautiful you looked today.' Gianfranco's husky drawl impinged on her musings, and suddenly he was beside her, his hand on her arm. 'My daughter reminded me.'

'You don't look so bad yourself,' Kelly murmured, her gaze resting lightly on his large, lithe body as he led her from the room.

'Thank you.' Gianfranco grinned. 'But I think our little princess took the prize, don't you?'

'Yes. Of course,' Kelly agreed and glanced speculatively up at him as they entered the sitting room of their suite. The wedding and Annalou seemed to have put him in a good mood, but then he usually was relaxed around Annalou. Maybe this was her chance to do some fishing and find out how he really felt about another child.

'She is growing up fast,' Kelly ventured, sinking down onto the sofa and kicking off her shoes; her heart was racing but she battled to remain cool.

'Yes, she is a darling child, and she looked a picture in that dress,' Gianfranco responded, walking across to the bar and pouring a good measure of whisky into a crystal glass. 'Want one?' He raised his glass.

Kelly shook her head. 'No,' and for a second wondered what he would say if she just came out with it. *Sorry, I can't—I'm pregnant.* But she wasn't prepared to take the chance. Instead she continued, 'But I sometimes wonder if maybe Annalou is a bit lonely with only adults for company,' she suggested. 'Maybe we should consider having another child—a brother or a sister for her.' She waited with bated breath for his response.

Gianfranco almost choked on the whisky and, draining the glass, he put it down, his dark brows drawing together in a frown. Had she taken leave of her senses? He crossed to where she sat, looking perfectly relaxed, and stared down at her. A tentative smile played around her luscious mouth, but her gorgeous eyes were oddly serious. He knew what she was like for leaping into things. Her latest idea had to be nipped in the bud immediately.

'No. Annalou is perfectly happy, and she has friends at pre-school. Another child is out of the question,' he told her bluntly. A nerve ticked in Gianfranco's temple, and he laid his hand on her shoulder, kneading her collarbone to emphasise the point. 'Forget it, Kelly. I don't want any more children.'

She trembled at the warmth of his hand on her flesh, but her blue eyes locked onto the implacable darkness of Gianfranco's and she had her answer. He was deadly serious and it hurt like hell. Deep down inside she had nursed the hope that perhaps her Italian had not been so good three years ago, that she had misinterpreted what Gianfranco had said. Now that hope was gone.

'Tough,' she said, shrugging off his hand and rising to her feet. 'Because I'm already pregnant.' She didn't wait to hear his response, but headed for the door.

'No—no.' Gianfranco grabbed her arm and whirled her

around to face him. 'Tell me it isn't true,' he demanded through clenched teeth.

His fingers bit into the flesh of her arm and a surge of anger coloured Kelly's cheeks, but she forced herself to remain calm; this was their unborn child they were discussing and anger would get them nowhere. 'It's true; get used to it,' she snapped, and watched as he closed his eyes for a moment. Perhaps now it was a *fait accompli* he might like the idea. But any hopes in that direction were squashed once and for all when he opened his eyes.

His face hardened into an impenetrable mask. 'Has the pregnancy been confirmed by a doctor?' he demanded, and his cold, clipped voice chilled her to the bone.

'Dr Credo. Two days ago.'

'Is it mine?'

A harsh, humourless laugh escaped her. That was the one question she had not expected, but she should have done, given he thought she had slept with Tom and was too dodgy to touch without a condom. 'Oh, yes. I am nine weeks pregnant—work it out for yourself. History repeating itself,' she drawled with bitter sarcasm. 'The tumble on the floor in Cornwall.'

His black eyes narrowed to mere slits in the harshness of his face. 'You were on the Pill.'

'No. You *said* I was on the Pill, because you told me to take it three years ago and Dr Credo told you I had done so,' Kelly said sweetly, but inside she was raging. Her husband, Count Gianfranco Maldini, was a very wealthy, very powerful man, one of an almost extinct breed of dinosaurs that believed once they had demanded a course of action it would be pursued *ad infinitum*. The conceit was colossal.

Gianfranco's dark eyes grazed over her slender but voluptuous body, and fear such as he had never imagined possible was staring him in the face. He frowned down at her. 'No matter, Kelly. Much as it goes against my belief, in this case it is not too late. A termination is in order.'

She shivered, closing her eyes against the pain. He had it all cut and dried.

'I will have a word with Dr Credo.' He was still talking, and Kelly saw red.

Her fingers curled into fists and her free hand swung though the air. She punched him straight on the nose. 'Take that, you no-good scum of the earth,' she yelled; it had hurt her hand but it was worth it, as Gianfranco reeled back, letting go of her arm in the process.

'I have had enough of you to last me a bloody lifetime.'

They hadn't spent as much as a year together as man and wife, and in that time Kelly had suffered every emotion known to man and then some, all because of Gianfranco. But his latest betrayal was the worst, the absolute pits. She glared at him with wild eyes; he had straightened up and was holding his nose, blood seeping through his elegant fingers. Serves the bastard right, she thought furiously. And all the hurt, the anger she had kept in check for so long, came spewing out.

'All you ever wanted from me was sex, from the first time we met. I was never good enough to be your wife or the mother of your child. You would never have married me, except you found out I was pregnant and your precious flaming Olivia wanted a baby. The pair of you decided to have mine. Olivia told me herself: the civil marriage in England meant nothing, but was just a means to get my baby. You could still marry her in church.'

She didn't hear Gianfranco's horrified, '*Dio, no.*' Her fury, unleashed, flowed like vitriol over his proud head.

'I saw you both in the study when I came back from the doctor's, wrapped in each other's arms. And you—you…' she shrieked. 'Telling her that we would certainly *not* have any more children. Caressing her while she said she loved *my baby* and would take care of her.'

Kelly didn't notice Gianfranco's sudden stiffening, his dark eyes fixed intently on her furious red face as he listened to her wild outburst while she was too bound up in her own emotional blood-letting…

'Well, I am glad I foiled the pair of you, and I am glad Olivia left you. My only regret is that you found me again. You don't deserve a daughter like Annalou. And to think I actually thought I loved you.' Kelly shook her head, her blonde hair falling from its precarious chignon to tumble around her shoulders. 'Even today I tried to convince myself—perhaps I had not understood the Italian language so well, maybe you had not said what I thought. More fool me!' Tears blinded her eyes. 'You soon put me right; I must have been mad.'

Kelly had never felt such complete and utter desolation in her life. But she squared her shoulders, steely determination in every line of her slender body. Her moist blue eyes glistened in her drawn face as she looked up at Gianfranco. 'Murder my baby, would you?' she grated in a raw voice. 'Over my dead body.'

His head jerked back as though she had punched him again, and every vestige of colour fled his hard face, leaving him looking grey and haggard, and his sensuous mouth was a taut, cruel line as he said through his clenched teeth one word, *'Exactly.'*

To have him admit everything she had feared was true with one word was like a knife skewering her heart. All the blood drained from her face and she drew a deep, unsteady breath, her blue eyes curiously blank. 'The truth at last.' Unconsciously rubbing her sore knuckles, she added in a voice devoid of all emotion, 'I will see you in hell before I let you near me again.' His large hand reached out to her and she batted it away. 'Don't touch me. Don't you dare touch me.'

His strong features were torn by some intolerable emotion. 'No, Kelly, no, you've got it wrong.' And before she could move he hauled her hard against his long body, his dark gaze moving over her anguished face. 'I know about your mother.'

Through the mist of her despair she looked into his eyes, and the anguish she saw there more than matched her own. 'My mother—you know she and Tom were lovers?' Why on earth was he harking back to what was ancient history?

'No, I didn't know that,' he said in a toneless voice. 'But I do know she died in childbirth, and the same could happen to you. When I said *exactly*, I was responding quite literally to your comment ''over my dead body''. Don't you see?'

She stared at him in complete confusion, then slowly, through the utter despair enfolding her, Kelly felt the first glimmer of something like hope. The pain, the passion as his dark gaze swept over her, was plain to see. He was worried about *her*, and she was so astonished she made no demur when he lowered her down onto the sofa and sat beside her.

'If I have to choose between you and another child...' He didn't look at her as he began to speak, his head bent, his hands clasped between his spread knees, the knuckles white with strain. 'I don't care if I condemn my immortal soul to hell. It has to be you. I can't bear to lose you again.'

Stunned blue eyes widening as the import of his words sank in, Kelly turned towards him and placed a hand on his arm. 'You're frightened?' she whispered.

He nodded and, sitting up, his head lifting to look at her, he gave her a somber, almost angry glance. 'Terrified,' he admitted, and Kelly instinctively knew his anger was not directed against her, but himself.

He agitatedly ran his fingers through his hair before continuing. 'The day I saw you in the hospital bed after giving birth to Annalou Dr Credo told me you had haemorrhaged, and then he told me your mother died in childbirth, but you didn't like to talk about it. But…'

He hesitated for so long Kelly thought he couldn't finish.

'So?' she prompted.

'In that moment, when I realised you could have died having my child when I wasn't even there, I recognised something I had never really thought existed: I love you quite desperately.'

'So you didn't love me when we married,' she murmured sadly to herself, but Gianfranco heard.

'I didn't know what love was,' Gianfranco said urgently and, grasping her slender shoulders, he made her face him. 'You want the truth?' His dark eyes blazed with a determined light. 'You shall have it. I met you, a bright, beautiful girl, and I wanted you. Then, because of a stupid masquerade about my name, I lost you. In my pride, my arrogance, I vowed I would not chase after you when you stood me up. So I did not. I saw other women, but it was no good, I suffered torment through months of celibacy.' He glanced at her. 'It had never happened to me before.'

Kelly amazed herself by smiling at his arrogance. 'Poor you.' But his words gave her the first glimmer of hope.

'Yes, well.' He grimaced with a wry twist of his lips. 'Even when I discovered you were pregnant and searched for you I still never thought of marriage. But the minute I saw you again I heard myself proposing marriage. I was as astounded as you were then; I justified it by telling myself it was the sensible thing to do. My mother was hinting I should marry and provide an heir, so why not?'

'I don't think I want to know this,' Kelly cut in

'You wanted the truth and you are getting it,' Gianfranco prompted bluntly, his mouth twisted and hard. 'It crossed my mind you might be a gold-digger, and Olivia certainly thought so, but I didn't care. Perhaps I loved you then but could not admit it, or didn't need to...' he offered with unconscious masculine conceit. 'All I knew was that I wanted you and the baby. I moved you into my home and my bed, and my life went on much the same as before.'

He shrugged as though he was ashamed of his lack of insight. 'I can remember wondering why my married male friends complained about the confines of married life. I felt no such constraint. I did not alter my lifestyle one iota, and I had the added bonus of having you in my bed at night. Then you complained about Olivia and I was hit by divided loyalties.'

'Was she your lover?' Kelly asked painfully. He had said he loved her, but not until after she had given birth to Annalou, and she did not know how that made her feel.

'No, never.' His hands tightened on her shoulders. 'You have to understand about Olivia. I was sailing with Alfredo the day of the accident. He died and I was saved, and I have carried the guilt with me ever since. I always thought it should have been the other way around.'

Her response was a long sigh. 'Oh, no.'

'Yes,' he admitted, his expression bleak. 'With hindsight I know I over-compensated. I dismissed your fears about Olivia because of my own feelings of guilt and because, if I am honest, it made for an easier life to blame your hormones. Hell, what did I know about pregnant women? When I should have supported you I failed miserably. I put up with more from that woman than you can imagine. But the last day, when you said you saw us in each other's arms plotting against you, I swear on our daughter's life it was not like that.'

Kelly drew in a sharp breath—to vow on Annalou's life, he had to be telling the truth. 'Then what *was* it like?' Kelly pressed him. She needed to know before she could let the tiny flame of hope in her heart blaze free.

'She knew you had gone to the doctor's, she knew I was planning to take you on holiday, and she flung herself at me ranting about how much she loved me, and when we could marry. I was horrified—I had never, ever thought of her in that way. It was then I finally realised she was very ill. I tried to calm her down, but she declared we would have to wait until you produced a boy before we could marry. I guess what you saw was me restraining her by the arms, after having told her she was talking rubbish and I was certainly having no more children.'

Kelly opened her mouth to speak, but Gianfranco went on in a harsh voice, 'She was back in the mental hospital two weeks after you left. She recovered, and the man she's married is a widower with three children. She got what she wanted. But it was too late for me; because of my own blind insensitivity and pride I had lost you and our child. Which brings me back to the present.' As if compelled, he bent his dark head and kissed her, hard and brief, before rearing back slightly, a dull red flush staining his high cheekbones. 'I love you too much, Kelly,' he grated in a tortured voice. 'I cannot let you take the risk of having another child. I couldn't live without you.'

She stared at him, and what she saw in his dark eyes, the love, the torment, made her heart expand in her chest until she thought it would burst with incredulous joy. There was no doubting his sincerity: Gianfranco did love her.

Suddenly the world was a marvellous place to Kelly, and

hope and happiness surged through her. Blue eyes glowing, she said, 'I love you too, but you are crazy, Gianfranco.'

'Crazy!' he exclaimed and, pulling her onto his lap, he added, 'Crazy in love. But as your husband I have to protect you from yourself,' he said seriously. 'No more children.'

Kelly curled up on his lap and linked one arm around his broad shoulders. She knew he needed to be convinced his very real fear was groundless. 'You can't stop me.' She lifted her finger and put it over his lips for a moment as he would have objected. 'And you're wrong; there is no risk, or none that every pregnant woman in the world does not face.' Her hand dropped from his face and she grasped his arm to emphasise her point. 'I am not my mother—she died from complications and, to be blunt, because, although she was forty-two and considered at risk, she insisted on having the child at home. The baby was delivered with the cord around his neck, dead. The midwife did her best, but when my mother haemorrhaged it was another two hours before she made it to the hospital.'

'Your father must have been mad to let her stay at home,' Gianfranco commented in typical autocratic macho fashion.

'That was exactly what Tom said.' Kelly felt the tension in his broad frame at the mention of Tom. 'Tom was a lifelong friend of my mother's—they were in the orphanage together, and were lovers in their youth. Tom went to sea, and when he came back my mother had married my dad. Tom was like an uncle to me, a friend of the family; he appeared now and then with hosts of gifts. But after my mother's death he had a furious fight with my father—he blamed him for Mum's death—and we never saw him again. But I always had his address.'

A dawning realisation made Gianfranco's dark eyes gleam with relief. 'No wonder my detective could not find you. No relation, and no contact since you were a child.' He shook his dark head and looked down into her lovely face, wrapping his arm more firmly around her waist, pressing her closer to the warmth of his body. 'You took a big chance searching him out,' he said seriously, an oddly speculative expression in his black eyes. 'He could have been an axe-murderer, anything.'

'You really are a worrier,' Kelly teased with a grin. 'Anyway, I knew no one else,' she said simply. 'And you haven't needed to use protection, because he was never my lover,' she added for good measure. It still hurt that Gianfranco had assumed the worst about her. 'I never had a lover, which is just as well, the speed at which I seem to get pregnant,' she added with dry humour.

His incredible dark eyes closed for a moment, and then he opened them and his voice was hard, quivering with emotion he no longer tried to hide. *'Dio grazie.'*

'Tom was a good man; he loved Annalou and I, and I miss him,' Kelly said softly.

Gianfranco drew in a deep breath and looked into her expressive sapphire eyes. He was going to tell her the truth, to exonerate his own behaviour, but the sadness he saw stopped him. His investigators had discovered Tom had never been a sailor, but he had travelled abroad—and spent quite a lot of time in jail for fraud. Gianfranco knew what went on in some jails, and he had genuinely feared for Kelly's health. The relief of knowing she had never slept with the man, or any other, was overwhelming, and he smiled gently down into her beautiful face. It was no wonder Tom had been able to keep Kelly hidden so successfully. The guy had been a master of the art.

He put his hand under her chin and tilted her face up. 'I'm sure he was, Kelly. He kept you and Annalou safe and he gave you both back to me. For that I will always be grateful.'

He brought his head down to cover her mouth with his own. She felt the rapid thumping of his heart against her breast as he eased her against him and her lips parted willingly, warmly, to the thrusting demand of his tongue. He kissed her with a hungry, desperate need until, lifting his head slightly, his lips moved against her smooth cheek. 'I loved you and longed for you for three years; I still do, and always will, Kelly.' His words vibrated against her skin, and echoed to her heart's core.

Kelly looked deep into his eyes, searching for the truth, and she shivered at the raw emotion she saw there. 'And the baby?' she had to ask.

He jerked his head back and looked straight at her. 'We will have the best medical care on the planet, and if it is a boy we will call him Tom.'

She laughed, her blue eyes sparkling with humour, and, reaching up, she wrapped her other arm around his neck. 'You don't have to go that far,' she teased, her fingers tangling in the dark silk of his hair, pulling his head back down towards hers. 'I rather like Gianni, after the first and only man I have ever loved or ever will love,' she confessed, and she brushed her mouth tantalisingly along his sexy lips.

'*Dio.* I used to lie in bed and dream of you in my arms, wake and reach for you, and find only an empty bed.' He groaned as his hand quickly unzipped her dress and pushed it from her shoulders. He gazed with feverish eyes on the soft curve of her breasts. 'Now I have you, I still wake in the night and simply watch you, terrified of losing you.'

'I had noticed,' Kelly confessed. Stunned by the golden glare of love in his eyes, the wonder of his love washing over her like a healing balm, Kelly did some undressing of her own.

'Not the sofa. Bed,' Gianfranco muttered frantically a few minutes later as he lifted her in his arms, he carried her into the bedroom and laid her gently on the bed. Sitting on the bed, in a trice he had dispensed with their clothes and swung his long legs up. He stretched out at her side, and, supporting himself on one elbow, stared down at her naked body.

One hand almost tentatively spread out over her flat stomach. 'I can't believe we have made a baby again the first time we made love after three years.' His hand swept up over her midriff and over the firm swell of one breast.

Kelly breathed a deep, shaky breath, trembling at the force of her emotions. 'You really don't mind?'

Gianfranco groaned and captured her mouth with his in a deeply tender kiss—a kiss like no other they had shared, an avowal of love and tenderness, commitment and hope. Finally he lifted his head and looked down at her. 'I love you, Kelly, and I want you to have my baby.' His dark eyes held hers, and surprisingly she discerned a certain vulnerability in their depths.

'But…?' she prompted, her body burning for him, and her heart suddenly fearful again as he hesitated, holding a terrific control over his emotions.

'Watching Anna and her groom and Annalou at the wedding today, listening to our daughter talking tonight, I realised I cheated you out of so many things. Kelly, will you marry me again—in church, with all our friends and neighbours and my mother in attendance?' He touched his lips to the elegant curve of her throat. 'I want there to be no doubt in your mind you are my wife and I love you.'

Meeting his eyes, Kelly parted her lips in a slow, sensual smile. 'Good idea,' she murmured throatily. Her small hands stroking up over his broad chest with tactile pleasure before curving around his neck, she pulled his head down and pressed a light kiss on his bruised nose. 'Sorry about the punch,' she apologised softly. 'But if you think for one moment I am going to be a pregnant bride for a second time, I'll give you another!' she teased. 'Try asking me again when I am not pregnant.'

Twelve months later, Kelly stood in the grand hall of the Casa Maldini, wearing an ivory satin wedding gown studded with seed-pearls and sequins, the train extending four feet behind her, with Annalou standing watching, looking equally lovely in a fairy-tale blue dress, and Judy Bertoni as maid of honour in a similar blue gown.

Carmela was elegant in a tailored suit in a subtle shade of cinnamon but the effect was spoilt somewhat by the five-month-old baby boy she was holding in her arms, Gianni Thomaso Maldini. 'You look beautiful, Kelly,' Carmela said, 'but let's go—we are forty minutes late.'

Gianfranco paced up and down the path to the church; his easy smile when he'd first arrived had long since turned to a frown. Father Rosso was waiting to begin the service. Where the hell was Kelly?

Then he saw the limousine draw up, and a relieved smile split his handsome face. Judy and Annalou skipped out, followed by his mother and son. Then his dark eyes widened with incredulity at the woman who followed.

Kelly, a vision in yards of bejewelled satin, with her silver-blonde hair swept up in a coronet of curls held in place by a diamond tiara, took his breath away. He drew in a ragged breath, his eyes suddenly darkening with deep emotion as they met hers, and she smiled, a dazzling smile only for him that lit her sapphire eyes and put the diamonds she was wearing to shame.

His hand, holding the posy of roses, trembled as he stepped forward to present them to his bride, a traditional Italian custom. 'For you.' He pushed the posy at her.

Kelly could not help smiling. He looked incredibly handsome in a pearl-grey tailcoat and a white wing-collar shirt, with a cream and gold cravat and matching waistcoat. Tall and elegant, every inch the aristocrat. But it was the expression in his eyes that thrilled Kelly to the bone: deeply possessive and blazing with the light of love.

'You look out of this world, incredibly beautiful, and I love you with a passion, a devotion, that will live through this world and the next,' Gianfranco said in a voice not quite steady as he led her into the church.

Her eyes misting with moisture, she squeezed his hand, her heart overflowing with love. 'Thank you,' Kelly said, and in that one word she was thanking him for everything: his love, their children, their life together.

It was the wedding of the year. Family and friends, dignitaries from all over Italy, business colleagues—no one was excluded. After the service the reception was held out of doors in the grounds of Casa Maldini.

'We have to leave soon…' Gianfranco's arm was wrapped firmly around his wife's waist, where it had been all afternoon. He glanced down at Kelly, his dark eyes glinting with raw desire. 'If we want to make the flight.'

Gianfranco adored Annalou, and had been at the birth of his son Gianni, and the experience had filled him with awe and humility. But, much as he loved his family, after two weddings they were finally going to get to go on honeymoon. Alone. He could not wait to get Kelly on her own for three whole weeks.

'OK.' Kelly beamed up at him. It had to be the best wedding any woman in the world had ever had, she thought, glowing with happiness and pride for the man at her side who had done all this for her.

'We don't want to be late. You were late at the church,' Gianfranco reminded her, just as the rather loud voice of a slightly inebriated Father Rosso, who was standing behind them, boomed out.

'Two children and five years late, but they got there in the end. *Dio grazie*.'

New York Times bestselling author **Anne Mather** has written since she was seven, but it was only when her first child was born that she fulfilled her dream of becoming a writer. Her first book, CAROLINE, appeared in 1966. It met with immediate success and, since then, Anne has written more than 150 novels, reaching a readership which spans the world. Born and raised in the north of England, Anne still makes her home there with her husband, two children and, now, grandchildren. Asked if she finds writing a lonely occupation, she replies that her characters always keep her company. In fact, she is so busy sorting out their lives that she often doesn't have time for her own! An avid reader herself, she devours everything from sagas and romances to mainstream fiction and suspense.

Look out for Anne Mather's next seductive story, coming in September 2005, in Modern Romance™!

SAVAGE INNOCENCE

by

Anne Mather

CHAPTER ONE

IT WAS incredibly hot and airless in the attic. Despite its being a fairly cool July day outside, whatever sun there'd been in recent weeks seemed to have been trapped here in the roof void, and Isobel panted a little as she clambered over trunks and cardboard boxes that hadn't seen the light of day for years.

It was her own fault, of course. She could have refused to do it—though she had to admit she hadn't expected that clearing the house would prove such an arduous task. Sitting back on her heels, surveying the accumulation of what was little more than junk that had collected here over the years, she tried not to feel anxious. But she wondered if she hadn't bitten off more than she could chew.

But there was no one else willing to do it. Marion wouldn't dream of soiling her hands by climbing up here. Besides, as she was always telling Isobel, there simply weren't enough hours in the day to do all she had to do anyway. And Malcolm wouldn't thank her if she gave what little time she had to sorting her late mother's rubbish. Her husband saw little enough of her as it was.

Isobel, who taught at the local comprehensive, was assumed to be able to take a day off to deal with the aftermath of a family bereavement without any problem at all. If her classes had to be covered by someone else, or she got behind in her marking schedule, she'd have to deal with it. Marion had people depending on her, staff, whom she couldn't possibly neglect to dispose of her mother's things.

Isobel supposed it was true. As well as having a husband and an eight-year-old daughter, Emily, Marion also ran her own employment agency. She was always busy interviewing people or attending 'important' meetings. Isobel sometimes wondered why she'd bothered to get married at all.

Isobel wasn't married, which she knew delighted Marion immensely. She knew little of her sister's private life, of course, but the fact that Isobel didn't have a steady boyfriend pleased her no end. Isobel's best friend, Michelle Chambers, said it was because Marion was jealous of her. But why Marion should be jealous of her adopted sister didn't seem to make much sense, in Isobel's view.

Isobel thought Marion was basically unhappy. Despite her assertions to the contrary, she never seemed to enjoy her success. Isobel knew their mother had seen more of Emily than Marion had been able to, and the little girl was going to miss her grandmother terribly.

Mrs Dorland had died six weeks ago. She'd been suffering from a terminal illness for the past three years, so no one was actually shocked by her death. But, for all that, Isobel was amazed at the gulf her mother's loss had left in her life. There was so much she hadn't told her; so much she wanted to tell her now.

Although she'd initially put off Marion's suggestion that the house should be cleared, she'd known that sooner or later she would have to do it. Their father had died some years ago, and although Isobel wasn't married she no longer lived at home, which meant the house in Jesmond Dene was now empty. But she'd known that disposing of her mother's belongings would be painful, and she'd waited until the emotional dust had settled before tackling the job.

Now, however, she didn't have a choice. She was going away herself soon, and Marion was agitating about selling the house while the market was still buoyant. Isobel knew Marion's share of the proceeds was earmarked for the business, and she wished she could insist that her sister had it all.

But the solicitor had been quite adamant on that point. Mrs Dorland's will stated clearly that *both* her daughters should inherit in equal shares. As far as her mother was concerned, she'd never made any distinction between them, and Isobel had sometimes wondered whether that was why Marion had always worked so hard to gain her parents' approval.

It had been easy enough arranging for the furniture to be dealt with. There were firms who specialised in house clearances and, apart from the one or two personal items Isobel had selected, everything else had been despatched to the saleroom.

It was not until Isobel had opened the trap door into the attic that she'd realised the enormity of her task. Unless they were willing to allow strangers to root around in family papers and suchlike, she would have to dispose of these old trunks and boxes herself. Despite the fact that all she'd discovered so far were old clothes and books and photograph albums, she couldn't find it in her heart to just burn them, unseen. There might be something of value. She owed it to her mother's memory to take the trouble to look.

All the same, she hadn't expected it to be so hot up here. And the nausea that had troubled her earlier that morning was beginning to make her sweat all over again. If she didn't get something to eat soon, she was going to start retching, and that was one consequence of her efforts she didn't want to face.

She was crawling back to where the loft ladder pointed down to the first-floor landing when she saw the small dust-covered suitcase. It had been pushed away beneath one of the beams, and it was doubtful if she'd have seen it if she hadn't been on all fours. As it was, she pulled it out, saying a not very ladylike word when the handle came away on one side and a screw scraped her finger. Then, tucking it beneath her arm, she climbed down to the landing below.

First things first, she thought, looping her curly hair behind her ears and descending the stairs to the ground floor. There was no food in the house, but she had brought a flask of coffee and some biscuits with her. Thank goodness, she thought weakly, stuffing a handful of arrowroot fingers into her mouth.

The nausea subsided, as she'd known it would, and, after pouring herself a cup of coffee from the flask, she carried the suitcase into the kitchen. Then, unlocking the back door, she stepped out into the watery sunshine and seated herself on the bench that circled the old apple tree.

This was where her mother used to sit in summer, she remembered sadly. And when she and Marion were schoolgirls, their father had hung a swing from one of its gnarled branches, but that had gone now. Even the blossom, that had flowered so incongruously, she'd felt, just after her mother died, had faded, the grass at her feet strewn with its decaying petals.

Sighing, she thrust her melancholy thoughts aside and turned to the suitcase. It was little more than the size of a briefcase, really, and Isobel couldn't remember ever having seen it before. Perhaps it hadn't belonged to her parents, she thought. Her grandparents had lived in the house before her father and mother were married, so it could have belonged to them. Whatever, it was unlikely to contain anything of importance. All her mother's private papers had been kept by her solicitor.

She thought at first that the case was locked. Her first attempts to flick the twin catches met with no success. But a foray into the toolshed, which still contained some rusty tools and a broken lawnmower, unearthed an old screwdriver, and when she used this to pry at the catches, they gave in.

As she'd expected, the box was just another repository for papers. Letters this time, postmarked from an address in Cornwall, all of them at least twenty-five years old. Isobel frowned. She was not aware that her parents had known anyone who lived in Cornwall. If they had, neither of them had ever mentioned it to her. And she doubted that if Marion had known about it she'd have kept something like that to herself.

Unless…

She shook her head. Were these letters anything to do with her adoption? She knew virtually nothing about her real parents. She'd been told that her birth mother had been killed in a car accident just after she was born, and that as she'd been an unmarried mother, living alone, her baby had been taken into care. Isobel had always assumed that she'd lived in Newcastle, too, which was how the Dorlands had come to adopt her. Mrs Dorland had always wanted a large family, but after Marion was born she'd discovered she couldn't have any more children.

Isobel wondered now why she hadn't asked more questions about her adoption. She supposed the truth was that her mother had always got very touchy whenever the subject was broached. Isobel had been taught from an early age that she was lucky to be part of a proper family, and somehow asking about her birth mother's background was ungrateful and disloyal.

Which probably had nothing to do with these letters, she decided, pulling off the elastic band, which had held them together, and studying the envelope with thoughtful eyes. It was addressed to her mother, she saw, and her nerves tightened, needlessly she was sure. She was regarding the letters far too seriously, she thought. They were probably from a friend her mother had known when she was young.

She felt a twinge of conscience as she pulled one of the letters out of its envelope. Perhaps she ought to wait and ask Marion what she should do with them. But then curiosity, and the knowledge that Marion had eschewed all interest in their mother's effects, encouraged her to investigate further. After all, it was only her imagination that was giving them a significance they probably didn't deserve.

She read the address at the top of the letter first: Tregarth Hall, Polgarron. Impressive, she though wryly, and, even though the letter was old, the quality of the paper was still evident. Then she noticed it started 'Dear *Iris*,' which was her mother's name, and not *Mrs Dorland.* Her unease slackened, and she glanced at the bottom of the page. The signature was Robert *Dorland.* She grimaced. They were obviously from some relation of her father's.

Wondering why that conclusion didn't douse her interest, she turned back to the beginning. *Dear Iris,* she read again, and then went on. *All the arrangements are now in place. Matty will bring the child to you on August 8th.*

The child? Matty?

Isobel's throat went dry, but she forced herself to read on.

I know you consider my actions reprehensible, but there is no way I can keep her even if I wished to, which I do not.

Isobel caught her breath, but she had to go on.

I trust George (her father, Isobel acknowledged tensely) *will learn to live with it. He was always a sanctimonious devil, even in his youth, and, had it not been for your intervention, I am sure the child would have found no favour with him. Still, who am I to judge him? As George would say, I have made my bed, now I should lie on it. He never could forgive anyone's weaknesses.*

Which is why, I suppose, my father left Tregarth to me, and not him. I doubt if we'll be in touch again, dear Iris. My thanks and my best wishes for the future.

The air escaped from Isobel's lungs in a pained rush, and the nausea she had defeated only minutes before attacked her again. This time there was no escape. She barely made it to the downstairs cloakroom before she was violently sick, and it was several minutes after that before she was able to drag herself to her feet again.

She felt chilled now. Whereas earlier she had been sweating in the heat of the attic, now goosebumps feathered her skin. She found the jacket she'd left hanging on the banister, and pushed her arms into the sleeves, clutching its warmth about her. But the chill she felt was as much psychological as physical, and it was some time before she could bring herself to return to the bench.

When she did, she found the dozen or so letters scattered in all directions. They'd tumbled from her lap as she'd rushed into the house, and, although she was tempted to toss the lot of them into the dustbin, she forced herself to pick them up again. Looking at the date of the postmarks on the envelopes, she discovered that the letter she'd been reading had been the last one to arrive. They must have been saved, one on top of the other, in reverse order, which was how she'd come to read the last letter first.

And that letter was dated August 1975, which was only a few weeks after she'd been born. According to her birth certificate, her birthday was the twelfth of July 1975, and it was highly improbable that her mother should have been involved with two babies at that time.

Which meant…? That this man, whoever he was, was her real father? That he'd got some poor girl pregnant and then reneged on his responsibilities towards her? Although George Dorland had always maintained that he had no relatives, it seemed obvious now that Robert Dorland must be his brother. His younger brother, by the sound of it. And instead of spending his early years in East Anglia, as he'd told his daughters, he'd actually been born in Cornwall instead.

Isobel swallowed, turning the other letters over in her hands. The last thing she wanted to do now was read them, yet she had to know how—*why?*—her own parents hadn't brought her up.

From the tone of the letter she'd read, she thought she could guess at least part of the story. If anything the Dorlands had told her was true, then her mother must have died, as they'd said. But if she'd lived in Newcastle, claiming to be a single mother, how had Robert Dorland become involved with the baby? And who on earth was Matty? Isobel knew from what she'd been told that her real mother's name had been Frances Parry.

She turned, somewhat apprehensively, to the earliest dated letter and drew the two sheets of paper out of the envelope. The address was the same: Tregarth Hall, Polgarron. And it both confirmed Robert Dorland's identity and proved that Mrs Dorland had known him personally.

Dear Iris,

I am writing to you and not to that hidebound brother of mine because I'm hoping that what I have to tell you may strike a chord of sympathy in your heart. Ten months ago, I did something totally selfish and totally stupid. I betrayed Justine by having a brief fling with a young woman I met while I was in London, visiting my solicitor. Believe me when I say that I've regretted it ever since, and I had no intention of having anything more to do with the woman involved. Unfortunately, circumstances have contrived against me, and I now find that a child resulted from that reckless union. How do

I know this? you ask. Because the child's mother has now died, leaving the infant in my care. Not literally, of course. At least, not yet. At present, she is in the care of Southwark Social Services, but I have been contacted, as the child's father, and I fear it's only a matter of time before Justine finds out. You know how distressed she's always been at not being able to have any children herself, and there's no way I can confess the truth to her. I've thought of denying any knowledge of the woman, but who knows what other incriminatory evidence she may have left? No. It's obvious that I've got to find an alternative home for the child, and, knowing how much you and George would have liked a larger family, I'm hoping you might agree to adopt your niece. Yes. In spite of everything, I know she is my daughter. I've seen her, and although her colouring is much darker than mine, the resemblance is there. Naturally, Justine must know none of this. Some other explanation must be found for your decision, but I'm sure we can work something out. What do you think? Will you do this for me? For Justine? For an innocent child? I beg you not to let me down.
Robert.

Isobel was shaking violently when she finished reading the letter. To think, all these years, when she'd believed she had no blood relations, she'd had an aunt, an uncle, a cousin—and a *father*! She couldn't believe it. She didn't want to believe it. Somehow it made a mockery of her life so far.

Why had no one ever told her? Why leave these letters for her to read when for more than twenty-five years she'd been kept in the dark? Surely her feelings had had as much relevance as Justine's? As soon as she was old enough to understand the significance of what had happened, she should have been told the truth.

Stuffing the letter back into its envelope, she reached for the second, and the third, flicking through them with trembling fingers. There were fifteen letters in all, and, however reluctant she was to continue, she knew she had to read them all. Somehow she had to come to terms with what she'd learned, and the only way to do that was to try and understand why it had happened.

But the tenor of the letters changed after that first one. It soon became evident that this was because Robert Dorland's plea had not met with universal approval. George Dorland had apparently refused at first to have anything to do with his brother's problems, and, judging by the response his reaction had earned, there'd been no love lost between the two men.

Slowly, however, perhaps because of Iris's intervention—Isobel would never know now—a compromise had been reached. However opposed to the idea her husband had been, Iris's wishes had prevailed, and he had eventually agreed to adopt the child.

Herself, thought Isobel disbelievingly. She was the child they'd fought over, and, ultimately, she was the one who'd benefited. But at what cost? George Dorland had driven a hard bargain, and his agreement had entailed stringent conditions.

The first was that he'd never wanted to see his brother again. There would be no familial visits; no opportunity for Robert Dorland to secretly drool over his handiwork; to feel a sense of pride in the child he'd been prepared to give away.

The second was that Isobel herself was never to know the truth, which explained her ignorance. Whatever bitterness there'd been between the brothers had been reinforced by her adoption, and was obviously why George Dorland had always denied any connection with his past.

And why she'd never been told she'd been born in London, instead of the north of England.

Spots of rain were dotting the knees of Isobel's leggings by the time she'd snapped the elastic band back around the bundle of letters. Returning them to the case, she closed the lid, and got to her feet. It was odd, she thought, she felt entirely different now from the woman she'd been before she opened the case. Pandora's Box, she thought painfully, as she walked back into the house. She should have burned the letters without reading them as her conscience had prompted her to do.

And yet…

She sighed. Why had her mother kept the letters? She suspected her father hadn't been aware of it, which might account for the fact that the case had been hidden away beneath the beam. It seemed that as far as George Dorland was concerned, his brother had ceased to exist on the day the baby—herself—had been handed over. But Iris had been made of gentler stuff. Was that why she'd hung onto the letters all these years?

Isobel frowned. She wondered if Marion had known anything about it. Did she remember her aunt and uncle, for example? Surely she'd have mentioned them if she had. And when their father died—and their mother—had anyone informed Robert Dorland? Always supposing he was still alive, of course. As the younger brother, it was reasonable that he might be.

The breath caught in Isobel's throat at that thought. My God, she thought. Her father—her real *father*—could still be living in another part of the country. The implications of that conclusion were both thrilling and terrifying. Had Robert Dorland thought about her at all since he'd abandoned her? Goodness, he might not even know that his brother and his wife were dead.

But what if he did…?

She ran a protective hand across the slight mound of

her stomach. Ever since she'd learned of her condition she'd been thinking that history always repeated itself. Like mother, like daughter, she'd thought, but without knowing all the facts. Now, the comparisons between them were even more pertinent. Except… She took a deep breath. She had no intention of putting Jared's name on the birth certificate…

CHAPTER TWO

THE sound of the front door opening brought her round with a start.

She hadn't been aware of leaving the door unlocked, but now she remembered that she hadn't intended to be so long. And if she hadn't opened the trap door into the loft, and realised the amount of work there was still to be done, she wouldn't have been. With the living areas of the house empty of her mother's belongings, she'd thought it was only a matter of tidying up.

How wrong she'd been.

'Belle?'

The attractive male voice was achingly familiar, and, in spite of all the warnings she'd given herself these past weeks, Isobel's heart leapt automatically at the sound. She knew it so well; knew every tone, every nuance, every sensual inflection. Which was why she had to get away, she thought, even though the knowledge pained her. There was no way she could avoid him if she continued to live at the apartment. Or in the area, she acknowledged wryly, even if a future without him in it looked abysmally black at this moment.

'I'm here,' she said, shedding her jacket onto the counter and emerging from the kitchen as Jared Kendall came strolling along the narrow hall. She forced herself to offer him a cool smile, even though she desperately wanted to run away from the temptation he represented. But she had to convince him that their relationship was over, and only by a show of total uninterest could she hope to arouse a similar response.

But God, it was hard, so hard, to disguise the fact that

her feelings hadn't changed. Just looking at him, knowing what they had once shared, turned every bone in her body to water. She didn't want to care about him; she *shouldn't* care about him; but she did. And it was that as much as anything that made her resent his coming here.

After the row they'd had two nights ago—the row she'd engineered—she'd been sure it would be several days before he'd attempt to see her again. If he ever did, she'd acknowledged honestly. There was just so much a man—any man—would take.

Yet now here he was, walking towards her with that loose-limbed gait that had always reminded her of the predator he represented. Tall, dark; if it wasn't for the metal-framed spectacles riding on his nose, he'd be every woman's fantasy, and even they only added to his appeal.

Though, to give him credit, he would have hated to think that that was so. Broad shoulders, lean hips, the muscles moving powerfully beneath his tanned skin, he had a toughness that didn't just come from working a good part of his life outdoors. Not handsome, she conceded. His features were too strongly sculpted to fit that image, and one of the first things that had drawn Isobel to him was his total lack of vanity.

But now was not the time to be categorising all his good points, she thought impatiently. Somehow, however painful it might be, she had to make him see that what they'd had was over, finished; before he destroyed them both…

'What are you doing here?' she demanded, wrapping her arms about her midriff in an unknowingly defensive gesture, and Jared arched a sardonic brow.

'Guess,' he said drily, coming to a halt and regarding her with faint resignation. 'If you start with the premise that I wanted to see you, you might come close.'

'Don't make fun of me.'

'Okay.' Jared pushed his hands into the pockets of his leather jacket. 'How about if I say I'm sorry?'

'You're sorry?' Isobel was caught off guard. 'What are you sorry for?'

Jared blew out a breath. 'How the hell do I know?' he exclaimed, revealing he wasn't quite as controlled as he'd like to appear. 'Anything, everything; whatever I've done to make you be like this.'

'Like this?' Isobel latched onto the words. 'Like what? What am I like?'

'Oh, for God's sake!' Jared turned sideways and rested his shoulders back against the wall. 'You know what I mean. Don't insult me by pretending you don't know what I'm talking about.'

'I don't.'

'Oh, right.' He turned his head and gave her a disparaging look. 'So why are we having this argument? Answer me that.'

Isobel was quivering inside, but she had to go on. 'I can't help it if you don't like the things I say,' she declared coolly. 'Just because you can't accept that I might be getting bored with our relationship—'

'That's not true!' He straightened away from the wall, his voice swollen now with anger. 'Our relationship may be many things, not all of them good, I'll grant you, but it's never been boring!'

'So you say.'

'So I know,' he corrected her harshly. He glared angrily at her, his dark eyes smouldering hotly behind the curved lenses of his glasses. 'What is this, Belle? What's happening? Who's been getting at you, for God's sake? Is it your sister? Has she said something to upset you?'

'Why should you think I'd need any encouragement?' Isobel managed to inject exactly the right amount of contempt into her voice. 'Just because you can't accept it, doesn't mean it isn't so.'

Jared wrenched off his glasses and rubbed the bridge of his nose with his forefinger and thumb. Then, taking a deep breath, he composed himself. 'So—what are you saying? That you don't think we should see one another again?'

Isobel felt as if her insides were being rent apart. 'Um—well, yes,' she said tightly. 'I think it would be best for—for both of us. Our relationship isn't going anywhere. And—and I'm not prepared to spend the rest of my life waiting for something that may never happen.'

Jared's face was dark with anguish when she'd finished. Without his glasses, which were still dangling from his hand, he had a vulnerability that wasn't evident when the lenses he wore to correct his short-sightedness were in place. It tore her heart just to look at him, and she wondered what malign fate had decreed that she and Jared should meet.

Which was why she had to go…

'You knew,' he began, his voice thickening with emotion as he spoke, 'you knew I was married when we first began seeing one another. I—never made any secret of the fact.'

'I know—'

'So why are you so impatient now?'

Why, indeed?

Isobel had to steel herself against the almost overwhelming urge she had to go to him then, to comfort him, to tell him that, far from wanting to split them up, she needed him more now than ever. She loved him; she'd known that from the minute she'd backed into his car.

She remembered that day on the supermarket car park now, how he'd uncoiled himself from behind the wheel of the huge Mercedes and come around to see what damage her small Ford had done. She'd expected many things, but not amusement, and his lazy smile had robbed the moment of any sting. She'd been hooked by that smile and by the easy assurance of his manner. The fact that he was also the sexiest man she'd ever seen was just the icing on the cake.

'Perhaps I've changed my mind,' she blurted now. Anything to distract herself from her thoughts. 'It was fun at first—'

'Fun!'

'But I'm not getting any younger. I've decided I—I want a normal life; a normal relationship. I want to get married. Have you thought of that?'

'I think of it all the time,' he retorted bitterly. 'But I'm not free, am I? I thought you understood.'

'I do.'

'It doesn't sound like it.'

'Well, it wasn't meant to sound like that,' she mumbled unhappily. Her heart ached, and she gripped herself tighter. 'I'm sorry.'

'Yeah, I bet you are.'

He shoved his glasses back onto his nose and thrust savage hands through his hair. His hair needed cutting again, Isobel noticed with unwilling tenderness, and there were streaks of grey among its silky dark strands. Were there more now than when she'd first met him? She hoped not, but there was no denying that their affair had taken its toll on both of them.

'So…' He took a deep breath. 'Who is he? Do I know him? Please don't tell me you've been seeing him behind my back.'

Isobel's jaw dropped. 'Who?'

Jared closed his eyes for a moment. 'Belle…' he said, and she could hear the edge of violence in his voice. 'Don't do this to me. You know perfectly well who I mean. This man—this paragon—the one who can give you everything I can't.'

'There is no one else.'

The words were out before Isobel could give any thought to what she was saying. Her denial had been instinctive, and she saw Jared's eyes open again and focus on her with piercing intensity.

'Do you mean that?' He gripped the back of his neck with a bruising hand. 'Or is this what they mean by letting me down lightly?'

Isobel shook her head. Despite the fact that it would be so much easier to pretend that there was someone else, she couldn't do that to him. 'It's the truth,' she said huskily, and then, unable to go on looking at him without revealing what she was trying so hard to hide, she turned back into the kitchen behind her.

Had she known he would follow her? She hardly knew any more. After the morning she had had, she was in no fit state to make any reasoned assessment about anything. Besides, if she was honest she would admit that she had never needed his strength and his commitment more than she did right now. Only he hadn't offered her any commitment, she reminded herself painfully, and she was a fool if she thought he ever would.

She sensed he was behind her even before he touched her. Where he was concerned she had always had a sixth sense, a sensory perception, that she'd used to tell herself proved that their relationship was meant to be. It was as if some energy arced between them, an electrical spark, that was as much spiritual as it was physical, so that when his hands cupped her neck she couldn't prevent the little moan of despair that escaped her. And when his tongue found the pulse that was racing behind her ear, she could only tip her head to one side to facilitate her own destruction.

'God, Belle,' he groaned, his breath cool against her hot skin, and the passion in his voice stroked her flesh with sensual fingers. 'Don't do this to me.'

At that moment it was beyond her capacity to do anything more than stand there, feeling the heat of him at her back, and trying like mad not to lean into him. But it was too much. His teeth had fastened on the skin of her neck now, skin that was the colour of thick cream, and which he had always insisted was just as rich and smooth, tugging the soft flesh into his mouth. There'd be a mark there now, she knew it, but she would willingly have stripped all the skin from her bones if it would have pleased him. She loved him. Ah, God, she was crazy about him. He had no idea what it was costing her to leave him.

His hands slid down her arms to her hands, linking their fingers together. Then, with just the slightest pressure, he urged her slim body to mould itself to his, his legs parting so that she was instantly aware of his arousal against her bottom. She was a tall girl herself, and Jared had always said they fitted one another perfectly.

She trembled then, and, sensing her weakening state, Jared uttered a muffled oath as he turned her towards him. Cradling her face between his palms, he stroked the faint shadows that had only recently appeared beneath her eyes with his thumbs, before tilting her head to his.

'I need you,' he said unsteadily, and she believed him. Their relationship would never have survived as long as it had without the friendship that had flowered between them. This past year had been the happiest time of her life, and if that damned her soul for all eternity, given the chance she'd do it all again.

He bent to kiss her, their mingled breaths causing the lenses of his glasses to film over, and Isobel lifted her hand to remove them. Her lips parted under the increasing pressure of his mouth, and when his tongue plunged deeply into that moist void, she clutched his glasses as if they were the only stable thing in a wildly unstable world.

Jared's hands moved down her back to her hips, bringing her more fully against him, the thrust of his erection nudging the junction of her thighs. His fingers shaped the rounded swell of her buttocks, finding the cleft that divided them easily through her thin leggings, and causing Isobel to arch helplessly against his insistent strength.

'I want you,' he told her thickly, his words barely audible as his mouth returned to hers with more urgency, and although she knew she was playing with fire, she wound her arms around his neck.

'Not here,' she got out jerkily, as her only concession to her departing sanity, but Jared seemed intent on proving to her that she wanted him just as much as he wanted her.

'Why not?' he demanded, his fingers slipping beneath the hem of her man-size tee shirt to find the softness of her bare flesh. He stroked her midriff with caressing hands, before seeking the unfettered freedom of her small breasts. 'It's what I want; it's what we both want.'

'No—'

'Yes.' He teased the sensitive nipples that swelled against his palms, and then peeled her tee shirt upward, exposing the rosy areolae to his possessive gaze. 'God, Belle, you can't stop me now!'

One hand curved along her thigh, bringing her leg up around his hips and lifting her off her feet. Realising what he intended to do, Isobel wrapped her other leg about his waist. It brought the sensitive place between her legs even closer to the taut seam of his trousers, and she was hardly aware that he'd carried her into the kitchen until he set her on the lip of the counter. Then, while she put his glasses aside and rested back on her hands, he peeled the close-fitting leggings down to her ankles.

When he spread her thighs and moved between them, she was more than ready for him, and her breathing quickened when the thickness of his erection probed her moist core.

But, just as she was giving herself over to the treacherous delight of feeling him a part of her again, he swore softly and drew back. 'Damn, I don't have anything with me,' he muttered. He groaned. 'I don't normally go to work with a pocket full of—well, you know what I mean.'

'It doesn't matter.'

Isobel's words were frantic, revealing how hopelessly eager she was, and Jared stared at her with dark, tormented eyes. 'Do you mean that?' he asked unsteadily. 'Is it the right time of the month or something?'

'Or something,' she agreed weakly, remembering another occasion when she had assured him that it was safe to take the risk. Of course it hadn't been so, which was why...

But she didn't want to think about that now, and, reaching down, she guided him towards her aching flesh. 'Just do it,' she said, and as she'd expected—as she'd *known*—Jared was not immune to such flagrant provocation, and he sighed with pleasure as he surged into her wet sheath.

'God, Belle,' he moaned, as her muscles tightened around him, and because she was no longer in control of herself, or her emotions, Isobel cupped his face in her hands and brought his open mouth to hers.

She thought she might have been content then just to know he was there, buried deep inside her, but as soon as he began to move she knew that being there wasn't enough. She wanted more, she wanted him, she wanted all of him, and his breathing grew hoarse and laboured as the irresistible demands of the flesh drove him to take them both to a glorious climax.

They came together, and Isobel felt the exquisite heat of Jared spilling his seed inside her. There was nothing to touch it. She sighed. The blissful union of male meeting female, skin to skin, flesh to flesh. The ripples of their lovemaking left them both shuddering in the aftermath, and Isobel would have liked nothing better than to spend the rest of the afternoon here or at her apartment, with Jared, repeating their closeness again and again.

But a chilling sense of reality returned when Jared bestowed one last lingering kiss at the corner of her mouth, and then drew away from her. While he fastened his trousers, she shuffled awkwardly off the edge of the counter, and bent to haul her leggings, and the bikini briefs he'd pulled down with them, up her legs.

'Are you okay?' he asked huskily, watching her, and she was warmed by the look in his eyes which told her he had been as reluctant to break their embrace as she was.

But that didn't alter the situation, and, making the excuse of needing to use the bathroom, she slipped into the cloakroom next door.

A glance at her reflection didn't help either. No one looking at her flushed face and swollen lips could be in any doubt as to what had been going on, and she wished she'd brought her make-up with her. Her hair, lustrous chestnut hair, which she usually wore short these days in an effort to quell its urge to curl, was a tousled mass about her creamy features. She looked—wanton, she thought unhappily. Which was not the image she'd wanted to convey.

She stayed in the cloakroom as long as she dared, and when she emerged she found Jared waiting for her in the kitchen. His hips were propped against the counter, where he had just made such passionate love with her, his arms folded across his broad chest, his glasses back in place.

The suitcase containing the letters she had been examining earlier—and which she had almost forgotten in the heat of their mating—was lying on the counter at his back, and he tipped his head towards it in obvious enquiry.

'Whose is this?'

Recognising the tension in his casual query, Isobel wondered if he thought it was hers. A hysterical sob rose in her throat at the unknowing irony of that suspicion, but she managed to fight it back, and, sliding her long fingers into the sides of her hair, she lifted her shoulders in a dismissing gesture.

'It was my mother's.'

Jared's dark brows drew together. 'Your mother's?' he echoed. 'I thought you'd got rid of all your mother's stuff.'

'I thought so, too.' Isobel took a deep breath. 'That was before I looked in the loft.'

'The loft? Here?' Jared glanced towards the ceiling. His eyes darkened. 'You haven't been crawling around in the loft on your own?'

Isobel gave him a retiring look. 'Someone has to do it,' she said drily.

'Not on your own,' retorted Jared, evidently disliking the proposition. He flicked back his cuff and looked at the plain gold watch on his wrist. 'Dammit, I've got to go. I've got a meeting with Howard and Ross Cameron at half-past one.'

'And it wouldn't do to keep your father-in-law waiting, would it?'

Isobel couldn't resist the mocking comment, and she saw the look of real pain that crossed his face. 'No, it wouldn't,' he conceded flatly. 'Particularly as he can probably smell you on me,' he said, straightening away from the bench, and Isobel felt instantly ashamed.

'Um—you could take a quick shower,' she offered, gesturing towards the stairs. 'I think there's an old towel still up there—'

'Did I say I cared?' Jared demanded, coming to slide caressing hands over her shoulders. He angled his head to rest his forehead against hers. 'Dammit, Belle, I don't want to go.'

She didn't want him to go either, but even thinking such a thought was breaking every promise she'd made to herself, and she knew she had to stop wishing for miracles. They didn't happen, and somehow she had to get over it—get over *him*—and move on.

Move on...

God, how cold that sounded. Isobel felt the prick of

unshed tears burning behind her eyes and she knew she had to make him go before he started suspecting that something was seriously wrong.

'I'll see you tonight, right?' he murmured, kissing her again, but Isobel shook her head.

'Not tonight,' she said, through dry lips. 'I—I've got too much to do. I've got to finish here, and then I've got some marking—'

'You're not going into that loft again,' said Jared harshly. He tipped her face up to his. 'Promise me you won't go up there unless someone else—preferably me—is with you.'

Isobel expelled an unsteady breath. 'I—all right,' she agreed, deciding that, whatever else was left up there, Marion's husband would have to move it. She forced a smile. 'You'd better go.'

'Okay.' Jared released her without further protest and started towards the door. 'I'll ring you,' he said, pausing at the end of the hall, and then, with an irrepressible grin, he let himself out of the door.

She cried after he'd gone. She told herself her hormones were responsible, that ever since she'd found out what was wrong with her she'd been in a state of emotional turmoil, but she knew she was just fooling herself. She wasn't crying because she was pregnant. She was crying because he'd never know.

Then, as she went to the sink to bathe her eyes with cool water, her gaze alighted on the suitcase again. And suddenly she knew what she was going to do. She'd planned on leaving Newcastle, but until now she'd had no clear idea of where she was going to go. The little money she'd saved and her share from the sale of the house would support her until she found a regular job, and she considered herself lucky to have an occupation that was not confined to any one area. Oddly enough, she'd thought of moving south and west, and now she knew her destination.

She was going to Cornwall, to a town not too far distant from Polgarron, wherever that was. And she was going to do her best to find out what kind of man her father was—or had been…

CHAPTER THREE

WHEN someone knocked at the door of her apartment that evening, Isobel's heart leapt into overdrive. She was expecting Michelle, but it was too early for her, and she wondered how she'd explain her friend's arrival to Jared if it was him. When she'd told him she couldn't see him, it had been because she'd planned to spend the evening packing things that would be put into storage until she found somewhere else to live. Michelle had agreed to help her, despite her own misgivings about Isobel's decision.

But when she eventually opened the door, she found her sister waiting on the landing outside. 'I was beginning to think you weren't in,' remarked Marion tersely, brushing past her into the living room. She loosened the jacket of her black business suit and glanced about her impatiently. 'What's going on?'

Isobel closed the door, a frown drawing her dark brows together as she followed Marion into the room. 'What do you mean?' she asked, her pulse palpitating at the thought that Marion might have somehow found out about what she intended to do. A quick glance assured her that she'd disposed of all the evidence. So long as her sister didn't go into the spare bedroom, she appeared to be safe.

'You were going to call at the agency after you'd finished at the house,' Marion reminded her shortly, and Isobel breathed a little more easily. After reading Robert Dorland's letters, and the disturbing emotions aroused by Jared's visit, she'd forgotten all about the promise she'd made to her sister.

'I—forgot,' she said lamely now, and Marion regarded her with scarcely concealed irritation.

'How could you forget?' she exclaimed, subsiding onto a braided sofa. 'You knew I'd promised to give the keys to the estate agent this afternoon.'

'Yes, well…' Isobel sighed. 'There's a problem.'

'A problem?' Marion looked sceptical. 'You haven't found something structurally wrong with the house, have you?'

'No.' Isobel shook her head. 'Why should you think that?'

Marion shrugged, and then, when it became apparent that Isobel expected an answer, she clicked her tongue. 'If you must know, Malcolm saw Howard Goldman's son-in-law going into the house at lunchtime,' she said shortly.

'Oh.' Isobel felt the heat in her cheeks, and she turned away towards the kitchen. 'Can I get you something to drink? Tea? Or something stronger? I think I have some sherry. And beer, of course—'

'Nothing, thanks.' Marion's lips were tight. 'You do know the risk you're taking, don't you, Isobel?' She shook her head. 'If Elizabeth Kendall finds out…'

'She won't.' Isobel pushed her hands into the back pockets of her jeans. She'd had a shower when she got back from the house and deliberately changed her clothes in an effort to forget what had happened. 'In any case, we were talking about something else—'

Marion ignored her. 'I thought you told me you'd finished with Jared Kendall.'

Isobel felt a flare of indignation at her sister's careless intrusion into her private affairs. She and Jared had been seeing one another for over six months before Marion had found out about their relationship, but ever since she had she'd been warning Isobel of the dire consequences, not just to her, but to Marion's agency, if Howard Goldman discovered the truth.

'Let's leave it, shall we?' Isobel suggested flatly, and, as if sensing she was on shaky ground, Marion contented herself with sniffing her disapproval. 'I was talking about what I found in the loft.'

'The loft?' She had Marion's attention now. 'What's the loft got to do with anything?'

'It's full of junk,' said Isobel evenly. 'At least, that's all I thought it was.'

'What do you mean?'

Marion looked genuinely puzzled, and Isobel walked across the room and extracted the bundle of letters from the suitcase she'd left hidden behind an armchair. Handing her sister the letter she'd seen first, she said, 'Read that.'

Marion frowned, handling the envelope as if its evident age and discoloration offended her sensibilities. 'What is it?'

'Read it,' urged Isobel, endeavouring to control her impatience, and Marion pulled a face as she extracted the letter.

'Very well,' she said, flicking a speck of dust from her fingers. 'But I can't imagine why you would think...'

Her voice trailed away as she began to read. Watching her expression, Isobel soon became convinced that what she was seeing was as much of a shock to Marion as it had been to her. Her sister looked up once, when she was about halfway through the letter, and gave Isobel a disbelieving stare, but she waited until she'd reached Robert Dorland's signature before making any comment.

'Do you think this has something to do with you?'

Isobel shrugged. 'Don't you?'

Marion looked down at the letter again. 'How would I know? Who is this Robert Dorland? Some relation of Daddy's, I suppose.'

'His brother,' Isobel told her. She flicked through the other letters she was holding. 'I've read all of these, and that one was the last.'

Marion held out her hand. 'Can I read them?'

'Of course.' Isobel handed them over. 'But not now. I—well, I'm expecting somebody.'

Marion's expression tightened. 'Not Jared Kendall?'

'No, not Jared,' agreed Isobel wearily. 'Though if he was coming here, it would be nothing to do with you.'

'It would if his father-in-law found out I'd known about it, and done nothing to try and put a stop to it.'

Isobel caught her breath. 'Marion, you're not my keeper.'

'No, but Howard and Elizabeth are friends,' declared Marion, fitting the letter back into the envelope. 'We've even had dinner with them occasionally.'

'Very occasionally,' remarked Isobel drily. Howard Goldman and the Rimmers happened to belong to the same golf club, and Marion had been trying for years to cultivate the right kind of social circle. So far their contact with the Goldmans had been restricted to charity dinners and the like, but Marion had ambitions.

'Nevertheless—'

'Nevertheless, nothing,' said Isobel shortly. She squared her shoulders. 'Did you know anything about this?'

'This?' Marion held up the letter. 'No. How could I?'

'You've never heard of Robert Dorland?'

Marion was indignant. 'Isobel, I was only three years old when Mum and Daddy adopted you.'

'Yes.' Isobel acknowledged what she'd already accepted herself. 'So what do you think I should do?'

'Do?' Marion blinked. 'What do you mean? What do *I* think you should do? What can you do? These letters are—what? Twenty-five, thirty years old?'

'I'm only twenty-six, Marion.'

'Oh, yes. Right.' Marion pulled a wry face. 'Well, it hardly matters now.'

Isobel dropped down into the armchair opposite. 'Don't you think so?'

'How could it? This man—this Robert Dorland—is probably dead by now.'

'He might not be.'

'No.' Marion conceded the fact with ill grace. 'But what are you going to do? Turn up on his doorstep and expose the secret he's been keeping all these years: you!'

'He is my father.'

'Is he?'

'Of course he is.' Isobel stared at her. 'Surely you don't think he'd have gone to all that trouble if—'

'Oh, I'm sure he *thought* he was your father,' declared Marion dismissively. 'But your mother was hardly a paragon of all the virtues, was she? I mean—' Her lips twisted, and Isobel could almost see what she was thinking. 'Getting involved with a married man! How do you know she wasn't lying about your paternity in the hope of making a better life for herself?'

'Because Robert Dorland wouldn't even have known he had a daughter if she hadn't been killed,' retorted Isobel tersely. 'For pity's sake, Marion, what are you implying here?'

'Well, you don't know anything about her, do you? She could have been—well, anything.'

Isobel sprang to her feet. 'I think you'd better go now.'

'Oh, Isobel, don't be so melodramatic.' But Marion got to her feet anyway, clearly aware that she had overstepped the mark. 'All right. Maybe I'm not being very—sympathetic about her, but you know I don't mean anything by it. It's just my way.'

'Yes.' Isobel knew Marion's ways very well. She snatched the bundle of letters out of her sister's hands and folded them within her arms. 'Well, I don't think you'll be needing these,' she said, stepping aside so that Marion could walk towards the door. She took a breath. 'Oh, and here are the keys,' she added, lifting them off the table by the door. 'But you'll have to get Malcolm or somebody else to clear out the rest of the junk. There's far too much for me to handle.'

'Isobel...'

Marion tried again to placate her sister, but Isobel had had as much as she could take for one day. 'I'll be in touch,' she said, guiltily, aware that she was planning to leave town without giving her sister her new address. 'Goodnight.'

'Goodnight.'

Marion took the keys and left, but after she'd gone Isobel found herself in tears again. Dammit, she thought, what was wrong with her? The sooner she got out of Newcastle the better.

She'd barely dried her eyes before Michelle arrived. Her friend came into the apartment looking at Isobel with anxious eyes. 'What's wrong?'

Isobel sighed. 'Don't ask.'

'Jared Kendall,' said Michelle disgustedly, taking off her jacket. 'Honestly, Issy, I thought you were going to be sensible about him.'

'I am being sensible.'

'Oh, right.' Michelle flicked her neck with a sardonic finger. 'So what's this? A mosquito bite?'

Isobel covered the mark Jared's teeth had made with defensive fingers. 'Jared hasn't upset me,' she denied. 'It was Marion, if you must know.'

'Oh, yeah?' Michelle flopped down onto the sofa, spreading her ample bulk over both cushions. 'So what's she done now?'

Isobel hesitated. 'I found some old letters in the loft today.'

'Big deal.' Michelle pulled a face. 'Isn't that what you usually find in lofts? Old papers; old letters; *junk*? What's that got to do with the green-eyed monster?'

'The letters were from my father.'

'So?'

Isobel sighed. 'My *real* father!'

Michelle frowned. 'Your real father?' She shook her head. 'I thought you didn't know who your real father was.'

'I didn't. Until today.' Isobel looked doubtful. 'It turns out he was my father's brother.'

'Are you serious?' Michelle's blue eyes were wide. 'Holy Moses! And they never told you?'

'They didn't tell anyone,' said Isobel unhappily. 'My father—my adoptive father, that is—made that a condition when he agreed to take me.'

Michelle still looked confused. 'But I didn't know your father had a brother.'

'Nor did I.'

'And your real mother—?'

'She's still dead.' Isobel looked wistful now. 'It turns out that when she was killed the authorities discovered that she'd named Robert Dorland as—as my father.'

'*Robert* Dorland?'

'That's right.'

'So where is he now?'

'I'm not sure. At the time the letters were written, he was living at somewhere called Tregarth Hall in Polgarron. That's in Cornwall.'

'Cornwall?'

'Mmm.' Isobel nodded. 'It turns out I was born in London, not Newcastle.'

'I don't believe it!' Michelle was amazed.

'Of course, the facts of—of my adoption are the same. My mother was still unmarried at the time I was born. Her—association with my father was very brief.'

She was feeling weepy again now, and when she turned away to go into the kitchen Michelle sprang up from the couch and went after her. 'Hey,' she said, putting her arm about the other woman's shoulders. 'It's nothing to cry about. At least you know who you are now.'

'Do I?'

'Sure you do.' Michelle sighed, searching for the right words. 'Are you telling me Marion knew about this all along?'

'I don't think so.' Isobel drew away from her, pulling a tissue out of the box she kept on the counter and blowing her nose before going on. 'She seemed as shocked as me.'

'Then, what—?'

'Oh, it was something and nothing,' said Isobel tiredly. 'She suggested that Robert Dorland might not be my father after all. That my mother might just have used his name—'

'To what advantage?'

'That's what I said,' said Isobel eagerly. 'I mean, if she hadn't been killed, he would never have known.'

'Precisely.' Michelle snorted. 'For goodness' sake, don't let her upset you. As I've said many times before, she's a jealous cow.'

'But why?' exclaimed Isobel blankly. 'She's the success of the family, not me.'

'Well, obviously she doesn't think so,' retorted her friend shrewdly. 'It must have been a sickener for her when she found out about you and Jared. I mean, doesn't she spend all her time trying to insinuate herself with the divine Elizabeth?'

'Don't say that.' Isobel couldn't allow Michelle to ridicule Jared's wife. 'Life hasn't been easy for Elizabeth, you know that.'

Michelle grimaced. 'I know what she wants everyone to believe,' she remarked drily. 'But, okay. I won't say anything bitchy about Mrs Kendall if you'll stop getting mopey over Marion's maliciousness. Hell, she's probably afraid you're going to go looking for him.'

Isobel frowned. 'Why should that bother her?'

'Come on.' Michelle was impatient now. 'What was that address you just told me? Tregarth Hall? That doesn't sound like a semi in a nice, but unspectacular, part of town.'

Isobel stared at her. 'You're saying you think my father might be a—a wealthy man?'

'It's possible,' said Michelle, shrugging as she opened Isobel's fridge. 'Ah, wine,' she noted approvingly. 'I thought you'd never ask.'

Isobel sniffed again, but her mouth tilted a little at her friend's good-humoured common-sense. 'I don't want any,' she said, helping herself to a can of Coke. 'It's all yours.'

Michelle lifted the bottle out of the fridge and looked for the corkscrew. 'So you're really going through with this, then?'

Isobel looked down at her stomach. 'You mean the baby?'

'I mean the baby,' agreed Michelle, pouring herself a glass of Chardonnay. 'Does Marion know about that?'

'Heaven forbid!' Isobel spoke fervently. 'She'd say, Like mother, like daughter.'

'Mmm.' Michelle headed back into the living room. 'And you're still determined that Jared doesn't need to know either?'

Isobel nodded vigorously. 'It was never meant to happen, Michelle. You know that. It'll be better for all of us when I go away.'

'Well, if you want my honest opinion, I think he's bloody lucky to have known you,' declared her friend staunchly. 'I hate to say anything good about the bastard, but he hasn't had the happiest of marriages with the—with Elizabeth, has he?'

'No.' Isobel's throat was tight.

'And, contrary to what you say, I think he would do something about it, if he knew.'

'What? Get a divorce? I don't think so. Apart from the

fact that Elizabeth's disabled, it's common knowledge that he was driving the car when the accident happened.'

Isobel was getting emotional again, and Michelle apparently decided it was time to back off. 'Who knows?' she said lightly. 'What he doesn't know won't hurt him, I guess.' She sank down onto the sofa again, and took a sip of her wine. 'So…what are you going to do about the letters?'

Isobel perched on the chair opposite. 'What do you think I should do?'

Michelle arched improbably thin eyebrows. 'How should I know?' Her eyes narrowed. 'But I guess, looking at you now, that you've got a plan in mind.'

'I had,' admitted Isobel ruefully. 'Now, I'm not so sure.'

'Why not?'

Isobel bit her lip. 'I had thought of looking for somewhere to live near—near Polgarron.'

'Ah. And?'

'Well, if your suspicions are true, and he—does have money, I don't want him to think I'm looking for him now because I think he—owes me something.'

'He does.'

'Michelle!'

'He does, dammit. You are his daughter.'

'If it's true.'

'Do you doubt it?'

'No.'

'There you are, then.' Michelle was triumphant. 'I suggest we drive down the first weekend of the holidays.'

Isobel caught her breath. 'You'll come with me?'

'And see you settled? What else?'

'Oh, Michelle, thank you.' Isobel went and gave her friend an impulsive hug. 'I thought I'd have to go on my own.'

'How are you going to haul all your stuff in that matchbox of yours?' demanded Michelle, disparaging Isobel's car with affectionate familiarity. 'No, we'll take the estate car. Phil can manage with my car for a few days, and we'll leave your car in our garage until you're settled. Then, you can either come back for it or get a local garage to deliver it for you.'

Isobel shook her head. 'Won't Phil object?' Michelle's husband was a sales rep and used the estate car to carry demonstration equipment.

'As I say, he can make do with the Peugeot. Honestly, he won't mind.'

'But your holiday—'

'We're not going away until the third week in August,' exclaimed Michelle impatiently. 'Stop making obstacles where there aren't any. With a bit of luck, you'll be installed in your new place before we go away. Hey—' she laughed '—after you move, Phil and I will have a permanent holiday home in the West Country, won't we?'

'The West Country.' Isobel echoed the words with a shiver of apprehension. Despite the news about her father, and the gratitude she felt towards Michelle for her help and understanding, she couldn't forget what she was leaving behind. 'It sounds so far away.'

'It is far away,' said Michelle mildly. 'I thought that was the idea.'

Isobel heaved a sigh. 'It is, of course, but—'

'You're going to miss me. I know,' said Michelle drily, but when Isobel turned pained eyes in her direction, she shook her head in knowing resignation. 'You've got to forget him, kid. You said yourself there's no future in it.'

'That doesn't stop me wishing—' Isobel cut herself off before she could finish the damning sentence and swung around towards the spare bedroom. 'Come on. Let's get started with the packing. It's only two weeks to the start of the summer holidays.'

CHAPTER FOUR

JARED dropped his hard hat onto the seat beside him, and rested his head against the soft leather upholstery. It had been a long, hot day and the hair at the back of his neck was damp with sweat. He needed a drink and a shower, not necessarily in that order, and then the prospect of spending the rest of the evening with the only woman he cared anything about.

Isobel…

But that wasn't going to happen. He scowled as he started the engine of the powerful Mercedes, barely acknowledging the salute of the security guard who was on duty at the gate of the building complex. Elizabeth had a dinner party for her father planned that he'd promised to attend. Instead of changing into jeans and a tee shirt and picking Isobel up for a bar-meal at some country pub, he was obliged to put on a dinner jacket and spend several hours talking to people he didn't even like.

He sighed. That wasn't absolutely true. Many of his in-laws' acquaintances were friends of his, too, and if he could have counted on looking at Isobel across the candlelit dinner table he'd have been content.

He was actually working on a plan to take her away for a few days. There was an architects' conference in Paris in August, and the prospect of several days—and nights—with Isobel caused his trousers to become unpleasantly tight. Dammit, they'd never spent a whole night together. He couldn't wait to wake up with her beside him.

The trouble was, while it was comparatively easy to find excuses for going out in the evenings, it was much harder to explain a night's absence. And, lately, Isobel had been finding excuses for not seeing him in the evenings either. On two or three occasions recently she'd turned him down in favour of other commitments, and, while he knew she had some crazy idea of breaking up with him, he also believed she was as helpless as he was to destroy what they shared.

His lips twisted. It was his own fault, after all. No one had forced him to marry Elizabeth. He'd gone into their relationship with his eyes open, and if the knowledge that as Howard Goldman's son-in-law he might be given the opportunity to gain recognition for his work had not been unpleasing to him, it had definitely not been the sole reason he'd made Elizabeth his wife.

He'd joined Goldman Lewis as a very junior draughtsman after getting his degree, and from the beginning he'd been aware of Howard Goldman's daughter watching him every time she came into the office. Elizabeth was easy on the eye, and he wouldn't have been human if he hadn't been flattered by her attention, but he'd never expected anything to come of it.

That it had had been more due to Elizabeth than himself. Young architects with big ideas were ten a penny, and he'd naturally assumed that Elizabeth would marry someone with a far different pedigree than his own. He'd actually hesitated before accepting that first invitation to a party at the Goldmans', unsure what her father would make of one his junior employees fraternising with the boss's daughter.

In fact, Howard Goldman had encouraged the relationship, but it hadn't been until they were married that Jared had found out why. Dazed by the speed with which he'd been promoted from a minor employee of the firm to a member of the family, Jared hadn't looked for reasons. He'd been far too busy congratulating himself on his good fortune to search for motives for his success.

His life with Elizabeth, however, had soon proved how naïve he had been. The woman he'd known far too fleetingly before the wedding bore little resemblance to his new wife, her black moods and violent depressions demonstrating that whatever feelings she had expressed for him before they were married, she could barely tolerate him now.

Within a few months, Jared had realised that Elizabeth's reasons for marrying him had had nothing to do with love or sex. She'd no longer been interested in him except as a means to pacify her father, and Jared had begun to understand that marrying him had been a way to get Howard off her back. The old man had confided in him before the wedding that his dearest wish was that his daughter should give him a grandchild, and, with Elizabeth approaching her thirtieth birthday, he'd been losing hope that she'd ever find a husband. Now that they were going to get married, he'd assumed Elizabeth would be proud to grant his wish.

How wrong he'd been.

Jared's lips compressed. Elizabeth's agenda had been totally different from her father's, from his own. She'd known all about his background before the wedding: the fact that his parents were dead, that he'd been brought up in a series of foster homes until he was sixteen and he'd run away to London, that there'd been little love of any kind in his life. He'd had to steel himself against his emotions; he'd been hurt too many times in the past to trust anything to change. He'd worked at a handful of jobs to earn the money to go to college, determined to get the qualifications necessary to get a decent job. And when he'd passed all his exams he'd returned to the north-east.

To a job with Goldman Lewis.

He sighed now. Elizabeth had apparently believed he'd be so grateful to her for what her father could do for him that whatever she did, however she behaved, he wouldn't object. She'd been sure he'd do nothing to jeopardise his privileged position, but she couldn't have been more wrong. For more than half his life already he'd been forced to do what other people—often strangers—told him, and he'd had no intention of allowing it to happen again.

Yet it had.

He scowled. He'd tried so hard to save the marriage, he remembered bitterly. He'd even convinced himself that he must be to blame for Elizabeth's change of attitude towards him, and when she'd suggested that their relationship might benefit from being given a little space, he'd happily agreed to her spending the weekend at a health farm with one of the women she played golf with.

The call that had shattered all his illusions had come on a Sunday morning. Jared had been sprawled on one of the sofas in the living room, the Sunday papers scattered around him in disarray. He'd actually been anticipating his wife's return with some enthusiasm, hoping against hope that whatever it was that had brought them together might still have the power to promote a reconciliation.

The call had killed any feelings he'd still had for her. It had been from a clinic in London. To begin with, Jared had assumed Elizabeth must have given him the wrong information. She'd said the health farm was in Northamptonshire, and as these places sometimes called themselves clinics, Jared had assumed he'd made a mistake.

He hadn't.

The young woman who'd contacted him—a very junior nurse, he'd learned later—had explained that there'd been a complication. She'd said that the operation Mrs Kendall had had the previous afternoon hadn't gone as satisfactorily as Dr Singh had anticipated.

Jared had been stunned. He hadn't known Elizabeth needed an operation and he'd briefly blamed himself for his ignorance. And when he'd expressed his concern the young nurse had taken pity on him, assuring him that his wife was in no danger, that the termination had been successful.

Jared had heard the rest of what she'd said in numbed disbelief. He hadn't wanted to hear that Elizabeth had developed an infection immediately after the operation, or that she wouldn't be able to return to Newcastle for a few days. His revulsion that she should do such a thing, without even telling him, had been all he could think about, and he'd been hard pressed to be civil to the girl who'd broken the news.

Of course, Elizabeth had never expected him to find out. As he'd discovered afterwards, the clinic was supposed to be totally confidential, and it was only the fact that a new—and very inexperienced—nurse had been on duty when Elizabeth had expressed her concern about the delay, and had taken it upon herself to call the number Elizabeth had given when she'd booked in, which had given the game away. Elizabeth herself had been a little groggy at the time, or she'd never have made such a stupid mistake. She'd have waited until she was well enough to call him herself, and given some other excuse for not returning home.

Jared didn't know how he'd got through the rest of that day or the days that followed. His first impulse had been to pack his bags and be out of there before his wife got back, but he'd wanted to see her first, to tell her what he thought of her, and that had been a mistake. When Elizabeth had got back she'd been still weak and shaken, but not too weak to remind him of the effect his intended actions would have on her father. The infection she'd developed after the abortion meant there could be no second chances, and the thought of Howard finding out that his daughter would never give him a grandchild was not a prospect Jared had wanted to face.

He'd been brought brutally back to earth when Howard had reminded him of the dinner he and Elizabeth were expected to attend in Alnwick the following evening. Howard had been invited, but it had clashed with another engagement he had in the city, and because these days Jared often acted as his deputy, the Kendalls had been invited in his stead.

The arrangements had been made weeks before or Jared wouldn't have hesitated in turning the invitation down. But to do so would have created questions he had not yet been ready to answer, and for Howard's sake he hadn't made any complaint.

Only when Elizabeth had insisted on driving home after the dinner had Jared objected. Knowing he'd had a thirty-mile drive ahead of him, he had drunk tonic water all evening, whereas Elizabeth had had several glasses of wine. She wasn't fit, he'd said coldly, expecting her to get out of the driving seat, but instead she'd started the engine, and he'd had no doubt she'd intended to leave him behind in the car park of the hotel.

He remembered grabbing the passenger door and jumping in beside her. The alternative would have been to let her drive off, leaving him to have to explain his plight to those who had still not emerged from the hotel.

It had been at a notorious bend in the road that the car had appeared to go out of control. Jared's stomach still roiled at the memory of jarring gears and squealing tyres, and the horrifying image of an enormous truck bearing down on them. He'd wondered since then whether Elizabeth hadn't had some crazy notion of killing herself and him, but he'd grabbed the wheel out of her hands and wrenched the car back from imminent disaster. Nevertheless it had lost too much traction, and he'd felt the wheels skidding over an icy patch on the road. There'd been no way to prevent the vehicle from mounting the kerb before it had lurched headlong into a ditch.

He didn't recall much after that, until he'd woken up in hospital the following day with two broken legs and a mild concussion. Howard had been sitting by his bed when he'd awakened, and for a moment he'd been sure the older man was there to break the news that Elizabeth was dead.

But Elizabeth hadn't been dead. Though she had been badly injured. Howard's reasons for keeping vigil by his son-in-law's bedside, however, had been to ensure that Jared would take the blame for the accident. Though he hadn't been sure then who had been at the wheel at the time of the crash—they'd both been flung out on impact—he'd wanted to protect his daughter's reputation. And the reputation of the firm, Jared had added silently. If Elizabeth had had to face charges of dangerous driving as well as having been drunk at the wheel, it would have proved a juicy piece of gossip for the press.

Besides, he'd added earnestly, Jared had nothing to lose.

Of course, that hadn't been true, as he'd found out later, when the consequences of the cover-up Howard had engineered had come to light. In addition to her injuries, it appeared that Elizabeth didn't remember anything about the accident, or about the evening, for that matter, and when those injuries had proved to be far more serious than anyone had expected, she'd blamed Jared for causing the paralysis that she was going to have to live with for the rest of her life.

Looking back now, Jared supposed he could have denied everything, but he'd given Howard his word and the old man still knew nothing of what had been going on. Short of destroying the old man emotionally, there was nothing he could have done, at least not then, and as Elizabeth had been going to be in hospital for some time, Jared had decided to wait.

In the three years since that night, Jared's life had, effectively, been put on hold. It had been a very sombre Elizabeth who'd eventually returned home from the hospital, and for a long time after that the house had been filled with nurses and doctors and other members of the medical profession so that any kind of normal routine had been impossible.

Howard had arranged for building work to be done to modify the house for Elizabeth's wheelchair. All doorways had been widened, and anything she used had been lowered accordingly. He'd even had a lift installed to give her access to the upper floors of the house, but if he'd ever suspected that things between his daughter and son-in-law were not as they should be, he'd kept it to himself.

By the time he'd been able to go home without encountering strangers in the house, Jared had shelved his own ambitions. Although he'd sometimes been tempted to confront Elizabeth with the truth about the accident, he never had. In many ways, their relationship had improved since the accident. Although she was still moody, particularly when things got frustrating for her, Howard had succeeded in convincing her that there was no way Jared could be held responsible for what had happened. The road had been icy; the car had skidded. It was a tragedy, but no one was to blame.

And Elizabeth knew she had Jared to thank for protecting her from her father's wrath. The abortion, and its aftermath, had had to take second place to the injuries she'd suffered, and even after all this time he had never betrayed her.

Jared suspected the improvement in their association was due to two things: one, they no longer made any pretence that theirs was a normal marriage, and, two, the live-in physiotherapist Howard had hired for her. Although Jared found Janet Brady too abrasive for his liking, there was no doubt she had the knack of keeping Elizabeth sweet.

Howard had also made Jared his deputy at Goldman Lewis, proving to outsiders, too, that he didn't harbour any grudges against his son-in-law. The irony of this was not lost on either of them, but Jared had become an expert at keeping his real feelings to himself.

His relationship with Isobel was not like any other. Meeting her had taught him to despise himself for the man he'd become. He'd realised that the feelings he'd had for Elizabeth were nothing like the way he felt about Isobel. He didn't know if it was love, but he couldn't bear the thought of never seeing her again. Of course he couldn't tell Isobel the truth about the crash without involving Howard. Although he had admitted that he and Elizabeth had been having difficulties long before the accident had occurred, he was loath to betray Howard's confidence when he didn't honestly know how Isobel felt.

He sighed, raking back the tumbled weight of his hair with a restless hand, forcefully closing his mind to what might have been. He had the evening ahead to face, and, unless he wanted to spend the next few hours torturing himself, he had to stop thinking of Isobel and put his own desires aside. But before she'd come along, he'd believed himself immune from any emotional attraction. He hadn't got a divorce because he'd had no intention of ever getting married again. Never wanted to—until now…

The house Howard had given them as a wedding present four years ago was situated in an exclusive development north-west of the city, and Jared contained his impatience as he joined the usual rush-hour press of traffic heading in that direction. As he waited at one of the numerous sets of traffic lights, he contemplated calling Isobel and asking her what she was doing this evening, but the knowledge of how he would feel if she told him she was free stopped him from picking up his mobile phone.

There was no way he could see her tonight, and he closed his eyes for a moment as the image of making love with her in her mother's kitchen of all places flashed across his mind. God, he thought, remembering that afternoon with sudden incredulity, anyone could have looked through the window and seen them there. All the doors had been unlocked. How would he have felt if that snobby sister of hers had walked in and found them?

The lights changed and he allowed the car to crawl forward to the next obstruction. The trouble was, when he was with Isobel such considerations went out the window, and he wondered if he wasn't in danger of not giving a damn…

He parked on the brick-paved forecourt in front of the triple garage which was situated to one side of the sprawling pseudo-mansion he'd learned to call home. It had never been his choice; he would have preferred something older. But appearances mattered to Elizabeth and this house said that they'd made it in the material world.

Gathering up his jacket, his briefcase, and his mobile phone, Jared pushed open the door and got out of the car. But he'd forgotten a portfolio of drawings that he'd brought from the current development, and by the time he'd rescued it from the back seat his hands were full.

He kicked the door closed with his foot, his lips twisting at the thought of treating a car he'd used to dream about when he was a teenager so shabbily. Then he saw Janet Brady watching him from Elizabeth's bedroom window, and all humour went of the situation. She was probably thinking he was venting his frustration on the vehicle, and he was. But it wasn't just the prospect of another formal dinner party that was souring his mood.

He heard the whine of the lift Howard had installed as soon as he entered the marble-tiled hallway. The ornamental cage came to a halt as Jared was shouldering the outer door closed behind him, and the wheelchair came gliding towards him.

'Did you get it?'

Elizabeth's first words were interrogative, and for a moment Jared couldn't think what on earth she meant. His own thoughts were still wrapped up with what he had been thinking on the drive home, and he looked at his wife without comprehension as she gazed up at him with enquiring eyes.

'Get what?' he asked, unloading the file and the briefcase onto the hall table, and her lips curled impatiently at any hint of opposition.

'The watch,' she exclaimed tersely, tucking a blonde strand behind her ear. 'Did you pick it up from the engraver's? Oh, don't tell me you forgot it, Jared. Temple's will be closed by now.'

Jared laid his mobile phone beside the portfolio, and bent to flick the catches on the briefcase. 'Oh, that,' he said carelessly, extracting a box from inside. He turned and handed it to her. 'I'm not entirely without sensitivity, you know.'

Elizabeth didn't bother to answer him. Her attention was focussed on the cardboard-covered leather case he'd handed her, and Jared was able to observe her without restraint. She was still a beautiful woman, though in recent years she'd gained some weight, but her features still possessed a certain sharpness even if her body was plumper than it used to be.

She slid the covering from the case now and opened it to gaze at the pocket watch that lay inside. It was a gold half-hunter, gleaming brightly on its bed of white satin, and Elizabeth picked it up and turned it over, smiling with satisfaction when she read the inscription on the back.

'"To Daddy on his sixtieth birthday,"' she murmured, the pad of her thumb rubbing the engraving as she spoke. '"With all my love."'

Jared winced. He doubted Elizabeth had it in her to love anyone. 'Is that what you had put on the back?' he asked tightly, and his wife looked up at him with scornful eyes.

Then, her own lips tightening with unwilling pique, she handed the watch to him and he saw the inscription for himself. '"With all *our* love,"' he read, '"Liza and Jared". Very nice.'

'It should be,' exclaimed Elizabeth, putting the watch back in its case. 'It cost plenty. I just hope it's enough.'

A headache was probing at Jared's temple, but her words demanded an explanation. 'Enough?' he echoed. 'Enough for what?'

Elizabeth shrugged. 'To distract him from his usual theme, of course,' she declared, as if Jared should have known what she was talking about. 'You know how irritating he's been lately.'

'Has he?'

Jared hadn't noticed any change in his father-in-law's attitude towards him, but Elizabeth's nostrils flared with evident impatience. 'Well, naturally, I wouldn't expect you to notice,' she said bitterly. 'You probably think that the fact that he's become such bosom buddies with Patrick Beaumont lately is just a coincidence.'

Jared sighed. 'Does it matter?'

'It matters to me.' Elizabeth twisted her hands together. 'Jared, Patrick's a consultant gynaecologist. Surely even you must know what Daddy's thinking.'

Jared began to understand. 'You're afraid he's going to bring up the possibility of you having a baby,' he said flatly. 'Well, you've got to tell him the truth sooner or later.'

'I can't.'

Jared shrugged. 'Just don't expect me to do it.'

Elizabeth bit her lip. 'You could tell him that in your opinion you don't think I could cope with a baby. That it wouldn't be fair on me to insist on my having a lot of unnecessary tests.'

Jared's mouth was grim. 'You have to be joking.' He would have brushed past her then, if she hadn't swung her chair and blocked his path. 'Dammit, Liz, you got rid of my child and, in the process, any chance you ever had of having another baby. Don't expect me to help you when you haven't even got the guts to tell your father yourself.'

Elizabeth's mouth compressed. 'Let's not forget that if it wasn't for you I wouldn't be in this wheelchair,' she said accusingly, and Jared had to bite his tongue to prevent himself from telling her the truth.

He pushed the chair aside and strode towards the stairs. He was making no promises to her when the only thing he really wanted was out of his reach. 'I need a shower,' he said, without giving her an answer, and vaulted up the stairs to the first floor.

He met Janet Brady on the landing. She was a tall woman, almost as tall as he was, with coarse red hair that she wore plaited in a single braid. She was overweight, too, and was invariably dressed in trousers with a loose blouse to hide her waistband, and the look she cast in Jared's direction was loaded with dislike.

'I should have thought you'd know better than to upset your wife, Mr Kendall,' she said sharply. 'Her therapy isn't just a physical thing, you know.'

'When I want your advice, Miss Brady, I'll ask for it,' retorted Jared, striding down the corridor to his bedroom, and it wasn't until he'd slammed the door behind him that he realised she must have been listening to everything he and Elizabeth had said.

CHAPTER FIVE

THE cottage stood at the end of a row of similar dwellings, but, unlike the others, it had been sadly neglected. A drooping gate gave onto a front garden that was choked with weeds, and the flagged path was covered with moss.

'You'll have to be careful you don't slip when it's wet,' Michelle remarked, following her friend though the gate. 'God, I hope the inside is better than this.'

Isobel was thinking the same, but she refused to be downhearted about it. She had so much else to be downhearted about, and finding this cottage had seemed the only bright spot in a rather dull day. When the estate agent in Polgarth had told her that there was a cottage to rent in Polgarron, she'd fairly jumped at the chance of finding a home so near to Tregarth Hall. But it was only now, when they came to inspect it, that they realised why the estate agent had been so willing to trust them with the key.

There were roses climbing over the porch, but she felt the unpleasant brush of spiders' webs as she stepped forward and put the key in the lock. It was obviously weeks, possibly even months, since anyone had visited here, and her heart sank a little when she had to apply her shoulder to open the door.

'Damp,' said Michelle resignedly, stepping inside and giving an involuntary shiver. 'Issy, you can't stay here. It's uninhabitable.'

Isobel put her own misgivings aside and looked about her with determined optimism. 'You're too pessimistic,' she said. 'And you've got soft, living in the lap of luxury as you do.'

'Issy, a three-bedroomed semi is not the lap of luxury.

Admit it: this isn't what you expected. No wonder that smarmy devil in the estate agent's was so eager to pass you the key. He probably thinks we're thick or something. I mean, no one in their right mind would rent this place.'

'We haven't seen it yet,' Isobel insisted, but she conceded to herself that the dismal room they were standing in would need more than soap and water to put it right. The windows were thick with dirt, but that didn't prevent them from seeing that the paper on the walls was peeling, and no one had touched the paintwork in heaven knew how many years.

'What's to see?' Michelle countered now, walking across the stained linoleum that covered the floor. She pushed open the door into the adjoining room, brushing away the cobwebs before venturing further. 'God, this must be the kitchen! Issy, have you ever seen anything like this?'

Isobel hadn't. She wasn't averse to primitive, but when it came to using a pump to get any water, cold or otherwise, she realised she had to draw the line. Besides which, there was no sign of any electrical appliances; not even a cooker.

'It is pretty—pretty—'

'I think the word you're looking for is ghastly,' declared Michelle fervently, backing out of the kitchen and turning away. 'Come on, Issy. Let's go and tell that estate agent what we think of him. I think we've got time before they close for the day.'

Isobel sighed, and as she did so a shadow further darkened the doorway behind them. A man had appeared in the entrance, and both women took a step backward as he came into the room.

'Can I help you?' he asked, and an errant ray of sunlight that had found its way between the smears of dirt on the windows highlighted reddish brown hair and a square, good-looking face.

Isobel glanced at Michelle, but her friend only arched a quizzical brow and she realised it was up to her to answer him. 'Um—I doubt it,' she said, wondering if he was another prospective tenant the agency had sent along. 'We were just leaving.'

'Really?' The man, who she could see now was somewhere in his late twenties, looked disappointed. 'I was hoping you might be interested in taking this place on.'

Isobel blinked. 'You were?' She frowned. 'Why should it matter to you?'

'Oh, forgive me.' The man, who was dressed in brown corduroy pants, a Barbour jacket and green boots, stepped forward, holding out his hand. 'I haven't introduced myself, have I? I'm Luke Herrington. My family owns this cottage, I'm afraid.'

And all the others as well, thought Isobel sagely, allowing him to shake her hand. 'How do you do? I'm Isobel D—Dawson.' She exchanged an appealing look with Michelle, begging her condolence. 'And this is my friend, Michelle Chambers.'

There were handshakes all round, but it was obvious that Luke Herrington was more interested in Isobel's dark slenderness than Michelle's more generous proportions. 'And am I right in thinking that the agency in Polgarth sent you here?' he asked, pulling a wry face, and Isobel nodded.

'Yes. But I'm afraid it's not what—what we're looking for.'

'Because of the state it's in, I'll bet,' agreed Luke Herrington warmly. 'I must admit, I hadn't realised just how dilapidated it had become.'

'It's a dump,' said Michelle flatly. 'I don't know how anyone could have expected us to take it.'

'Oh, I agree.' Herrington nodded his head vigorously. 'I'd never have allowed Gillings to send anybody here if I'd known.'

Both women took that with a pinch of salt, but the man's next words gave them pause. 'Of course, if you were interested, I'd be happy to have the place renovated for you. I mean,' he pressed on, when it appeared possible that at least one of the women was listening to him, 'no one wants to leave a property standing empty for months on end. Particularly not when a few rolls of paper and a few pots of paint could make it habitable.'

'Oh, I think it would take more than that,' said Michelle disparagingly, ignoring Isobel's reaction. 'The kitchen doesn't even have running water.'

'Oh, I'm sure it does.' Luke Herrington frowned now. 'Let me see...'

But when Michelle turned back towards the open doorway, he stopped her. 'That's not the kitchen,' he said, and Isobel didn't know whether to be glad or sorry. 'That's just a storeroom. The kitchen's this way.'

He led them out of another door into a narrow passageway that ran towards the back of the cottage. The kitchen was the only door opening off the hall, with a narrow flight of stairs curving towards the upper floor opposite.

'Here we are,' he said, dipping his head under the low lintel. 'What do you think?'

The kitchen was tiny, but he was right, it did have running hot and cold water—or it would have if the boiler was working—and there was a small gas cooker and electric fridge.

'It's—antique,' declared Michelle, before Isobel could find some polite adjective to use, and just for a moment a look of irritation crossed Herrington's handsome face.

'It's—primitive, I'll give you that,' he said, running the tip of one finger along the rim of the fridge and then grimacing at the smear of dirt it left behind. 'But, as I say, it could be made quite—comfortable.'

'And how long do you think that would take?' asked Isobel, wondering if she was mad to be even thinking of living here. She'd already given him a false surname, and she was glad that Michelle had given her name and address as a guarantee when the estate agent had handed over the key.

'Oh—let me see.' Herrington glanced about him. 'Two or three weeks, I suppose.'

'Two or three months, more like,' muttered Michelle, making her opinion very plain, and once again he gave her an impatient look.

'Will you be living here, too, Miss Chambers?' he asked politely, and Isobel guessed that Gillings had phoned and told him that only one of them was looking for accommodation.

'It's *Mrs* Chambers,' replied Michelle coldly. 'And, no, I won't be living here. But I think Issy should think again about where she wants to live.'

Taking a deep breath, Herrington turned back to Isobel. 'Do you have some connection with this area, Miss Dawson?' he asked, and for a moment Isobel wondered if he'd detected that she had some ulterior motive for choosing Polgarron. But then, realising he was only making conversation, she shook her head.

'I was just looking for somewhere to rent in this area,' she admitted. 'This cottage was vacant, so...'

She shrugged, and he inclined his head. 'I see.' He gestured that they should move out into the hall again. 'Come, let me show you upstairs.'

There were two bedrooms, and a minuscule bathroom that contained a suite that, like the kitchen downstairs, had seen better days. But the bedrooms themselves were considerably less off-putting, the view from the windows making up in no small part for what they lacked in size.

'What do you think?'

Herrington was looking at her now, and Isobel didn't know what to say. The cottage wasn't really what she was looking for. It was small, even by her standards, and there was no central heating, which she'd told herself she had to have for when the baby was born.

'I'm not sure...' she said awkwardly, and Michelle took the opportunity to endorse her own feelings.

'You need somewhere more modern, Issy,' she exclaimed. 'An apartment would be better than this.'

With a baby? Isobel didn't say the words but the thought passed between them, and she had to admit that although having a baby in an apartment wasn't ideal, it was gaining more merit. After all, this wasn't the first house they'd been offered, but all of them had had something wrong with them, most usually the rent.

'I don't know...'

She was loath to dismiss the cottage out of hand. Despite its bedraggled appearance, she tended to agree with Luke Herrington; it could be made habitable, and not too expensively. Besides which, she'd never had a garden of her own before, and she could already see a lawn and a rose garden, and a pram standing in the sunshine beside the door...

'Let me get my bailiff to take a look at it,' said Luke eagerly, sensing her reluctance to turn him down. 'Are you staying locally? Let me get him to give you an estimate of how long it will take to put the place in order.'

'Oh, I—'

'I've got to do something about this place anyway,' he persisted. 'As I said before, if I'd realised just how run-down it had become, I'd have done something about it before now.'

Isobel looked at Michelle for guidance, but her friend was saying nothing more. Isobel knew what she was thinking without having to be told, but the knowledge that she might have to spend another week trailing round unsuitable properties was urging her to at least give Luke a chance.

'We're staying in Polgarth,' she said, making a decision. 'At the White Hart. Do you know it?'

'Indeed I do.' Luke beamed now. 'Frank Culver, the landlord, you know, is a good friend of mine. I'm sure he's making you very comfortable there.'

'Better than here,' said Michelle under her breath, but Isobel heard her.

'We're very comfortable,' she said, hoping her would-be landlord hadn't heard Michelle's comment. 'All right. I suggest I leave it for the time being. I'll keep looking round, and you can let me know when your bailiff has had the chance to give his assessment.'

'Excellent.' Clearly, he was looking forward to having her as his tenant, and Isobel hoped he would feel just as enthusiastic when he realised she wasn't going to be entirely alone at the cottage.

But, back in the car again, Michelle let her feel the brunt of her frustration. 'I can't believe you're going to consider that dump,' she exclaimed, accelerating through the village in an effort to expunge her irritation. 'For God's sake, Issy, I know you want to find somewhere to live and we haven't been having a great deal of success lately, but—'

'We only have another week,' Isobel reminded her desperately. 'Then you'll be going back to Newcastle, and I'll have to go looking at places on foot. Unless I get someone to deliver my car. Not to mention the fact that I'd rather not go alone.'

'But you don't want my opinion,' Michelle pointed out shortly. 'I couldn't believe it when you told that ass where we were staying. You as good as accepted his offer there and then.'

'No, I didn't.' Isobel sighed. 'Oh, Michelle, don't be angry with me, please. You know how much I want to live in this area. What are the chances of us finding anywhere else to rent that's as convenient as this?'

'Pretty slim, I suppose,' Michelle conceded, opening her

window and resting her arm on the sill. 'And this is a pretty village, I suppose. I like all the grey stonework, and that church looks interesting.'

'Hmm.' Isobel squeezed Michelle's arm with grateful fingers. 'Thanks.'

Then, her eyes widened. 'My God!'

'What? What?' Michelle grabbed the wheel with both hands, nearly steering off the road in her efforts to control the car.

'There. *There!*' said Isobel, pointing a shaking finger. 'That sign; can you see it? It says, "Tregarth Hall"! Oh, God, Michelle, that must be where those letters came from.'

Michelle left for home six days later.

She was loath to leave her friend, still staying at the inn in Polgarth, but it was a long journey back to Newcastle and she and her husband were leaving for Portugal in a few days.

'What do I say to Marion, if I see her?' she asked, as she and Isobel lingered over dinner the night before she left. So far, all Isobel's sister knew was that she and Michelle were holidaying together, but sooner or later Marion would have to be given a proper explanation.

Even so, Isobel was loath to tell her about the baby just in case Marion happened to mention it to someone at the golf club. The idea that Jared might find out via some crony of Howard Goldman's was unacceptable, but Michelle wasn't convinced that she should keep it a secret from her family.

'If you have to, tell her I've decided to prolong my holiday,' Isobel said now, avoiding the other woman's eyes. 'There's another four weeks before term's due to start. It'll be easier if I'm settled into the cottage before I tell her and Malcolm I'm not coming back.'

Michelle sighed. 'I still think you should have been

straight with her. About moving, at least. Whether you tell her about the baby is up to you, but I think she deserves to know that you've resigned from your job.'

'I know.' Isobel pulled a wry face. 'But you know why I didn't.'

'Of course. Because you were afraid someone else would find out. But he didn't and you're here now. What have you got to lose?'

Isobel shrugged. 'Nothing, I suppose.' But the knowledge of how Jared would react when he discovered what she'd done was tearing her apart, and she knew it was foolish but, so long as she didn't tell anyone else, she could fool herself into believing that it wasn't a final break.

It had been so hard not seeing him again before she left. She hadn't been able to avoid speaking to him on the phone, of course, but she'd managed to find excuses for not meeting him in the two weeks after his visit to her mother's house. After that scene, and its aftermath, she'd known she couldn't see him again. She was too weak, too vulnerable; he only had to lay his hands on her and she went to pieces.

God knew what he was thinking of her now. He'd have called the apartment and discovered that her number had been discontinued, but would he have been indiscreet enough to ask Marion where she was? He knew her sister had found out about their relationship, but he also knew that Isobel had told him that it was over, and that she had probably told Marion the same thing, so…

'So does that mean that if she asks I can tell her where you are?' Michelle persisted now, and, forcing thoughts of Jared to the back of her mind, Isobel took a deep breath.

'I'm not sure—'

'But you can't expect her to believe that I don't know where you are,' said Michelle impatiently. 'Issy, accept it.

You've made the break. Kendall's going to have to live with it.'

'I know.'

'I'm not sure you do.' Michelle looked worried now. 'Dammit, I wish I didn't have to go back.'

'But you do,' said Isobel, finishing the mineral water in her glass. She forced a smile. 'I'll be all right. Honestly. I'm not a complete fool, you know.'

'Remember, you've got to check in with a doctor at the first possible moment. And make arrangements about—well, about when the baby's due.'

'I know.'

'The provisional date you have is January eighteenth, isn't it?'

'You know it is.'

'I wonder if that coincides with a weekend?' Michelle bit her lip. 'Perhaps I could get a flight to Penzance or somewhere. It would be so much quicker than bringing the car, and if the weather's bad—'

'Michelle.' Isobel reached across the table and covered her friend's hand with her own. 'I don't expect you to be here when I have the baby.'

'But someone has to be.'

'Not necessarily.'

Isobel suppressed the panicky little feeling that assailed her at the thought of going into labour at the cottage and having to drive herself to the hospital in—where? She didn't even know where the nearest hospital was. Polgarth was the nearest small town, but not all small towns had maternity units. She might have to go to Truro or St Austell. God, how far away was that?

A little of her anxiety must have shown in her face, because Michelle gripped her fingers now. 'What is it? What are you thinking? Issy, I'll try to be here. I will.'

Isobel shook her head. 'I'm just being silly.' She made

herself give a short laugh. 'I was thinking, I don't even know where the nearest hospital is.'

'Well, at least you'll have plenty of time to find out before it happens,' Michelle reassured her. 'And I'll be down again in the October break.'

'Phil's going to get sick of you leaving him on his own,' said Isobel at once. 'There's no need—'

'Hey, Phil may come with me,' Michelle interrupted her quickly. 'He gets more than two weeks' holiday a year, you know.'

Isobel's eyes widened. 'Do you think he would? Come, I mean?'

'Why not?' Michelle grinned. 'So if you find you've got any little jobs that need doing, just leave them to him.'

Isobel's smile was tearful. 'What would I do without you?'

'You'd manage.' Michelle was philosophical. 'I dare say that if Herrington has anything to do with it, you won't be on your own for long.'

'Until he finds out I'm expecting another man's child,' remarked Isobel drily.

'Well…' Michelle shrugged. 'He wasn't the reason you decided to take the cottage, was he?'

'No.' Isobel was thoughtful. 'I wonder if he is still alive. My father, I mean. It's going to be interesting finding out.'

'Well, be careful,' said Michelle warningly. 'Don't forget, his wife may still be alive, and he may not want to acknowledge something he's spent the last twenty-five—twenty-six years trying to forget.'

Isobel nodded. 'I realise that. And I'm not planning on doing anything rash. But—I would like to see him. You can understand that?'

Michelle regarded her gently. 'I understand,' she assured her. 'I just wish I could stay around to see it.'

CHAPTER SIX

JARED gazed at the plans for the new Hermitage shopping complex and leisure centre without really seeing them. He'd had this particular set of drawings on his desk for the past week, and, although he knew he had to have them ready to present to the board of Hermitage Developments in a few days, he couldn't seem to concentrate on anything at present.

No matter how he tried to apply himself, the knowledge that Isobel had apparently disappeared gnawed like a continuous pain in his gut. If he managed to divert himself for a few minutes, it didn't last: some action, some memory, bringing it all back into painful focus.

He couldn't believe she'd done this to him. Oh, he knew what she'd said the last time they'd been together, but she'd tried to finish with him before and it had never worked. They needed one another; they enjoyed being together too much to allow anyone to come between them. Or so he'd thought. How the hell was he supposed to know what she was thinking now?

He stifled a groan.

He supposed that was what was crippling him most: the knowledge that she had indeed left town without even telling him she was going, let alone where. She'd closed up her apartment, had her phone disconnected, and then simply disappeared. And there was no one he could turn to for information.

How could she do that? How could she abandon him without a word of explanation? He'd even tried to find that friend of hers, Michelle Chambers, but she was apparently away, too. Were they together? Was it just a prolonged holiday? Or did she really have something more permanent in mind?

Everything he'd been able to find out for himself pointed to the latter. Her apartment was empty. Jared had managed to use his contacts to speak to the landlord on the pretext of looking for an apartment for someone else. He'd confirmed that Isobel had cancelled her lease before she left. The phone was another obvious give-away. No one had their phone disconnected for just a couple of weeks.

So where had she gone? *Why* had she gone? And, please God, was she ever coming back?

The opening of his office door curtailed any further introspection. Howard Goldman came into the room, brandishing a sheaf of contracts that he wanted Jared to have a look at before they were signed. 'You're not still working on those drawings?' the older man asked, coming round the desk to peer over his son-in-law's shoulder. 'Dammit, Jared, they're coming on Friday. I don't want any last-minute hitches to hold up this deal.'

'There won't be.' Jared wished he could feel as sure as he sounded. 'I'm just having a bad day, that's all.'

Howard frowned, drawing back to look at him. 'Yes,' he said, after a few moments' study. 'I can see you are. Hell, Jared, you're not sickening for something, are you? I need you on this project. Mercer asked specifically for your participation.'

A thin smile crossed Jared's lips. 'That sounds like a compliment, Howard. Should I be flattered or what?' It was rare that his father-in-law handed out any plaudits, and now he gave the younger man a rueful look.

'You know damn well your designs are appreciated,' he declared gruffly. 'You don't think I'd be giving you the cream of the work that comes in here if I didn't think you were the best man for the job.' He paused, taking a breath. 'But I have to say I've been disappointed in the lack of enthusiasm you've shown over the Hermitage development. What's wrong with you, man? Is Liza making your life difficult? I've told you, I've arranged for us all to go on that cruise in September. You'll enjoy it and we all need a break.'

The cruise!

Jared lay back in his chair as Howard moved round the desk again, and, giving the older man a rueful smile, he said, 'Holidays! Aren't they supposed to be the third most stressful event in your life? After divorce and moving house?'

Howard stared at him. 'You don't want to go?'

Jared straightened his spine. 'I'm not a holiday person, Howard. You should know that.'

Howard's disappointment was evident. 'Does Liza know how you feel?'

'No.' Jared was defensive now. It was bad enough that he couldn't take any satisfaction from his work in his present mood without his father-in-law putting his mistaken interpretation to the facts. 'Besides, I don't think that's relevant. So long as Janet Brady's around, she won't give a damn.'

Howard's expression softened. 'You don't have to swear at me, boy. I'm not your enemy.' He sighed. 'I know Liza can be difficult. Who better? It would be different if she had someone other than that Brady woman to distract her from her own problems. I know she's always going to be paralysed, but that doesn't mean she can't live a normal life.'

Jared stiffened. He could guess what was coming. 'Don't you think she lives a reasonably normal life now?' he asked.

Howard didn't immediately answer him. Instead, he flung himself down into the chair opposite and rolled the sheaf of contracts between his hands. 'I was talking to Pat Beaumont the other day,' he said. 'You know Beaumont, don't you? He works at the County. Hospital, that is. He and I have a similar handicap.' He grimaced. 'I mean on the golf course, of course.'

'So?'

Jared's response was wary, but Howard didn't seem to notice. 'He's a good chap. Used to work at some well-known teaching hospital in London. He knows what he's talking about.' He nodded. 'You can take it from me.'

'A good man to know, then.' Jared was sardonic. 'What is he? A cardiologist? A neurosurgeon?'

'He's a gynaecologist,' exclaimed Howard shortly, looking impatient. 'He's had quite a lot of experience with women in Liza's condition. According to him, there's absolutely no reason why she shouldn't have a baby even now.'

Jared blew out a breath. 'What if she doesn't want a baby?'

Howard's brows ascended. 'What kind of a question is that? Of course she wants a baby. Hasn't she always said how much she wishes she could give me a grandchild?'

Had she? Jared didn't know anything about that, but it was typical of Elizabeth to try and pass the blame.

'I don't think it's practical, in the circumstances,' he declared flatly. 'Our marriage is hardly normal as it is.'

'That's just what I'm saying. Elizabeth needs something to distract her.' Howard snorted. 'Naturally, we'd employ a full-time nanny. But the baby would be ours—yours! What do you say?'

What could he say?

'I think you'd better talk to her about it,' he said, straightening the papers on his desk. There was no way he and Elizabeth could have a child, even if it were possible. He realised he was getting older too, and he wanted his life back.

'But she won't talk to me,' protested his father-in-law frustratedly. 'Not about her condition, anyway. When it comes to discussing the future, she just clams up. You know that. I don't want to upset her, Jared, but I'm not getting any younger.

'You're hardly in your dotage,' said Jared evenly, but Howard was serious.

'I spoke to Dr Hardesty last week,' he admitted heavily. 'I've been having some indigestion lately, and I wanted him to check me out.'

'And?' Jared was concerned.

'Well, he thinks there's nothing wrong. But no one can be sure of their own longevity, and Liza doesn't seem to realise it.'

Jared shook his head, relieved to find it was nothing more serious, and, unwilling to destroy all the old man's hopes so arbitrarily, he blew out a breath. 'I'm sorry,' he said. 'I really must get on with this presentation. Do you think I should concentrate on the overall concept or point out that certain building regulations may limit us on height levels and so on?'

Howard's jaw clamped. 'So you won't talk to her?' He grimaced. 'Oh, well, we'll have plenty of time to discuss it while we're away.' His eyes narrowed. 'Don't let me down, Jared. We need each other too much to let Liza's pig-headedness come between us.'

Jared didn't contradict him. There'd be time enough to marshal his arguments why he couldn't accompany them on the cruise later on. After he'd found Isobel, he reflected tautly. After he'd found her and persuaded her to come back.

Apparently deciding he'd done as much as he could for the present, too, Howard turned to business matters, and by the time he'd left Jared was reasonably sure the old man had put it out of his mind. There was no room for sentiment when it came to business. And his observations were as sharp as ever.

Which was all to the good, thought Jared, taking off his

glasses. Then, after massaging his lids with his finger and thumb, he replaced them again. And, ironically enough, he worked better for the rest of the afternoon. Howard's comments had caused him to take an unbiased look at himself. Perhaps it was time to take a harder look at his life.

He phoned Marion Rimmer later that evening.

He'd met Isobel's sister a couple of times, at charity events and the like, but this was the first time he'd spoken to her personally. Isobel had told him she'd found out about their relationship, so he had no fears that he was betraying her confidence. But he was also aware that Marion resented him, though he never could decide whether it was because he was deceiving Elizabeth or because he was doing it with her sister.

A young girl's voice answered the phone. Emily, he guessed. Isobel had told him her niece's name, but he knew better than to appear too familiar with the child.

'Is your mother there?' he asked, and with the innocent honesty of youth Emily went to get her.

'Who is it?' He could hear Isobel's sister chiding her daughter in the background, and then, having received an unsatisfactory reply, Marion herself came on the line. 'Hello? Marion Rimmer speaking.'

'Um—Mrs Rimmer.' Now that he had her undivided attention, Jared felt briefly stunned at his audacity. And then, before she could begin to think it was a crank call, he added, 'This is Jared Kendall.'

There was a silence that was almost palpably chilly, and then Marion seemed to remember he was related to the Goldmans, and recovered her composure. 'Mr Kendall,' she said, with cool politeness. 'How can I help you?'

Jared dragged his lower lip between his teeth and bit down hard. Then, steeling himself for her response, he said evenly, 'I wonder if you could tell me when Isobel will be back.'

'Isobel!' The woman repeated her sister's name with evident irritation. 'I'd have thought you'd know that better than me, Mr Kendall.'

'Well, I don't.' Jared couldn't prevent the harsh rejoinder. But getting angry with Marion wasn't going to solve anything, and, calming himself again, he continued, 'I thought you might have a forwarding address.'

'A forwarding address?' If he hadn't known better, he'd have sworn that Marion's reaction was as blank as his had been. 'People who go on a touring holiday don't leave a forwarding address, Mr Kendall. And now, if you—'

'She hasn't gone on a holiday,' put in Jared quickly, revising his earlier opinion of her understanding. 'Her apartment's empty.'

There was another silence, a shorter one this time, and then Marion said faintly, 'What do you mean, her apartment's empty? Of course it is. I've told you: she's away.'

'She's cancelled the lease,' Jared told her flatly, his heart sinking at the news that her family was as much in the dark as he was. 'I don't think she's coming back.'

'Oh, no. No. You must be mistaken.' He was relieved to hear anxiety in her voice now. However disapproving she might be of him, she still cared about her sister, and it must be worrying to realise that Isobel had left without telling anyone where she was going and what she planned to do. 'She'd have said something, given me some inkling—'

'And she didn't?'

'No. No.' He heard her swallow rather convulsively. 'Unless—unless this has something to do with those letters.'

'Letters?'

Jared's senses were alert to any clue that might explain Isobel's disappearance, and although he was sure that at any other time Marion would have bitten her tongue out rather than give him any information, she was still in a state of shock and she'd briefly forgotten who she was talking to.

'Those letters from her father,' she said, almost unthinkingly. 'Surely she told you about them? You knew she was adopted, didn't you?'

Jared's fingers were in danger of crushing the receiver. 'Oh—those letters,' he said, as if he knew all about them. 'I'd—forgotten about them. Do you think they're relevant?'

'Yes.' Marion was obviously still trying to put two and two together. 'She knew I didn't approve of her tampering with the past, of course. I mean, if her real father had wanted to meet her—' She broke off, and then went on more thoughtfully, 'Oh, where was that place they were from? Tregarth or Tregarron or something.'

Jared hardly dared to breathe for fear of diverting her. 'I'm not sure,' he said, his mind already working on a plan that would give him a few days to find out. 'But—you think she might have gone to find her father?' He was feeling his way blindly now. 'Is that likely?'

'Well, it's possible.' But Marion was recovering her composure. He could hear it in her voice. 'Not that it's any business of yours.'

Jared's smile was bitter. 'No.'

'And if she'd wanted you to know where she was going, she'd have told you,' she continued, and Jared had to suppress a very real urge to say the same was true for her.

But he didn't. When Marion cut the call short, he put the phone down with the first real feeling of optimism he'd had for weeks. It wasn't much, but he had a name. Well, two names, actually. And, as he'd never heard of either of them, he thought it was a safe bet that they weren't large municipalities. Most likely they were small towns or villages, and surely someone, a hotel receptionist, an estate agent, somebody, would remember a woman as unfamiliar—as beautiful—as Isobel.

If only Marion had mentioned the father's name…

CHAPTER SEVEN

ISOBEL moved into the cottage four weeks later.

She wouldn't have believed that so much could be accomplished in so short a period of time, but Luke Herrington had kept his word and the transformation of Raven Cottage from its previously run-down state was quite remarkable.

To begin with, the whole place had been cleaned and redecorated. The chimneys had been swept and fires lighted, and modern appliances had replaced the ancient fixtures in the kitchen. The bathroom fitments were the original ones, but Isobel had been enchanted to discover that beneath the dirt and grime the cast-iron bath and basin were as pure and unstained as any she'd seen in specialist catalogues that catered to people's tastes for Victoriana.

She'd visited the cottage several times during the renovations, trying to work out where she was going to put her furniture when it arrived. It had been put in storage before she and Michelle left Newcastle, and she was looking forward to having her own things around her again. She missed having a radio, and her own bed, and she got quite excited at the thought of having a whole house at her disposal. Apart from when she'd lived at home, she'd been confined to the apartment, and two bedrooms, a bath and kitchen/diner, all on one floor, were not as spacious as this.

Most of the men who had worked at the cottage were local, but although Isobel had tried to strike up a conversation with them they hadn't been very forthcoming. It could have been because they were very conscientious about getting their work done, but Isobel suspected it was more personal than that. She'd noticed a certain standoffishness about most of the people in the village, and she guessed they were suspicious of her reasons for being there.

She could hardly blame them. From what she'd gathered from the landlord at the White Hart in Polgarth, strangers were few and far between in Polgarron, and they were probably curious as to why someone young and apparently unattached like herself should choose to move from one end of the country to the other.

Of course, she hadn't gone into her reasons with the landlord. No matter how tempting it would have been to ask if he knew the owner of Tregarth Hall, she'd contained her impatience, contenting herself with ringing directory enquiries and affirming that there were indeed Dorlands still living there. The number was ex-directory, as she'd half expected, and she still had no clear idea how—or even if—she was going to try and contact her father. For the present, it was enough to know that he was there.

On a more practical note, she'd contacted the local education authorities and had her name put on the supply list for the new term. At present, they could give her no information as to possible placements, but once the new term was underway they would have a better idea of future vacancies.

She'd also had her car transported from Newcastle to Polgarth. After speaking to Michelle when she got back from Portugal, and discovering that Jared had been seen visiting the apartments where she used to live, she'd decided it would probably be wiser to contact a local garage in Cornwall and have them effect the transfer. Dealing with a garage in Newcastle would leave too many loose ends, and she didn't trust Jared not to use any means to try and find her.

That was why, when she eventually gave her new address to Marion, she intended to ask her not to discuss it with anyone. Although she didn't expect Jared would be reckless enough to contact her sister direct, word could get around and she wanted to cut it off at source. She knew Michelle was totally trustworthy. Her friend wouldn't betray her whereabouts, and there was no one else.

She had encountered Luke Herrington at the cottage just two days before she was due to move in. His bailiff had given her the keys the day before, and as her furniture was being delivered the following day, she'd decided to do some preliminary shopping and fill the fridge.

She'd been unpacking a few personal belongings she'd brought with her from the inn in Polgarth when she had heard the sound of a car outside. On the off-chance that she might have to take a furnished apartment, Michelle had suggested she bring such things as books and ornaments, towels and linens, away with her, which was why the Chambers' estate car had been so much more useful than Isobel's small saloon when they'd first driven down here. Ever since then they'd been stored in a pile of boxes in the corner of her room at the White Hart, and she'd realised it would take more than just one trip to transport them to the cottage.

However, when she'd heard the sudden cessation of the car's engine, her hands had stilled over the box of books she'd been stowing on some fitted shelves beside the fireplace in the living room. Her mouth had gone dry, and a nervous quiver had gripped her stomach, and for a heart-stopping moment she had wondered if Jared could have found her after all. But then common sense had overcome her involuntary panic, and, smoothing her hands over the seat of her black leggings, she had gone to meet her visitor.

'Oh—Mr Herrington,' she said, not without some relief, when she opened the door. He'd knocked as she was heading for the door, but she'd deliberately steeled herself not to look out of the window like some frightened rabbit. 'Um—won't you come in?'

'Thank you.' He stepped immediately into the newly decorated living room, glancing about him with some satisfaction at the gleaming white paintwork and subtly patterned walls. 'Well, this looks much better,' he remarked pleasantly. 'Does it meet with your approval?'

Isobel smiled. 'Very much,' she said. Then, seeing his glance move to the box of books, 'I was just making a start at moving in.'

'I can see that.' He strolled casually across the room and rescued a copy of *Pride and Prejudice* from the floor. 'Ah, Jane Austen.' He smiled. 'Are you a romantic, Miss Dawson?'

Isobel took a deep breath. 'It's—it's not Dawson,' she said, coming to a decision. 'It's Dorland, actually. I—didn't like to correct you before.'

Luke's reddish-gold brows drew together in some confusion. 'Oh, but—' He put the book down and pulled a rent book from his pocket. 'I was about to give you this.' He grimaced. 'I'll have to change the name.'

'Yes.' Isobel twisted her hands together at her waist, feeling awful for having deceived him. 'It was an easy mistake to make.'

'I suppose so.' He frowned. 'Dorland. That's quite an unusual name, isn't it? Did you know there are Dorlands living in the village?'

'No!' Isobel hoped she didn't look as guilty as she felt. 'How interesting.' She hesitated. 'Not such an unusual name, after all, then.'

'Perhaps not.' Luke frowned. 'Where was it you said you came from? Newark? Newmarket?'

'Newcastle,' said Isobel at once, perfectly sure he knew exactly where she'd said. Then, in an effort to distract him, she added, 'I can't tell you how grateful I am for what you've done to the cottage. I've never had a house to myself before.'

His expression softened. 'I'm sure your parents will miss you terribly. It's a long way from Newcastle to Polgarron. But then, their loss is our gain.'

'My parents are dead,' said Isobel automatically. 'My mother died just a few months ago.'

'I'm sorry.' She hadn't realised it before but in his eyes that provided her with a legitimate reason for wanting to make a new start. 'I wasn't attempting to pry.'

He was, but Isobel chose not to pursue it. 'That's all right,' she said, forcing a smile. 'It's natural that you'd want to know something about your new tenant.'

'Only if you want to tell me,' insisted Luke, evidently prepared to be generous now, and Isobel explained that she was a secondary school teacher, and that she was hoping to find a position in or near Polgarth.

'Well, I'm not absolutely sure of the situation at present,' he said. 'But I have connections with the local education authority, and I'd be happy to make enquiries on your behalf.'

'Thank you.' Isobel would have preferred not to have to feel beholden to him for anything else, but she was aware that a personal endorsement could improve her chances of being offered a position, and she couldn't afford to be churlish.

'Good. Good.' His smile was friendly now, and she hoped she'd passed whatever test he'd felt was warranted. 'Well…' He gestured with the rent book. 'If you hadn't been here, I was just going to push this through the letterbox, but I'm glad we've had this opportunity to cement our association.'

'Yes. So'm I.'

Isobel nodded, but when she stepped aside, in expectation of him going to the door, he sauntered through to the kitchen instead.

Trying not to resent his presumption, Isobel followed him. Things were probably done differently in the country, she told herself, remembering the indifference with which her previous landlord had treated his tenants. She'd never seen Harry Lofthouse unless there'd been some kind of problem with either the plumbing or the heating, the rent having been collected by a monthly direct debit from her account.

Luke was examining the new appliances, but at least he didn't open the fridge door to see what was inside. His interest seemed to stem from a genuine desire to check on the improvements, and Isobel could hardly fault him for that.

'And you expect to move in—when?' he asked, turning to rest against the new Formica-topped counter.

'In a couple of days, I hope,' she answered, half wishing she could offer him a cup of tea. She would have preferred to put their relationship on a more formal footing, but unfortunately she hadn't yet brought the box containing her least mis-matched china from the inn. 'The furniture's being delivered tomorrow.'

'From Newcastle?' He inclined his head. 'You will let me know if you need any assistance, won't you?'

'I'm sure that won't be necessary.' Isobel was grateful to him, but she was beginning to wish that he would go. 'You've done enough.'

'Not nearly.' To her relief he straightened then, and when she retreated to the living room he followed her. 'Perhaps you'd permit me to buy you dinner one evening, as a kind of celebration, perhaps? After you've moved in, of course.'

Isobel's jaw dropped, but she quickly rescued it. 'Oh—I—that's very kind of you, but—'

'But, what?'

'Well, it's not necessary...'

'I know that.' He sounded impatient now. 'But it would

give me a great deal of pleasure.' He paused. 'If you'll agree?'

Isobel shook her head. 'Well...'

'Good.' He took her hesitation as an acceptance. 'I'll be in touch as soon as the phone's connected.'

'The phone?' Isobel's eyes widened. She'd been thinking she would have to get herself a mobile.

'Of course.' Luke looked a little smug now. 'We can't have you living here all alone without one. I've been in touch with the phone company and they're coming to install it at the end of the week. With your approval, of course.'

Isobel was disarmed by his kindness. 'I don't know what to say.'

'It's my pleasure,' he assured her, and this time he made an unsolicited move towards the door. He tapped the rent book against his thigh as he reached for the handle. 'I'll make sure this is amended, too. We can't have a prospective employer addressing you as Miss Dawson, can we?'

It wasn't until after he'd gone that Isobel's doubts about getting socially involved with her landlord resurfaced. She wasn't interested in getting involved with anyone, and although she assured herself that he would probably forget all about his invitation, she didn't want to create any difficulties for herself now that she'd found herself a home.

Still, there was no point in worrying about it now, she conceded, resuming the unpacking she'd been doing before Luke Herrington arrived. And one date didn't constitute an involvement, anyway. If he did insist on taking her to dinner, she would have to explain about the baby and hope it wouldn't make any difference to her lease.

She phoned Michelle from the inn the night before she was due to move into the cottage. Her furniture had arrived, as arranged, that morning, and for a few extra pounds the delivery men had unrolled the carpets in the living room and bedroom, and helped her assemble her bed before they left.

The carpets were not a perfect fit, naturally, but she intended to make some adjustments later. She didn't even have a carpet for the hall and stairs, and she intended to make that her first priority when she went into Polgarth again. For the moment, however, she was content to have a place she could call her own again, and once she'd got the furniture arranged to her satisfaction she'd begin to feel it was a home.

Michelle was delighted to hear that things were going according to plan, and she was particularly pleased when Isobel told her about the phone. 'I must confess, I was a bit anxious about you living there without any form of communication with the outside world,' she said. 'Don't forget to let me have the number as soon as you have it.'

'I won't.' Isobel forced a light tone, but she was beginning to wonder if ringing Michelle had been such a good idea, after all. She sounded so far away, and she was, which automatically led to the thought that other people were a long way away, too. And, unable to help herself, she added, 'How's—everything?'

'Do you mean everything—or everybody?' asked Michelle drily, and Isobel immediately knew that her friend had heard from Jared.

'Whatever,' she said, fighting back the urge to ask the question she was dying to ask. 'Um—have you spoken to Marion?'

'Marion?' Michelle's surprise was not feigned. 'No, I haven't. Should I have?'

'Well, I thought she might have wondered where I was,' muttered Isobel, feeling an absurd desire to burst into tears. 'Does she know I'm not coming back?'

'She does now.'

Michelle's answer was confusing, and Isobel wondered

if she'd misunderstood her before. 'But—I thought you said you hadn't spoken to her.'

'I haven't.' Michelle sighed. 'But Kendall has.'

'Jared!' Even saying his name caused a wave of warmth to invade her stomach. 'You've seen Jared, then?'

'I didn't say that.'

'Then, what—?'

'Oh, Issy, are you sure you want to hear this? I mean, I thought you went away because you wanted to sever the ties between you and Jared. What on earth was the point of that if you're going to ask me about him every time I come on the phone?'

Isobel sniffed. 'I didn't ask you about him.'

'Didn't you?'

Isobel sighed. 'All right. Maybe indirectly.'

'Indirectly, my eye.' Michelle snorted. 'All right. I'll tell you. He rang me last week.'

'Last week!' Isobel had to bite back the urge to ask Michelle why she hadn't bothered to let her know before this. Only the fear of inviting another rebuke kept her silent. 'I—what did he want?'

'What do you think he wanted?' Michelle demanded shortly. 'Needless to say, he didn't get any joy from me.'

'Oh.' Isobel despised herself for the sinking feeling that enveloped her. 'Well, good.'

'Do you mean that?'

Isobel struggled to hide her misery. 'Of course I mean it,' she said, with admirable fortitude. She hesitated. 'I just don't understand how—how he could approach Marion.'

'What you mean is, what has he said to Marion, don't you?' Michelle was cynical. 'Well, from what I gathered, she told him about the letters.'

Isobel caught her breath. 'Marion told Jared about the letters! I don't believe it.'

'Well, I didn't tell him,' said Michelle huffily. 'And he knows all about them.' She gave a sardonic grunt. 'If you ask me, Marion was so shocked when he told her you'd disappeared, she automatically assumed you'd told him about them.'

Isobel licked her dry lips. 'So—did she give him the address that was on the letters?'

'No.' Michelle was positive. 'That was why he rang me. He assumed—quite rightly, as it happens—that I'd know where you were.'

'Oh, Michelle!'

'You didn't want me to give him your address, did you?'

'No!' Isobel was horrified that her friend should even think she might.

'Are you sure?'

'Of course I'm sure.' Isobel made a sound of indignation. 'All right. I admit I was curious about how—how he was taking it. My leaving, I mean. But it was the right thing to do.' She paused. 'Wasn't it?'

Michelle didn't answer for a moment. Then, almost wearily, she conceded, 'I guess.'

'You guess?' Isobel felt anxiety pricking her nerves.

'Hey…' Michelle groaned. 'I don't profess to be an expert on human relationships. Sure, your affair with Kendall was going nowhere. And, in your present condition, I'd say that going away has probably saved you a hell of a lot of heartache, not to mention making it easier for—well, for everyone, if you get my meaning. But—oh.' She expelled a weary breath. 'I have to admit to feeling a bit sorry for him. Kendall, that is. I guess I thought that he'd feel really peeved when he found you'd walked out on him and all, but that deep down he'd be relieved. Hell, Elizabeth's father is Goldman-Lewis, after all.' She paused. 'Jared must know he took a hell of a risk in contacting your sister. Particularly as we all know how desperate she is to cosy up to the Goldmans.'

Isobel's throat was dry. 'So what are you saying?'

'I don't know.' Michelle sighed. 'I don't know what I'm saying. Whatever it is, I'm pretty sure you're better off out of it.'

Isobel blew out a breath. 'So—did he say anything else?'

'What about?'

'The letters, I suppose.' Isobel wished she could see her friend's face. 'Was he—worried? Angry? What?'

'I'd say he was—hurt,' admitted Michelle, turning the knife. 'I'm sorry, Issy. But you did ask.'

'I know.'

'As far as the letters were concerned, he asked me if I'd known about them. I said yes. I saw no point in lying about that.'

'No.' Isobel pressed two fingers to her throbbing temple. 'I suppose I should have told him.'

'What? And have him turn up on your doorstep within days of your leaving? Oh, yeah, Issy. That would have been the sensible thing to do.'

Isobel shook her head. 'Well…' She tried to be optimistic. 'It looks as if I've done it, doesn't it? Made a complete break. Just what I wanted.'

'Why don't I find that as convincing as I should?' asked Michelle sardonically. 'But, okay. Enough about Jared Kendall. How are you? Have you registered with a doctor yet?'

'No, but I will, once I'm settled into the cottage,' Isobel promised. 'And I'll ring you just as soon as the phone's been installed.'

There didn't seem much more to say right then, but after she'd rung off Isobel wondered why she hadn't told her friend about Luke Herrington's invitation. Was it really because she hadn't considered it important enough to mention? Or would it be truer to say that so long as Michelle didn't know about it, she couldn't tell Jared?

*   *   *

Isobel spent the first day at the cottage trying to get her bedroom in some kind of order. The downstairs rooms could wait, but she was still plagued by feelings of nausea, and it was important that she had somewhere where she could rest and relax. Besides, she got tired quickly these days, and she had no desire to have to tackle her bed at a time when she wanted nothing so much as to fall into it.

The paper in the bedroom was light and airy, sprigs of mauve blossom on a white background that added space to what was really quite a small room. It might not have been her choice of decoration, but she quite liked it, and with her own rose-printed curtains billowing at the open windows, it looked very pretty.

The windows themselves were set under the eaves, the ceiling sloping slightly at that side of the room. She managed to position her bed so that she was able to see out of the windows when she awoke in the morning. For the first time in her life, she had an uninterrupted view.

Her clothes were the next things to unpack. She'd been living out of suitcases for the past four weeks and it was going to be so nice to know where everything was again. On top of which, there were cartons containing shoes and other odds and ends that she'd had stored along with the furniture, as well as handbags and winter clothing that she hadn't had an immediate use for.

Before she knew it, it was one o'clock, and after casting a satisfied glance around the room she went downstairs to make herself some lunch. She was making good progress, and she had no intention of overdoing it. It wasn't as if she had a deadline.

Her breath caught in her throat. Deadlines were for people who had something to do and somewhere to go. She didn't. At least, not yet. And it was annoying to realise that even something as innocuous as that could bring back painful memories of her life as it used to be.

It was a short step from that to allowing thoughts of the

conversation she'd had with Michelle the previous evening to fill her mind. She didn't want to think about what her friend had told her, or face the doubts that had been evident in Michelle's voice. It was enough that they'd tormented her sleep without them destroying what little pleasure she'd found in moving into the cottage.

She was making herself a sandwich when a shadow passed the kitchen window. Someone had walked along the side of the house, she realised, and she was hardly surprised when there was a knock at the back door. Luke Herrington again, she thought frustratedly. Dear God, he hadn't wasted any time.

She wondered whether, if she'd still been working upstairs, she'd have risked not answering the door. But, no. Her car was parked in the lane outside, and all the windows were open.

She glanced down at the cropped vest she was wearing, together with denim shorts that were frayed and bleached almost white in places from frequent washings, and pulled a face. She'd changed before tackling the unpacking, guessing, quite rightly as it turned out, that she'd find it hot work, but now she wished she wasn't wearing something quite so revealing. Not that anyone who didn't know would guess that the waistband of the shorts was abnormally tight. And, taking a deep breath, she opened the door—to Jared.

CHAPTER EIGHT

DIZZINESS assailed her, and she clung to the handle of the door, praying she wasn't about to faint. Isobel had never fainted before, and if she did so now Jared might easily suspect that there was something wrong with her. And she couldn't have that.

All the same, as she stood there, struggling to recover her senses, she couldn't deny how good it was to see him again. Her eyes moved with indecent haste over his lean tanned face—surely paler than she remembered, his eyes narrowed and guarded behind his glasses—to the muscled strength of his arms, exposed below the short sleeves of a black tee shirt. Pleated khaki trousers completed his outfit, a matching jacket hooked carelessly over one shoulder.

How had he found her? she wondered, as the dizziness subsided. Michelle had insisted that she hadn't told him anything and surely Marion never would…

'Surprise, surprise,' he said at last, when it appeared that she was incapable of making the first overture. 'If it isn't the incredible disappearing woman!'

Isobel stiffened. 'Don't be sarcastic.'

'Why not?' He shifted his weight from one foot to the other. 'Believe me, sarcastic is good.'

'As opposed to what?' Isobel tried desperately to sound as if he hadn't just swept the ground out from under her, but it was obvious that Jared wasn't in the mood to humour her.

'Take it from me, you don't want to go there,' he remarked, his voice clipped and unfriendly. 'May I come in?'

Isobel gave a shrug and moved aside, holding onto the

door as he stepped into the small kitchen. As he'd gone to the trouble of seeking her out, he deserved an explanation—albeit an edited one. She just wished she knew what she was going to say.

'I was just making myself a sandwich,' she murmured rather obviously after closing the door. 'Would you like one?'

Jared swung his jacket off his shoulder and folded it over one arm. 'No, thanks,' he said, and she realised he wasn't just unfriendly, he was hostile. 'I just want to know why you didn't tell me you were leaving.'

Isobel swallowed a little convulsively and moved back to the counter. Picking up the knife again, she started buttering a slice of bread, only to utter an involuntary cry of protest when he snatched the knife out of her hand and tossed it into the sink.

'Dammit, answer me!'

Isobel quivered, her hand going automatically to protect her stomach. 'Are you mad?' she exclaimed tremulously. 'What gives you the right to think you can come here and intimidate me?'

Jared stared at her, breathing hard, and for a second she thought he meant to do her some actual physical harm. But then, uttering a harsh obscenity, he turned away.

'God knows,' he said, at last, when he'd got himself under control again. 'It's obvious you don't give a damn about what I think.'

Isobel expelled the breath she'd hardly been aware she was holding. 'I—I suppose it does look that way,' she muttered awkwardly, wringing her hands before pushing them into the back pockets of her shorts.

Jared turned his head to give her a pitying glance. 'How's that for understatement?' he asked contemptuously. 'God, I've had some pretty foul things done to me in my time, but this beats all!'

'I'm sorry—'

'I bet you are. That I've found you, I guess.' He grimaced. 'Who'd have thought I'd have to thank your sister for anything?'

Isobel stared at him. 'Marion told you where I was?'

'Oh, yeah.' He was sardonic. 'And gave me written instructions on how to get here! Yeah, right.'

Isobel blinked. 'Then, how—?'

'How did I find you?' He turned back to face her, swiping away the sweat that had beaded on his forehead and dampened the hair at his temples. 'Give me one good reason why I should tell you that.'

'I can't.' Isobel shook her head, and then, because she could see he was exhausted, she gestured towards the front room. 'Look—why don't you go and sit down? Surely you'll have a beer or something? It is lunchtime.'

'Is it?' He sounded weary. 'I don't even know what day it is any more.'

Isobel sighed. 'It's Thursday,' she said, waiting for him to do as she'd asked. 'Have you had anything to eat or drink today?'

'Don't tell me you care,' he taunted bitterly, and, refusing to answer him, she reached for a clean knife out of the drawer.

She didn't move when he eventually gave in and walked past her, even though the heated brush of his arm against her back caused every nerve in her body to rise up in protest. Instead, she forced herself to finish making her sandwich, and then made another, just in case. She'd already made the tea, and, after adding another cup and saucer and a bottle of beer to the tray, she took a deep breath and carried it into the other room.

He'd tossed his jacket onto the back of a chair and was presently standing staring out of the window. Now that the windows were clean, they gleamed brilliantly between leaded lights, showing up the tangled wilderness of the garden outside.

'I've made you a sandwich,' she said, setting the tray on the coffee table and perching on the edge of the sofa closest to it. 'It's only egg and tomato, I'm afraid.'

He turned. 'Egg and *tomato*?' he echoed. 'I thought you didn't like uncooked tomatoes.'

'Oh—' Isobel could feel herself colouring. 'Well, I don't, usually. But this tastes all right.' She could hardly admit to having a sudden craving for the fruit. 'And they're yellow tomatoes anyway.'

Jared arched a disbelieving brow. 'Are you sure it's not just another attempt to prove to me that you've changed?' he asked flatly. He walked towards her. 'Is this for me?'

He'd picked up the bottle of beer, and she nodded shakily, aware that for another anxious moment she'd been half afraid he was going to touch her. But he didn't. As she buried her teeth in one of the quartered sandwiches she'd cut for herself, praying that by getting something substantial inside her she could quell the uneasy turbulence of her stomach, Jared twisted off the cap and retired to the window again.

He propped his hips on the narrow ledge and raised the bottle to his lips, and she had to steel herself not to watch the muscles in his throat moving beneath the tanned skin. It was hard enough trying to ignore him watching her as she struggled to get the sandwich down, without torturing herself with the knowledge that what she really wanted him to do was take her to bed.

Which was madness…

'Have you spoken to your father yet?'

His question caught her by surprise, and she almost choked on a crust, staring at him with watering eyes. 'My father?'

'Don't look as if you don't know what I'm talking about.' Jared's tone was biting. 'That is what you're doing here, isn't it? Setting up house on his doorstep, hoping he's had a change of heart.'

Isobel gasped. 'What do you know about my father?'

'About as much as you do, by the sound of it,' he retorted contemptuously. And then, as if regretting his cruel words, 'Marion said you'd found some letters.'

Isobel quivered, getting to her feet and rubbing nervous palms over the seat of her shorts. 'She had no right to tell you anything.'

'I'm sure she would agree with you,' Jared concurred, giving her a bitter look. 'You certainly believe in covering your tracks, don't you?'

'Do you blame me?'

Her response was automatic, and she determinedly crushed the emotion she felt when she saw the spasm of pain that crossed his face.

'I guess not,' he said at last, flatly, weighing the empty bottle in his hands. 'If this is what you really want.'

'It is.'

'Are you sure?' He stared at her disbelievingly. 'My God, Belle, if you really don't want to see me again, then I'm going to have to live with it. But was there any need to put the length of the country between us?'

'I think so.'

'Why? *Why?*' he demanded, almost dropping the bottle in his agitation and then bending to place it on the floor at his feet with hands that were obviously unsteady. 'Do you really hate me that much?'

She didn't hate him at all; that was the trouble. And Isobel's heart ached at the obvious confusion in his expression. 'You shouldn't have come after me,' she said, staring down at the toes of her scuffed trainers. 'You must have known—'

'What?' He waited for her to go on, but she couldn't. 'What should I have known? That having sex with me in your mother's kitchen was your way of finishing it? Of showing me how little it meant to you?'

'That's not true.' She couldn't let him think that. 'I told you at the time…'

'Oh, yeah, you told me,' he muttered. 'What was it you said: *Just do it*? I guess I should have known then that you were planning on walking out on me.'

Isobel's sigh was shaky. 'It just seemed—'

'Easier that way?'

'Something like that.' Isobel tucked her thumbs into her waistband.

'So—' Jared got up from the windowsill. 'Have you seen him?'

'Seen who?' For a moment Isobel's mind was a total blank.

'Your father, of course,' said Jared tiredly. 'I wish you'd told me about those letters.'

'I only found them that afternoon—' Isobel broke off, not wanting to bring up the events of that afternoon again, but he had always had the uncanny ability to read her thoughts.

'*That* afternoon?' he echoed. 'Do you mean when you were crawling around the loft at Jesmond Dene?'

Isobel nodded. 'Yes.'

'The case,' he said suddenly, and she knew he was remembering what she had said about it. 'They were in that case, weren't they?' His eyes narrowed. 'Was that when you decided to give me the push?'

'No!' She was vehement. 'They had nothing to do with it.' She took a calming breath. 'What did Marion tell you?'

Jared's lips curled. 'Not a lot.'

'But enough to find me.'

'Hardly.' He paused. 'If I hadn't let her think I knew about the letters, she'd never have let the name slip.'

'The name of the village?'

'I wish.' Jared was cynical. 'No, not the name of the village. Just Tregarth or Tregarron; she wasn't sure which. And the fact that it was in Cornwall.'

'Tregarron?' Isobel frowned in confusion.

'As I said, she was only groping for the address the letters had come from at the time.'

'But how did you find it? Tregarth isn't even the name of the place.'

'Tell me about it.' Jared grimaced. 'That was when I had the bright idea of trying your friend, Michelle. But, as you probably know, I don't rate very highly in her opinion either.'

He looked as if he would have liked to have left it there, but she was obviously waiting for him to go on, so after a few moments he said, 'Then I tried looking up the names in a road atlas. But the only listings there were were in Wales, and Marion had definitely said Cornwall.'

'So what did you do?' Isobel was amazed at his persistence. 'How on earth did you expect to find me even with the name of the town?'

'A town I might have had difficulty with,' he agreed wryly. 'But I went on the assumption that, as I hadn't heard of them, they were probably villages; hamlets, something like that. A strange woman moving into a small village would surely arouse some curiosity. At least, that's what I was banking on, anyway.'

Isobel shook her head. 'But I might not have moved into the village.'

'I know that.' Jared shrugged wearily. 'I'm not denying it was a gamble. But when you're desperate enough, you'll go to any lengths to make it work.'

Isobel hesitated. 'Yet you said the names weren't listed.'

'They weren't.' Jared nodded. 'So I ran them though the computer instead. It's amazing what you can find out if you're determined to get a result.'

'And?'

'And—I found the name of a house: Tregarth Hall, Polgarron. As there weren't any Tregarron houses or halls in the program I was using, I decided to run with it. I figured Marion was unlikely to have remembered the name unless it was a particular place.'

Isobel was reluctantly impressed. 'Even so...' she murmured.

'Hell, I know. I could have been making entirely the wrong connection. But, obviously, I wasn't.'

Isobel was shaking her head, staggered at the success he'd had, when another thought struck her. Her mouth went dry. 'You—you didn't go to Tregarth Hall, did you?' she faltered. 'Oh, God, as far as I know, they don't even know I'm here.'

Jared gave her a scornful look. 'Oh, yeah,' he said. 'I was going to do that, wasn't I? I didn't even know if this was the right village, let alone the right house. What do you think I'd have said, hmm?' He pretended to think for a minute. 'Oh—I've got it: *Hey, I'm looking for a woman who thinks you gave her up for adoption—what? Twenty-six years ago? Got any idea where she is?*'

Isobel held up her head. 'That's not funny.'

'You're telling me.' Jared was bitter. 'Believe it or not, I recognised the car. I was driving around the village, trying to concoct a convincing story to tell the publican at the Black Bull, and there it was. Parked at the gate.' His lips twisted. 'So you haven't contacted this man yet? But you intend to.'

'I don't know.' Isobel didn't want to admit it, but she was having some doubts now that she was here. 'I'm not sure if it's the right thing to do.'

'I'm bloody sure it's not,' said Jared forcefully. 'For God's sake, Belle, you don't know anything about the man. He could be a serial child molester for all you know.'

'Oh, thanks.' Isobel caught her breath. 'It's good to know you think I might come from such distinguished stock!'

'Don't be so—stupid!' Jared bit off the epithet he had been going to use and grasped her shoulders. With his fingers digging into her flesh, he thrust his face close to hers. 'I don't give a damn who he is. As far as I'm concerned, he's not important. You are. All I'm trying to say is that if he'd been any kind of a father, he wouldn't have abandoned your mother when she needed him all those years ago.'

Isobel was trembling, as much from the goosebumps his touch was causing as from the violence of his reaction. 'He—he's my uncle,' she got out jerkily, and used his momentary lack of concentration to free herself from his hands. 'He's my father's brother.'

Jared dragged his spectacles from his nose and blinked myopically at her. 'My God!'

'It's true.' Isobel realised she had to elaborate and went on, 'I was the result of a brief liaison he'd had when he was in London visiting his solicitor. That's where I was born. He didn't know anything about me until my mother was killed and the authorities discovered his name on my birth certificate.'

Jared replaced his glasses. 'So how come you ended up with your real uncle? Didn't anyone think to tell you the truth?'

'Not until I read the letters, no,' admitted Isobel uncomfortably. 'It's a long story. I'm sure you're not really interested.'

Jared arched a speculative brow. 'Wait a minute: you said you'd never met him.'

'I haven't.'

'Your own uncle?' Jared made a disbelieving sound. 'How the hell did they manage that?'

'It sounds incredible, I know.' Isobel heaved a sigh. 'But I didn't know my father—my adoptive father, that is—had any brothers or sisters. It's true. I wouldn't lie about something like that.'

Jared was obviously finding it difficult to get a handle on what she was saying, and, deciding she had nothing to lose, Isobel quickly outlined the conditions George Dorland had made at the time of her adoption. 'There was obviously no love lost between them,' she murmured unwillingly. 'As far as I know, there's been no contact since then.'

'But why couldn't your real father take care of you?' exclaimed Jared, and once again Isobel was obliged to explain the circumstances behind Robert Dorland's appeal to her mother.

'Dear God,' Jared said at last, and, glimpsing the look of repugnance that had darkened his face as he'd absorbed what she was saying, Isobel wondered if what he'd learned had somehow cheapened her in his eyes.

'Things were different then,' she said hurriedly, aware that she was trying to excuse what had happened. 'And—and if his wife—my aunt—couldn't have children, it would have been quite a blow to her.'

'Not to mention exposing his behaviour,' remarked Jared scornfully, and Isobel caught her breath.

'You know what they say about people in glass houses,' she observed curtly, and had the satisfaction of seeing the heat darken his tanned face.

'I hope you're not comparing our relationship to a one-night stand with some—some—'

'Hooker?' supplied Isobel coldly, and once again Jared's colour deepened at the accusation.

'I was going to say with some woman he'd met by accident,' he retorted harshly. 'Dammit, Belle, you said yourself their association had been brief. Stop trying to put words into my mouth. You know our relationship isn't like that.'

'Do I?'

He didn't bother to dignify that with an answer. 'I just don't know how he could have done such a thing,' he muttered, his mind on other things.

'Done what?' she asked. 'Gone in for one-night stands

or abandoned me? I guess you'd say he can't be a very honourable man.'

'I was talking about George Dorland, actually,' said Jared shortly. 'I was wondering how the hell he could cut his own brother out of his life.'

Isobel sighed now. 'He must have thought it was for the best.'

'For whom?' Jared was sceptical. 'I still don't see why he kept the truth from you.'

'Because he probably guessed—rightly, as it happens—that I'd be curious about him,' said Isobel ruefully. 'Look, do you mind if we talk about something else? I've told you as much as I know about it. And I still haven't decided whether I'm going to tell him who I am or not.'

'Haven't you?'

Jared's tone was gentler now, and Isobel despised herself for the weakening she felt towards him. If he didn't go soon she was in danger of saying something really stupid, and she couldn't afford to make any more mistakes.

'No,' she said now. Then, with deliberate emphasis, 'How's Elizabeth?'

The look that crossed his face then was chilling. If her earlier words hadn't struck a nerve, it was obvious that that question had. 'I guess that's a polite way of saying I've wasted my time in coming here,' he said darkly. His mouth curled. 'Since when did my association with my wife have anything to do with us?'

CHAPTER NINE

THE engineer from the telephone company arrived the next morning before Isobel had had time to swallow the dry toast she usually ate at breakfast. She was still nauseous some mornings and she thought the man looked at her a little oddly when she let him in.

She knew she was pale and she guessed her lack of colour had drawn his attention to the hollow circles around her eyes. But there was nothing she could do about it now. Her first night at the cottage hadn't been as restful as she'd anticipated, and it wasn't just the trauma of Jared's visit that had left her feeling so tired and depressed.

The unfamiliar quiet of the village had unsettled her, and the creaks and groans as the boards in the cottage contracted had kept her constantly on edge. Perhaps she should get herself a dog, she'd speculated, dragging herself out of bed at eight o'clock, and, confronting her haggard reflection in the mirror, she was glad Jared couldn't see her now.

By the time she'd quelled a rising surge of nausea, cleaned her teeth and pulled on a baggy tee shirt and sweat pants, the engineer was on her doorstep. Happily he wasn't a young man, so she didn't feel so bad about looking a mess. All the same, she wished the cottage had a shower. She missed washing her hair every day.

After telling the man where she'd like the phone situated, Isobel went into the kitchen and made some tea. Then, after swallowing a slice of toast, she felt well enough to offer him some refreshment, smiling rather wanly when he asked if she was feeling all right.

'I think I must have a cold coming on,' she offered, not

wanting to tell him what was really wrong with her. 'It's a lovely morning, isn't it?'

'Not bad,' the man agreed, thanking her for his tea. He glanced around, noticing the unpacked boxes. 'I guess you've just moved in.'

'Yesterday,' she acknowledged, feeling a pang at the memory of Jared's departure. 'Do—do you live in the village yourself?'

'No. I live in Polgarth,' he answered, putting the cup down and resuming his task, but although Isobel was sure he'd have been willing to go on talking, she made an excuse and retreated to the kitchen again.

It didn't take him long to install the phone. Apparently there'd been a line to the cottage when it was last occupied, and it was just a matter of reconnecting the wires. Isobel had her hands in a bowl of soapy water, and was staring unseeingly though the kitchen window, when the engineer came to tell her he was finished, and she hurriedly dried her hands before taking the clipboard he offered to her.

'If you'll just sign here,' he said, indicating the job sheet, and Isobel signed her name and accompanied him to the door.

'Your name's Dorland?' The man had glanced at the sheet and now he halted in the open doorway. 'I suppose you're related to the Dorlands at Tregarth Hall?'

Isobel swallowed. 'I—no,' she said, aware that a trace of colour had entered her cheeks at the lie. 'Are there other Dorlands in the village?'

'Just the family at Tregarth.' The man nodded. 'There've been Dorlands there for—well, for as long as I can remember anyway.'

Isobel hesitated. 'You know them?'

'Only slightly.' The man grimaced. 'I've fixed Mrs Dorland's phone a time or two, but I don't know the rest of them very well.' He grinned. 'Well, I'd better be going. I'll never get finished at this rate. Thanks for the tea.'

'Thank you.'

Isobel forced a smile, but after she'd closed the door she leant back against it, feeling utterly bereft. In his letters, Robert Dorland had insisted his wife couldn't have children. So who else was living at the Hall?

Of course, he could have married again, she considered, pushing away from the door and glancing somewhat bleakly about her. That was something she hadn't considered, and she wondered once again if she hadn't made the biggest mistake of her life in coming here. It was only a matter of time before someone told Robert Dorland that there was someone of the same name, with a northern accent, living at Raven Cottage. How long would it take for him to suspect who she might be?

Would he care?

With tears pricking at her eyes, she went to finish the dishes. Perhaps she should have found herself a bolt-hole nearer to the people who really cared about her, instead of risking being rejected for the second time in her life. Jared was right. If Robert Dorland had cared about her, he would never have abandoned her. Whatever conceit had made her think he'd ever want to see her again?

Drying her hands, she went back into the living room again. The newly installed phone was a distraction and she determinedly reached for the receiver. She'd done it now, so there was no point in feeling sorry for herself. It was time to tell her sister where she was.

She phoned Marion's office, and for once she seemed genuinely relieved to hear from her. 'When that Kendall man told me you'd given up your apartment and moved away, I couldn't believe it,' she exclaimed. 'Are you all right?'

'I'm fine. And—and his name is Jared,' said Isobel automatically. 'I—wanted to wait until I knew where I was going to be living before giving you an address.'

'Well, I suppose I can understand that.' Marion was surprisingly amiable. 'I dare say you suspected he might contact me for information as to your whereabouts, and the less I knew, the better.'

'Well—'

'And you were right.' Marion snorted with satisfaction. 'He did come to me, and I sent him away with a flea in his ear.'

'You—saw—Jared?' Isobel's tongue circled her upper lip. He hadn't told her he'd seen Marion.

'No.' Marion clicked her tongue. 'He phoned me. I don't know how he had the nerve to do it. I mean, he knows I'm a friend of his wife's.'

Isobel sank down weakly onto the arm of the nearest chair. 'You're saying you didn't tell him anything, then?' she ventured softly, and Marion sounded almost offended at the suggestion.

'As if I would,' she said. 'Oh, I'm not denying he tried to pump me about those letters. But I told him. I said, It's nothing whatsoever to do with you.' She chuckled smugly. 'He got the message.'

'Did he?'

Isobel felt a momentary twinge of humour. If Marion only knew, she thought wryly. She'd be mortified to think she'd let anything slip. She thought she'd been so clever, when in fact Jared had been more clever than either of them.

'So, come on: where are you?' asked Marion impatiently. 'I think it's a good idea, by the way. Making a complete break like this. It was obvious that the man was never going to leave you alone so long as you stayed in Newcastle. I suppose Michelle Chambers knew all about it. You and she taking a holiday indeed! I should have suspected that her husband wouldn't have been very enthusiastic if he'd thought you were trying to split them up.'

'It was nothing like that,' said Isobel, a little crossly. Marion always had the knack of rubbing her up the wrong way. 'Michelle just—helped me move my things. Their estate car holds so much more than my Fiesta.'

'I see.' Marion absorbed this without comment. 'So you'd obviously been thinking about it for some time.'

'Well, it was time for a change,' agreed Isobel, not wanting to go too deeply into her reasons for leaving. 'With Mum dying and all, it seemed like a good time to make a fresh start.'

'And I suppose those letters you found couldn't have helped,' said Marion thoughtfully. 'I can't imagine why Mum kept them. I'm sure Daddy knew nothing about it. He'd have felt—offended, I think, if he had.'

'I had a right to know,' insisted Isobel, not prepared to compromise on that principle. 'He had no right to keep it from me. Not once I was old enough to understand.'

'To understand what?' Marion was scathing. 'Isobel, he knew what a sentimental—emotional—creature you are. I expect he doubted your ability to view what he'd done in a sane and rational way.'

'Well, I suppose he was right about that.' Isobel drew a breath. 'I do find it hard to believe how he could just cut his own brother out of his life.'

'Well, you would.' Marion sighed, and then, apparently deciding it wasn't worth arguing about, she turned back to the reason why Isobel had called. 'So, where are you? You don't know how hard it's been to convince Emily that her auntie Isobel hasn't gone to heaven, like her nana.'

'Oh, I'm sorry.' Isobel felt genuinely concerned for her niece. 'I never thought she'd think that.'

'I could say you don't think, period,' remarked Marion drily. 'But never mind that; give me your address.'

Isobel moistened her lips. 'It's—Raven Cottage,' she said reluctantly. 'Polgarron.'

'Polgarron!' Marion's gasp was audible. 'You're staying with Uncle Robert?'

Uncle Robert!

Isobel was surprised at the way his name tripped off her sister's tongue. She had yet to come to terms with the fact that he'd been her father's brother, let alone…

'As if,' she said now. 'The Dorlands live at Tregarth Hall.' And, recalling what Jared had told her, 'You remember the address, don't you?'

'Oh—yes.' Marion still sounded agitated. 'So, have you been in touch with him?'

'Not yet.'

'But you're thinking of it, aren't you?' Marion gave an impatient exclamation. 'Of course you are. Why else would you have moved to Polgarth when you had the whole country to choose from? Oh, Isobel, I can't believe you'd do such a thing!'

Isobel was taken aback at the vehemence of Marion's condemnation. 'Why not?'

'Why not?' Marion spoke fiercely. 'You know how Daddy felt about him, about what he'd done. If it hadn't been for my mother, he'd never have agreed to the arrangement.'

'Yes, I had gathered that.' But Isobel was surprised that Marion had garnered as much from the brief glance she'd taken of the letter Isobel had shown her.

'There you are, then. Surely it's obvious that neither of the parents wanted you to know about it—about him.'

'Then why keep the letters?'

'How should I know?' Marion was irritable now. 'You know what Mum was like. She hated to throw anything away.'

'Even so…'

'Even so, what? You're not suggesting she left them

there deliberately for you to find? Come on, Isobel, she couldn't be sure you would be the one to find them. Malcolm or I could have volunteered to clear out the loft.'

'Could have' being the operative words, thought Isobel cynically. Her mother would have had a fairly good idea that she'd get the job.

'Anyway, I still haven't decided what I'm going to do,' she admitted. 'For the present, I'm just going to play it by ear.'

'Well, you'd better give me your phone number,' said Marion shortly. 'Fortunately, we haven't found a buyer for the house yet. I'd hate to think what I'd have done if I'd needed to get in touch with you urgently.'

'In an emergency, Michelle would have given you my address,' said Isobel practically, beginning to feel the familiar sense of oppression Marion's domineering attitude always evoked. She gave her sister the number, and then declared with forced brightness, 'I'd better go now. I've got a lot to do today and this call must be costing me the earth.'

'But you'll keep me informed of what you're doing, won't you?' Marion persisted, and Isobel knew exactly what she meant. 'And you will think seriously before doing anything—rash. I mean, Mum and Daddy didn't have to adopt you, you know. The least you can do is respect their wishes now they're dead.'

Isobel made some non-committal response, but after she'd hung up the phone she found herself wondering if Marion didn't have a point. Yet the letters had been there for her to find, and surely someone who'd wanted so desperately to keep the facts of her adoption hidden would have burned them long ago.

She scrambled some eggs for her lunch and then, realising it was time she familiarised herself with her surroundings, she decided to go for a walk. She needed some bread, and she knew that she couldn't remain a prisoner in her own home for ever. She didn't want to admit that she had wondered if Jared would come back, and the prospect of spending the afternoon listening for the familiar sound of his car in the lane outside was too pitiful to countenance. He'd gone; she had to accept it and get on with her life.

The village consisted of little more than a main street with two pubs, a church and its attendant vicarage, and the general stores-cum-post office taking up most of one side. There were several substantial houses, standing in their own grounds, with poplar and cypress trees set behind wrought-iron fences, and a row of what might once have been miners' cottages that had been lovingly restored and maintained. An open expanse marked the village green, with a small pond where a family of ducks clucked in lazy contentment. The gardens she could see were still bright with flowering shrubs, and, noticing the late-flowering lilies and richly coloured dahlias, Isobel was unhappily reminded of the unkempt gardens at the cottage. She would have to tackle them soon, and she wondered if there was a lawn mower lurking in the garden shed.

There were few people about. She saw an elderly man walking his dog and some young children careering up and down on bicycles. A group of teenagers were perched on the wall outside the village stores, and she was conscious of them watching her as she walked towards them. But she was used to teenagers, and they soon lost interest when she didn't react to their subtle intimidation.

Entering the stores was far more daunting. Although she kept telling herself that she had as much right to be here as anyone else, she couldn't help the quiver of apprehension she felt when the two women who had been chatting with the postmistress broke off what they were saying when she came in. She was aware that they all watched her take a loaf of bread from the display and approach the till, and despite herself her hands trembled as she fumbled her purse from her bag.

But before she could offer payment, a curious tremor swept over her. It was not like any feeling she'd ever had before, and for an awful moment she wondered if she was going to faint. She took a trembling breath as the sensation that she could only liken to butterflies in her stomach caused her to grope urgently for the edge of the counter, and, as if her weakness had breached their standoffishness, all three women hurried to her aid.

'Here, sit you down,' said the younger of the two women who had been chatting to the shopkeeper. She dragged an old cane chair that had been standing in a corner forward and helped Isobel into it as the postmistress hurried away to get her a glass of water. 'There, just take it easy.'

'You've been overdoing it.' The other woman was not to be outdone. 'We all know what it's like when you've just moved house. And it's been so hot.'

Isobel managed a faint smile. Evidently they all knew who she was. But her hand went automatically to the curve of her abdomen and she prayed that this wasn't a forerunner to her losing her baby.

The shopkeeper came back with the water and Isobel sipped it gratefully. But she was aware of them exchanging knowing glances above her head and she guessed that little escaped their notice.

'Feeling better?'

It was the shopkeeper who spoke now. A plump woman, in her late forties, Isobel guessed. She had a friendly smile, and Isobel nodded. 'Much better,' she agreed, looking round at them. 'I don't know what happened. I'm not normally affected by the heat.'

'You have to look after yourself when you're in your condition,' declared the second woman sharply, and Isobel realised she wasn't the only one to be embarrassed by such plain speaking.

'Sarah,' protested the shopkeeper, giving her a horrified look, and the younger woman took the opportunity to introduce herself.

'I'm Joanne James,' she said ruefully. 'And you'll have to forgive Mrs Creighton. She has a reputation to uphold.'

'I can speak for myself, thank you.' Sarah Creighton regarded the other women indignantly. 'And it's not as if we didn't all guess what was wrong with Mrs—Ms—'

'Dorland,' Isobel conceded reluctantly. 'And it's all right. It's not as if I'll be able to hide it for long.'

'Dorland,' echoed Joanne, arching an inquisitive brow, but to Isobel's relief the woman who owned the shop came unwittingly to her rescue.

'And isn't that just like a man?' she remarked slyly, taking the empty glass from Isobel's hand. 'Never around when you need them.'

Isobel forced herself to get up from the chair. 'I'm—separated from my partner,' she said, wincing at yet another lie. 'And—well, I think I'm all right now.' She found her purse again. 'If I can just pay for the bread…'

Yet, despite her eagerness to get away from the women, Isobel left the shop with some reluctance. She should have brought the car, she thought worriedly, facing the walk home with real trepidation. Perhaps she had been overdoing things. There was no doubt that she had been bending and lifting for the better part of the last two days.

She made it back to the cottage without further incident and let herself into her own domain with an enormous feeling of relief. It was unfortunate, perhaps, that the facts of her situation were likely to be common knowledge around the village very shortly, but at least she'd broken the ice. And cut off any speculation as to the possible whereabouts of her 'partner', she acknowledged wryly. Or, at least, she hoped she had. So long as no one had seen Jared's car and jumped to the wrong conclusion.

Jared…

A sob rose unbidden into her throat and she fought it back. Damn, was she never going to be able to think about him without feeling close to tears? Jared was history; he had to be. That was the reason she was here, for heaven's sake. The idea of contacting Robert Dorland had come much later.

And was likely to remain dormant, she thought, somewhat painfully. After what the telephone engineer had said, she was having serious doubts about Robert Dorland's honesty, and the conversation she had had with Marion had only added to her uncertainty. The question of whether he'd have ignored her existence for so long if he'd really cared about her couldn't be ignored. And what if she wasn't his daughter? Her sister's opinion of her biological mother couldn't entirely be dismissed either.

The jangle of the phone almost scared the life out of her. She'd got out of the habit of hearing a phone ring. At the hotel, she'd made calls, but she couldn't remember the last time she'd received one. And it was weeks since she'd had a phone of her own.

But as she went to answer it another quiver rippled across her abdomen and she halted abruptly, pressing an anxious hand to her stomach. And felt it again. A faint, but unmistakable tremor that she suddenly identified. It was the baby, she thought incredulously. She could feel her baby moving.

Her excitement was so intense she wanted to share it with somebody, and she hurried to pick up the receiver, hoping against hope that it might be Michelle. She'd left her new number on Michelle's answering machine that morning and it was about the time her friend got in from school.

'Polgarth 4542,' she said breathily, after snatching up

the phone, and then was taken aback when a man's voice answered.

'Miss Dorland?'

'Yes,' she said wearily, swallowing her disappointment. 'Who is this?'

'Luke Herrington here,' declared her landlord pleasantly. 'Just checking that everything's okay.'

'Oh—yes.' Isobel endeavoured to sound more upbeat than before. 'Everything's fine, thank you.' She managed a short laugh. 'You're my first caller.'

'Ah, you mean the phone,' he responded lightly. 'Yes. I have to admit, I had to pull a few strings there.'

'Did you?' Isobel realised that sounded as if she was questioning his integrity and amended it. 'You did.' She took a breath. 'Well—thanks.'

'It was my pleasure,' he assured her warmly. 'If there's anything I can do to help, you only have to ask.'

'You're very kind.'

'Not at all.' He waited a beat. 'By the way, you haven't forgotten about my invitation, have you?'

Isobel grimaced, glad he couldn't see her expression at that moment. 'Er—your invitation?' she murmured faintly, hoping he would take the hint and make some excuse for not being able to follow up on it. 'I'm afraid I've been too busy to think about anything except how exhausting moving house can be.'

'You've obviously been working too hard,' he said firmly, and she could tell from his tone that had no intention of letting her off the hook. 'What you need is an escape from all your endeavours, however worthy they might be. An evening of pampering, where the only effort that will be expected of you is to make yourself look beautiful. And that will take no effort at all.'

Isobel suppressed a groan. 'Oh, really, I—'

'You're going to turn me down?'

'Would you mind?'

'You've made other arrangements?' His voice was cooler. 'I'm sorry. I thought you said you didn't know anyone in the district.'

'I don't.' Isobel realised she was in danger of arousing his suspicions. 'Um—what time were you thinking of?'

'Well, not early,' he exclaimed, the warmth seeping back into his voice. 'I'm sure you've had a busy day, and you'll need time to recover. I recommend a long soak in a warm bath. Shall we say—eight o'clock?'

Isobel blew out a breath. Eight o'clock! The way she was feeling, she would have preferred an early night, but at least it would be a short evening.

'That sounds good to me,' she managed, and as he made arrangements to pick her up she reflected that at least he was unlikely to hear any gossip before then.

CHAPTER TEN

JARED had initially booked a room for two nights at the Moat House Hotel in Polgarth.

He supposed he'd had some wild idea—futile, as it had turned out—that as soon as Isobel saw him again she'd fall into his arms and the booking could be cancelled. Even knowing she'd come here to find her father, he'd been confident that he could persuade her to come back.

Of course he hadn't. But he hadn't driven home that night. As his anger had cooled, so had his intellect, and he'd known that he had to see her again. He hadn't given her time to think over what he'd said, and it was possible that she'd been so shocked to see him that her reactions had been coloured by an instinctive desire to defend herself.

If she'd never found those letters and conceived this crazy notion of finding her biological father she'd never have dreamt of moving to Cornwall. He was sure of it. She might have left Newcastle: he had to accept that she'd had that in mind for some time, and, however painful it was to stomach, he had to try and understand her motives.

He spent Friday kicking his heels in Polgarth. It was a nice little town, with one or two decent hotels and a shopping precinct surrounding a central square. There was even a museum, and he spent some time examining the tools and other implements that were all that was left of the tin-mining that used to be so prevalent in the area. These days, most of the mines had closed, and, reading about the conditions the miners used to work under, Jared couldn't help but think that that was a good thing. Having been raised in the north-east of England, he was very familiar with mining and its difficulties, and although people missed the camaraderie that had existed in mining communities, there was no doubt that they didn't miss the dangers.

It crossed his mind that he might run into Isobel in Polgarth. He remembered she'd always used to make her weekly visit to the supermarket on Fridays, and that brought back memories of how they'd first met.

She'd been so mortified at reversing her car into his, he recalled ruefully. Particularly when she'd had to confess to being a teacher, as well. She'd admitted that she'd always impressed upon her pupils the necessity to take especial care in car parks. People often reversed out of bays without thinking, she'd told them, and the possible consequences of her carelessness had stayed with her for weeks.

From Jared's point of view, he'd been grateful for the introduction. His attraction to her had seemed as natural as breathing and he'd hated the thought of having to tell her he was a married man. But, as it happened, he hadn't had to. She'd recognised his name from things her sister had said. As usual, Marion had been shamelessly social climbing, and she had already been pretending that the Goldmans were close friends.

To begin with, he knew, Isobel had had no intention of becoming involved with him. She'd liked him; he'd known that. But she'd kept their association an impersonal one, concerned simply with arranging for her insurance company to cover his repairs. The damage to his car had been minimal, and he could easily have attended to it himself without involving her. But it had been a means of keeping in touch with her, and he'd exploited it shamelessly for his own ends.

From the beginning of their association Jared had insisted that they were doing no harm. The predictable excuse of any married man, he conceded now. But when he'd told her that he and Elizabeth were living separate lives, he hadn't been lying. He'd assured Isobel that he was asking for her friendship, nothing more…

Jared bought a sandwich for his lunch and ate it in his car, overlooking a wooded ravine just outside of town. Then, leaving the car, he hiked down into the valley, following the course of a tumbling stream that had been swollen by recent rains.

It was a beautiful part of the country, he acknowledged, wondering why he had chosen to return to the north of England after he'd got his degree. Perhaps he'd been destined to go back to Newcastle to meet Isobel, he reflected. Flinging himself down onto a flat rock beside the stream, he raked frustrated fingers through his hair. He didn't even want to think of how he'd feel if she insisted on staying here.

He took a deep breath and stared blindly across the stream to where a few late pansies were still blooming. It was his own fault, he thought bitterly. If he'd kept his promise, she'd never have felt the need to get away. She probably thought he'd lied when he'd said that all he wanted was her friendship. Of course he'd wanted to make love with her, but to begin with just being with her had been enough.

And he hadn't made any undue demands upon her. For weeks, months, even, he'd contented himself with being in her company, sharing her humour, delighting in making her smile. From the very beginning, their relationship had not been like any other relationship he had had.

He grimaced, taking off his glasses and wearily tipping back his head. Was that entirely true? Hadn't he taken every opportunity he could to touch her? From putting his arm around her to guide her into a restaurant, to taking her hand whenever they walked together?

But she'd let him do it, he defended himself. Smiling up at him so confidently, laughing at his jokes, teasing him mercilessly. She'd even massaged his shoulders when he'd gone to her apartment with the tensions of the day still stiffening his spine. She'd done everything except kiss him, and gradually the strain had begun to tell on both of them.

Ironically enough, it had been Isobel who'd broken their self-imposed abstinence. Three years before, her mother had been diagnosed with a certain virulent form of cancer, and, although she had had surgery and chemotherapy treatment at the time, nine months ago it had reappeared.

Isobel had been devastated when the doctor had given her the news, and she'd done something she'd never done before: she'd called him on his mobile phone and begged him to come to the apartment. And when he'd arrived—barely thirty minutes later, he remembered, having broken every speed limit in the city to get to her—she'd virtually thrown herself into his arms.

Between incoherent sobs, she'd told him about her mother, and although Jared had comforted her, he'd never imagined that she wanted anything more from him than that. He'd thought he'd understood how she was feeling, but he'd been wrong. She hadn't just wanted his sympathy, she'd wanted him, wholly and completely, an affirmation of life at a time when she'd seemed surrounded by the shadows of death.

But, dammit, he didn't want to think about making love with her now; didn't want to remember how sweet that first time had been; how sweet and trusting *she* had been, offering herself to him with a complete lack of guile or artifice. God, it had been so good then, so satisfying, and that fledgling encounter had been the start of their affair.

He drove back to his hotel in the late afternoon, resisting the impulse to go to the cottage with a distinct effort. Better to wait, he told himself. Better to give her a whole day to think about what she'd said. If he went back now, she would know that he hadn't taken her seriously, and that would defeat the object.

He considered ordering his dinner from Room Service, but the idea of spending the whole evening with only himself for company didn't appeal. He hadn't bothered with dinner at all the night before, but the considerable quantity of alcohol he'd swallowed in the bar had filled the empty space inside him. Tonight, however, he had no intention of getting drunk, and watching his fellow guests couldn't be any less entertaining than staring at the four walls of his room.

The restaurant was fairly full when he went downstairs, and he was glad he'd taken the trouble to wear a jacket and tie. It was obviously a favourite place to eat for the people of Polgarth, because he didn't recognise many faces from when he'd had breakfast that morning. He guessed that most of the diners were just out for the evening, but at least he didn't feel conspicuous as he accompanied the *maître d'* to his table by the window.

Yet, for all that, he sensed his arrival had not gone unremarked. He might be flattering himself, and it was probably nothing more than the unfamiliarity of dining on his own, but after he'd been seated and the waiter had supplied him with a menu, he took a surreptitious inventory of the room.

And suffered an immediate blow to his gut.

Isobel was sitting not twenty feet away, sharing a table for two with a man he'd never seen before. But she was staring at him as if she couldn't believe the evidence of her own eyes and he could hardly blame her. She'd obviously assumed he'd returned to Newcastle, and as she hadn't known where he was staying anyway, the chances of them both dining in the same restaurant must have been hundreds to one. Although, remembering Polgarth's limitations when it came to gourmet eating, perhaps not.

His eyes consumed her. She looked so beautiful, her dark hair, which had grown in the six weeks since she'd left Newcastle, a curly halo about her face. He thought she looked pale, but that was probably just the shock she'd had upon seeing him, and as she was wearing a simple black dress, her pallor was impossibly pronounced.

The man she was with leant towards her then and said something, and Isobel dragged her eyes away to answer him. Whatever he'd said, it brought a faint smile to her lips and, seeing it, Jared knew he had to get out of there before he did something unforgivable. Already the collar of his shirt was feeling unpleasantly tight and hot colour was sweeping up his neck to darken his skin. He needed a drink, he thought savagely. Something strong and powerful, that would cut through the constriction in his throat that was threatening to strangle him.

He thrust back his chair and got to his feet, aware that by doing so he was creating exactly the spectacle he'd most wanted to avoid. The *maître d'* came hurrying towards him, evidently alarmed that the waiter had said or done something to offend him, and what with reassuring him, and avoiding the eyes of the other diners, Jared was unaware that Isobel had left her seat and come to join them.

'Jared,' she said, her low voice reaching him even over the flustered protestations of the manager, but although he could hear the anxiety in her tone, he couldn't bear to look at her.

'Go back to your friend, Isobel,' he said harshly, fighting back the urge to go and bury his fist in the other man's face, and, uncaring of what anybody thought of him now, he pushed both of them aside and strode out of the restaurant.

He couldn't wait to get out of his formal clothes, and he was already loosening the neck of his shirt and pulling his tie free of his collar as he vaulted up the stairs. God, what a fool he'd been, he berated himself bitterly. He'd believed her when she'd told him there was no one else, but it was obvious now why she'd really left town. There was no way in hell that the guy with her was her father, and she had hardly had time to get to know anyone else.

'Jared!'

She was at the foot of the stairs now, gazing up at him with an imploring expression on her face, and he thought how pitiful it was that he still wanted to give her the benefit of the doubt.

'Go away, Isobel,' he said coldly, pausing only long enough to deliver these words, and he heard the sob that marked her intake of breath.

'Jared, you don't understand.'

'You got that right,' muttered Jared to himself as he stalked along the corridor to his room. He was hurt, and he told himself his feelings were justifiable, even if the knowledge that he had no real right to blame her was gnawing at his conscience.

He had his keycard in his hand before he reached his room, and, jabbing it into the lock, he thrust the door open with enough force to ensure that the recoil slammed it shut behind him. Then, pulling off his tie and tossing it onto the bed, he walked straight across to the phone and punched out the number for Room Service.

He was waiting impatiently for someone to answer when there was a tentative tap at his door. He stiffened abruptly, but before he could abandon his call and go and answer it Room Service came on the line.

Deciding whoever was outside would have to wait, he turned his back on the door deliberately. 'I want a bottle of Scotch,' he said shortly to the woman who had responded, and after giving his room number he slammed the phone down again.

The tap at his door was repeated.

Taking a deep breath, he considered ignoring it, but the suspicion of who it was drove him across the room again. Flinging open the door, he was hardly surprised to find

Isobel outside, but he had no intention of listening to any more lies from her.

'Go away,' he said flatly, but when he would have shut the door again, she insinuated herself into the opening.

'Please, Jared—'

'Please, what?' He was in no mood to bandy words with her, and only the fact that he would have to physically man-handle her out of the doorway prevented him from accomplishing his objective. The last thing he wanted to do was lay his hands on her. He had the uneasy feeling that if he did he might not be able to let her go again. 'You're wasting your time, Isobel.'

'Isobel?' Her lips quivered at his formal use of her name. 'Please—can't we talk? I don't want you to—to go away with the wrong impression.'

'Is that possible?' Jared was sardonic, but his will was weakening, he could feel it, and, stifling a curse, he left the door and put some space between them. 'Make it quick.'

Isobel didn't say anything immediately. She simply came into the room, closing the door with more care than he'd shown, and then stood there like a schoolgirl, her hands, one on top of the other, forming a horizontal line at the apex of her thighs.

Jared's jacket joined his tie on the bed and he turned to face her, arms crossed at his midriff. He didn't want to feel any sympathy for her, but he couldn't help noticing that she was paler even than before.

Yet she seemed to have gained a little weight, he observed sourly, wondering if it was the natural result of several weeks without work or because she no longer had to live with the stress of their relationship. Whatever, it suited her, and he had to drag his eyes away from the unknowingly provocative thrust of her breasts.

But he could feel himself hardening, and, in an effort

to keep her off-guard, he arched a mocking brow. 'Is he good?'

Isobel's gasp was pained. 'How can you ask something like that?'

Jared shrugged. 'Well, I can't imagine what else you have to tell me. I just wish you'd been honest when I came to the cottage. It would have saved me from kicking my heels around here for the last twenty-four hours.'

'So, why did you?' she protested unsteadily. 'Stay here, I mean? I—I thought you must have gone back to Newcastle.'

'Hoped,' Jared corrected her caustically. 'The word you're looking for is 'hoped'. You *hoped* I'd gone back to Newcastle, didn't you?'

'I—yes.' Her momentary hesitation was no recompense. 'Of course I hoped you'd gone back. We—we'd said all there was to say. Hadn't we?'

'So what are you doing here, then?'

She shook her head, as if he'd disappointed her. 'You know what I'm doing here,' she insisted. 'I don't want you to think—to imagine that Luke and I—'

'Luke?' His lips curled.

'Yes, Luke. Luke Herrington,' she said defensively. 'He's my landlord. He owns the cottage I'm renting.' She gestured behind her. 'This—this evening was intended to be a kind of celebration of me moving in.'

'Oh, yeah, right.'

It was obvious that he didn't believe her, and Isobel spread her hands in helpless appeal. 'It's the truth.' She gazed at him entreatingly. 'Why would I lie to you?'

'I can think of a number of reasons,' he retorted bitterly. 'Like, you've thought I was a bastard for so long, you wouldn't want to lose your advantage.'

Isobel's lips parted. '*I* thought you were a bastard?'

'You said it.'

She left the door and came towards him. 'I don't know

what the hell you're talking about,' she got out chokingly. She swallowed, her throat working convulsively. 'I—I have never—never thought you were—' She couldn't seem to say it. 'I—I loved you, Jared.'

'Loved?' His contempt was audible. 'What is love? I don't know, and I doubt it to hell that you do either. What is this? Some kind of guilt trip? D'you expect me to believe you left me because you loved me? Come on, Isobel. I've been down this path before.'

'And I'm not Elizabeth,' said Isobel fiercely, moving her head agitatedly from side to side. 'Why are you saying these things, Jared? Can't we at least part as friends?'

'I'm not your friend,' snarled Jared, hardly knowing what he was saying, and, uncaring of the hands she raised to stop him, he jerked her into his arms. His mouth fastened on hers, taking advantage of her parted lips, and he thrust his tongue hungrily between her teeth.

He knew the moment she stopped fighting him. Her hands, which had curled into fists at his midriff, opened and spread against the fine fabric of his shirt. Her breasts flattened against his chest, and as she arched against him his arousal was cushioned by the womanly softness of her stomach.

'God, Belle,' he groaned, releasing her mouth to seek the scented hollow of her neck, and, almost against her will, it seemed, her hands curved up to pull off his glasses and bring his mouth back to hers.

He was hungry for the taste of her, for the feel of her warm body in his arms. He wanted to touch every part of her, to strip away the barriers of their clothes that separated them and enclose her securely within the possessive circle of his embrace.

His hands slid down the slender column of her spine to the rounded swell of her bottom and brought her even closer to his aching loins. Hiking up the silky skirt of her dress, he wedged one leg between the sensual heat of her thighs. She was wearing black stockings, and above their lacy tops sexy suspenders gave a tantalising glimpse of pale flesh.

Jared's breathing quickened in concert with the accelerated beat of his heart. Opening her mouth wider, to give him greater access to the moist cavern within, he nibbled at the sensitive softness of her inner flesh, biting the provocative curl of her tongue when it came to duel with his.

Her mouth was so hot, so sweet, so familiar, and his senses reeled beneath the onslaught of so many dizzying sensations. She'd thrown his glasses onto the bed and her hands were in his hair, her nails raking his scalp, sliding into the collar of his shirt, loosening buttons to expose his hair-roughened chest.

His erection throbbed painfully, eager for release, eager to bury itself in the wet curls that pulsed against his leg. Desire, like a ravening beast, blinded him to everything but the consummation of his own needs. He wanted her; ah, God, she was as important to his survival as the air he breathed, and somehow he had to convince her of that.

He'd forgotten about the man downstairs, the man she'd been having dinner with. He'd forgotten the betrayal he'd felt when he'd seen them together, or how much he'd despised himself for his own selfishness in not wanting to let her go. Right now, the idea that this woman, *his* woman, might be operating under a different agenda from his own didn't even occur to him. He'd even forgotten where they were, and why he was here, miles from everything that was familiar to him. All his bemused brain was telling him was that Isobel was here, they were together, and soon, very soon, he was going to feel her responsive flesh opening to his. Her muscles, those tight demanding muscles, would close around him, and his aching body would find its release in the sensual sweetness of hers.

His guard was down, he was briefly vulnerable, and when someone knocked at the door it took him a few precious seconds to comprehend its significance. Precious seconds that Isobel used to her advantage. With a groan, she thrust him away from her; thrust him away with such force that the backs of his knees hit the edge of the bed and he toppled helplessly onto the mattress, only narrowly avoiding crushing his glasses.

He rebounded at once, the shock instantly rousing him from the mindless confusion his senses had created. But it was too late. Isobel had already reached the door and was pulling it open, and any chance of grabbing her and trying to regain the advantage was thwarted by the appearance of the hotel waiter with the Scotch he'd ordered earlier.

'Your whisky, sir,' said the man politely, but Jared could tell from his expression that he wasn't unaware of what had been going on before he knocked at the door. Even without his glasses Jared could see that Isobel's mouth was swollen, and there were creases in her skirt that hadn't been there before. Besides which, his shirt was unbuttoned almost to his waist, and, although his erection had subsided, his own frustration must have been unmistakable.

'Goodbye, Jared.'

Evidently, Isobel felt obliged to say something to try and normalise the situation, and, uncaring what the man thought, Jared bounded across the room and caught her arm as she was hurrying away along the corridor.

'Wait!'

'I can't.'

She was stiff now, her face pale and unyielding, and Jared's teeth ground together. 'Dammit, you can't go like this,' he muttered, conscious of the waiter behind him. 'Please, Belle: I won't touch you if you don't want me to, but come back into the room.'

'No.' She looked down at his fingers gripping her arm, and with a muffled oath he released her, knowing he wasn't aiding his case by holding her against her will. 'Luke will be wondering where I am.'

Jared was tempted to say, To hell with Luke, but he had the sense to realise that losing his temper was unlikely to achieve anything either. Instead, with enforced patience, he said, 'He can wait a few minutes longer.'

'No, he can't.' She was determined not to compromise with him. 'I should never have come up here. I don't know why I did, really, except that—that—'

'You couldn't help yourself?' he suggested huskily, but she turned her head away.

'I was going to say that I—felt I owed you an explanation,' she responded. 'I should have known better.' Her lips twisted bitterly. 'I should have realised you'd take any advantage and use it to your own ends.'

'They were your ends too.'

'Not any more.' She glanced at him with tormented eyes. 'I've tried to tell you I don't know how many times, Jared. We're finished. It's over. I'll get over it. So will you. And we'll both get over it a whole lot sooner if you stop trying to rekindle a dying fire.'

'This—is—not—a—dying—fire,' he enunciated harshly, but when he would have grasped her hands, she thrust them behind her back.

'It is. Accept it, Jared, and go home. Please. I don't know why you're still here, but if you're planning on visiting the cottage again, forget it. I won't answer the door.'

CHAPTER ELEVEN

IT WAS raining again.

Having forced herself to crawl out of bed when the alarm rang for the second time, Isobel crossed to the window and gazed out at the overcast skies with weary resignation. It seemed to have done nothing but rain since she started work and she was heartily sick of it.

Sick of everything, herself included, she acknowledged miserably, padding into the bathroom. Why had she ever thought that making a fresh start would give her life new meaning? Sometimes it was even hard to remember what her motivation for coming to Polgarron had been, and the idea of making some contact with the Dorlands of Tregarth Hall grew more unlikely with every passing day.

She had successfully severed her relationship with Jared, of course, even if the advantages of that were sometimes equally hard to justify. Which was stupid, she reminded herself now, viewing the reflection of her steadily burgeoning stomach in the mirror above the washbasin. There was no way she could have allowed Jared to find out about the baby. He wanted her, but he didn't love her. He'd made that painfully clear. And the fact that he and Elizabeth had never had any children must surely prove that they were not on his agenda either.

She shivered. It was definitely getting colder in the mornings, and already she was missing the benefits of central heating. Perhaps she could suggest to Luke that radiators were no longer considered a luxury, she considered. Though, since she'd told him she was expecting a baby, his interest in his new tenant had seriously waned.

So long as he didn't cancel her lease, she could live

with it, she thought wryly. At least until the baby was born, anyway. So far, she hadn't considered what she was going to do afterwards. There was no doubt she was missing her friends and family more than she could have imagined, the long phone conversations she had with Michelle only partly compensating for the gulf there was between them.

Between you and Jared, you mean. Her hormones kicked in grumpily, and she felt the familiar pull of tears. Despite all the warnings she had given herself, she still thought about him—a lot. Every time the baby moved, every time she noticed some new change in her body, she wanted to share it with him, and it was agony knowing she never could.

If she occasionally felt a pang of guilt at keeping her condition a secret from him, she quelled it. But there were still nights when she lay awake for hours on end, the knowledge of her own duplicity an inescapable burden.

Perhaps if she'd made some contact with the Dorlands it would have been easier for her, she conceded. She had wondered if the Dorlands themselves might show some interest in her, but so far their paths hadn't crossed. She didn't even know if they knew that another person of the same name was living in the village. From what little she had gathered, they didn't mix much with the local people.

She wished there was someone she could ask about them, but she was afraid of appearing too nosy. The snippets she had learned she'd gleaned from Joanne James, who also worked at the school where she was supply-teaching at present. Joanne was the school secretary, and although it had been natural enough during their early conversations for Isobel to comment on the fact that she'd heard there were other Dorlands living in the village, she'd realised that any subsequent interest in them was bound to arouse Joanne's curiosity.

The water was only lukewarm, so Isobel didn't linger

long in the bathroom. At least the sense of nausea had left her, she thought gratefully. She would have hated to have to deal with that as well in her current state of depression.

Then, she had the frustrating task of finding something to wear that didn't overtly advertise her condition. So far, she'd managed to get away with loose-fitting dresses, but it was getting too cold for summer clothes, and her winter clothes were much too tight.

She really would have to make an effort and go into Polgarth at the weekend, she conceded unwillingly. It would be October next week, and, just because she hadn't a lot of interest in her appearance at the moment, that was no reason to go round looking like a frump. She needed some maternity clothes, and no one else was going to buy them for her.

Rummaging through the drawers, she discovered a cream sweater that she'd once borrowed from Jared and never returned. It was big and bulky, the long sleeves falling over her hands so that she had to keep pushing them up over her forearms. But it was warm, and comforting, and teamed with a wrap-around navy skirt it looked pretty good.

She lit the fire in the living room while the kettle was boiling. It wasn't that she had much time to benefit from it before she went to work, but it made the cottage warm and cosy for when she came home. In fact, it was the one aspect of living in the cottage that she really appreciated. It was years since she'd enjoyed the advantages of an open fire.

The school where she had a temporary teaching position was in the nearby village of Rose Cross. Rose Cross was a much bigger village than Polgarron, and the secondary school catered to the needs of the children from all the surrounding villages. Isobel was helping out because a member of the English department was just recovering from a serious operation, and she expected to stay there until Christmas, at least.

Which meant she was unlikely to need another post until after the baby was born. The date she'd been given, of the middle of January, seemed fairly definite according to Dr Wilson, whose practice was in Rose Cross, too. Joanne had said the doctor who'd used to have a surgery in Polgarron had retired, and it was convenient to fit in her appointments after school was over for the day.

Of course, Isobel had had to visit the hospital in Polgarth for her scan, which had taken place a few weeks ago. Michelle had pressed her not to put off the examination, and she'd been relieved to find she wouldn't have to go to St Austell when the baby was due.

But it had been another stage of her pregnancy that she would have liked to have shared with Jared, she reflected now, as she got into her car. She'd chosen not to be told the baby's sex, but she had learned that he—or she—was perfectly normal, and once again her hand curved possessively over her womb.

She usually stopped at the stores before driving out of the village. Mrs Scott, who owned the stores and ran the post office, also supplied newspapers and magazines, and Isobel had started to collect a paper on her way to work. It made her feel more like a local, despite her sense of alienation, and Mrs Scott never failed to ask how she was when she came in.

There was another woman in the shop this morning, a tall young woman, with hair as dark as her own, who was apparently complaining about a magazine that hadn't been delivered. Her voice, an unusually arrogant voice, Isobel noticed, was raised in protest, and she glanced round impatiently when Isobel came into the shop.

'Morning, Ms Dorland,' called Mrs Scott cheerfully, before resuming her attempt to pacify the girl. But the young woman had heard Isobel's name and turned again to regard her with suspicious eyes.

'Your name's Dorland?' she enquired, as if she had every right to ask the question, and Isobel felt herself stiffening.

'Just the *Mail*, Mrs Scott,' she said, without answering her, handing over the necessary change. 'Thanks.'

She was obviously going to leave without speaking to the girl, and, as if she felt obliged to say something in mitigation, Mrs Scott hurriedly intervened. 'Er—this young lady is called Dorland, too,' she said, with an appealing look at Isobel. 'You may have heard of Mrs Dorland of Tregarth Hall?'

Isobel's jaw dropped. 'You're Mrs Dorland?' she said faintly, and the young woman tossed Mrs Scott a disparaging look.

'Of course not,' she exclaimed scornfully, but it was hardly a reassurance. 'I'm Barbara Dorland. Her daughter.'

Her *daughter*!

So, it was true, then. Robert Dorland had been lying when he'd told his sister-in-law that his wife couldn't have children. This girl was proof of it, and Isobel wondered why the news didn't come as any surprise to her.

'Well—I'd better be going,' she began, but Barbara Dorland had another question.

'You don't know my mother, do you?' she probed, and despite herself Isobel felt the colour draining out of her cheeks.

'No,' she said quickly, reaching for the handle of the door, but Barbara still wasn't finished with her.

'You don't come from around here, do you?' she persisted. 'Are you staying in the village?'

'Ms Dorland's renting Raven Cottage,' put in Mrs Scott, before Isobel could stop her. She smiled beneficently. 'Barbara's just got back from the United States,' she added to Isobel, as if to even the score.

'How nice.' Isobel found it difficult to be friendly towards the young woman, but, reminding herself that her feelings had nothing to do with Barbara, she forced a smile. 'Well—'

'Does your—er—husband work in Polgarth?' The girl's eyes were moving assessingly over Isobel's thickening waistline now, but once again it was Mrs Scott who answered her.

'Ms Dorland's partner isn't living with her at present,' she declared firmly, giving Isobel an encouraging smile. 'And we mustn't keep her or she'll be late for work.'

'You're still working?'

Barbara made it sound incredibly foolish, and Isobel wondered if it was just jealousy that made her want to slap the other woman's face. 'Some of us have to,' she remarked, guessing from the designer cut of Barbara Dorland's clothes that she wasn't one of them. 'Bye.'

She was shaking when she got back into her car, and she couldn't decide if it was the shock of meeting her half-sister or simple anger at Barbara's obvious insensitivity.

Michelle rang that evening.

'Hey, how're you doing, kid?' she asked cheerfully, and instantly sensed from Isobel's tone that something was up. 'Have I rung at the wrong time?'

'As if.' Isobel's voice was a little gruff. 'No, I'm fine. How about you?'

'Same old, same old,' said Michelle ruefully. 'What can I tell you? Oh, yeah. Mr Seton's excluded Wayne Harris for the second time, and Karen Weaver is pregnant.'

'Pregnant!' Isobel forgot her own problems for a moment in the familiar politics of her old school. 'I bet her father's pleased about that!'

'He's spitting blood, I can tell you.' Michelle chuckled. 'Particularly as Karen's mother is insisting that Karen should be allowed to decide if she wants to have the baby or not.'

'And the fact that Mr Weaver has custody doesn't have anything to do with it, I suppose,' remarked Isobel drily. 'So what's going to happen?'

'Your guess is as good as mine.' Michelle snorted. 'If Social Services have their way, she'll probably be encouraged to have the baby and then have it adopted. I think that's the current philosophy. Naturally, Karen's father was hoping for a termination.'

'He would be.'

Isobel sounded wistful, and Michelle picked up on her uncertainty. 'Hey, you're not having second thoughts about having your baby, are you?'

'No.' Isobel was vehement. 'That's one thing I've got no doubts about.'

'So what's that supposed to mean?' Michelle hesitated. 'Help me out here, Issy. Do I take it you're still having doubts about breaking up with Jared?'

'No.' But Isobel sounded less convinced of that. 'I—I was talking to Barbara Dorland today,' she added, with some reluctance.

'Barbara Dorland?' Michelle was startled. 'I thought you said your aunt's name was Justine?'

'It was. It is.' Isobel sighed. 'Barbara's her daughter.'

'My God!' Michelle's gulp was audible. 'I see.'

Isobel sighed again. 'I thought you would.'

'I gather you still haven't told them who you are?'

'No.'

'Are you going to?'

'I don't know.' Isobel was resigned. 'I keep telling myself that—that if he'd wanted to speak to me, he'd have made some overture before now.'

'There is that.' Michelle obviously sympathised. 'So what did she say?'

'Barbara?' Isobel was thoughtful. 'Not a lot. But she was obviously curious about me.'

'Was she?'

'Yes, but not the way you think.' Isobel paused, and then explained, 'She was in the shop when I called for my paper this morning. She heard Mrs Scott call me Ms *Dorland*, and she must have thought that gave her the right to ask me all sorts of questions.'

'What questions?'

'Oh—' Isobel tried to think. 'Well, she asked if I knew her mother, for one thing. And then she asked if I came from this area, and so on. Oh, and she asked if my husband worked in Polgarth.'

'Your *husband*?' Michelle gave a short incredulous laugh. 'That was pretty nosy, wasn't it?'

'I thought so.' Isobel tried to sound indignant, but her anxiety was showing again. 'I think she noticed—that I was pregnant, I mean.'

'Ah.' Michelle was beginning to understand. 'And you're afraid she may tell her father?'

'Something like that.'

'Well, what does it matter? He was bound to find out sooner or later.'

'I know.'

'Issy, don't let these people get to you. Okay, I guess finding out that you've possibly got half-sisters and brothers is upsetting, but you don't have to stay there. You know that. You could move somewhere else.'

'Yeah, right.'

'I mean it.' Michelle sighed now. 'Look, why don't you take a break? Come up here for a few days. You can stay with us. No one need know you're here if you don't want them to. And you don't have to worry about meeting Jared because he's away.'

Isobel gasped. 'Away?' she echoed weakly, not realising until that moment that, in spite of everything, she still relied on the fact that, if she really needed him, he was just at the end of a phone line.

'Yeah.' Michelle seemed to regret having mentioned it

now, but she had no choice but to go on. 'They've all gone away. Mr Goldman; Elizabeth; Jared; oh, and that physiotherapist Elizabeth seems to think so highly of.'

Isobel swallowed. 'What do you mean—gone away?'

'As in, on holiday,' explained Michelle reluctantly. 'I wouldn't have known myself if I hadn't seen Marion in town a couple of nights ago. I'm surprised she hasn't rung and told you all about it. That's the sort of thing she usually does, isn't it?'

Isobel stifled a groan. It was possible that Marion had rung the day before. The phone had been ringing when she got in from work, but she'd been too late to answer it.

But now she said, 'So—where've they gone?' endeavouring not to sound as devastated as she felt.

'Would you believe on a cruise?' Michelle attempted a sardonic laugh. 'Not Jared's cup of tea, I'd have thought, but Elizabeth will be lapping it up. A swish stateroom; dining at the Captain's table! Just what the doctor ordered.'

Isobel wet her dry lips. 'Isn't it a bit late in the season to be going on a cruise?'

'Hey, people go cruising all the year round. And it's still pretty warm around the Mediterranean.' Michelle paused. 'Anyway, what about you taking a holiday? Doesn't a few days in the old place have any appeal?'

It did, more than Isobel cared to admit, and the prospect of getting away from the cottage for a few days was irresistibly appealing.

'How can I?' she asked now. 'I've only been working at Rose Cross for a little over three weeks. I can't leave them in the lurch.'

'There's always the weekend,' pointed out Michelle, undeterred. 'Surely that old car of yours can make the journey. Come up on Friday evening and go back Sunday. What do you say?'

CHAPTER TWELVE

JARED got back from London on Friday evening.

The house was quiet when he let himself into the hall and he breathed a sigh of relief. For the next week, at least, he would have the place to himself, and he welcomed the prospect. With Elizabeth and Janet away, he'd have time to think, to plan; to decide what in hell he was going to do with his life.

Since coming back from Cornwall he'd been bitter and unsettled. He'd been forced to reappraise his future, and he didn't like what he'd found. He'd been drifting; he realised that now. For the past three years he'd been living a life in limbo, and he'd been selfish enough to expect Isobel to share it with him.

No wonder she'd cut him out of her life. No wonder she'd taken the first opportunity to move away. He believed her when she said she wanted a real relationship, a real family. Dammit, wasn't that what he'd wanted before he'd managed to screw everything up?

He tossed his jacket over the banister, and, switching on lamps as he went, he crossed the hall and entered the steel and chrome sophistication of the kitchen. A strip of angled spotlights lit up the various working surfaces, but Jared had always thought the place had a clinical appearance. It wasn't his design, and he entered it only infrequently these days. Howard had insisted on employing a housekeeper after Elizabeth's accident, and Mrs Webster kept it gleaming like a new pin.

Now, however, the housekeeper was away, too. Elizabeth had insisted that Mrs Webster deserved a holiday as well, but if she'd hoped that threatening him with having to look after himself would make him change his mind about accompanying them on the cruise, she'd been mistaken.

Jared had already had it out with Howard, and, although he'd been sorry to disappoint the older man, his threats no longer held any fears either. He'd reached the point where he didn't much care what happened in the future, and he suspected Howard had realised that, and that was why he'd backed off.

In the event, it had been Howard who'd eventually justified Jared's reasons for staying in England. Despite the unlikelihood of them being offered the contract, his father-in-law had decided that they should tender for a proposed development at Spitalfields. Which was why Jared had spent the first week they were away in London, viewing the site and holding meetings with the various authorities, and making preliminary drawings in his hotel room at night.

They'd all flown to Heathrow together. Then Howard and the two women had flown on to Malta, to rendezvous with the ship, and Jared had taken a taxi into town.

It had been a fairly hectic week and he'd met some interesting people, but he couldn't deny he was glad to be back. He still hoped that Isobel might have had a change of heart, and he intended to speak to Michelle Chambers if he could.

Crazy? He grimaced. Perhaps, but he was desperate. Despite the fact that he could fill his days with work, he couldn't keep Isobel out of his thoughts when he went to bed. He tortured himself wondering where she might be and what she was doing. And, more agonising still, who she might be with.

He'd tried to tell himself that he didn't believe she was involved with Herrington. Although he couldn't forget what he'd seen at the hotel in Polgarth, his inner self rejected the interpretation he'd made. Isobel wasn't like

Elizabeth; she didn't lie to save her own face. But if she was serious about ending their relationship—and he had to believe she was—he wanted her to know exactly what it was she was giving up.

If she didn't already know, he chided himself contemptuously. His lips twisted. He was fooling himself if he thought he could salvage anything worthwhile from this mess. She despised him now for taking advantage of her without offering her any commitment. He had to tell her he was sorry. He had to ask her to forgive him.

Filling the coffee pot with water, he left it to filter through the beans he'd ground while he made himself an omelette. He wasn't particularly hungry, but, as he hadn't had anything since a slice of toast that morning at the hotel, he knew he had to eat something.

There was no fresh bread in the house, but he would worry about that in morning. For the present, the eggs would do, and, after pouring himself a mug of black coffee, he set the meal on a tray and carried it through to his study at the back of the house.

The message light on the answering machine was winking at him, and although he told himself that it could wait until morning, too, the unlikely thought that it could be something urgent forced him to press the button.

As he'd expected, all the calls were business-related. Even the invitations from other firms and colleagues to social events were all slanted towards his position at Goldman Lewis, and with an exclamation of disgust he switched the machine off. Dammit, that was what his life had become and he was sick of it. It was time to tell Elizabeth he wanted out.

Michelle Chambers and her husband lived in the Fenham district of the city.

According to Isobel, she and Michelle had known one another since their schooldays, when they'd both lived near Jesmond Dene, and, although they'd lost touch with one another afterwards, they'd met up again teaching at the same school. Jared knew her only slightly, but he was well aware that Michelle didn't approve of him. A situation that he hoped to reverse. He needed her help, not her condemnation, however well deserved it might be.

He knew where Michelle lived. He'd passed the house a couple of times since Isobel went away, originally in the hope of seeing Michelle and begging her to tell him where her friend had gone. He'd even spoken to her on the phone on one abortive occasion, when she'd told him in no uncertain terms that if Isobel wanted him to know where she was, she'd tell him herself.

Which had been fair enough, he supposed honestly. And, in the event, he'd managed to find Isobel without her help. But now he wanted something different from her: he wanted to know if Isobel was seeing anyone else. If Michelle thought he had any chance of persuading her to come back to him.

As if she'd tell him.

But he had to try.

He saw the little grey Fiesta the minute he turned into Cunningham Grove. It wasn't a large cul-de-sac, and the Chambers' house was situated at the end, in full view of anyone who turned off the main thoroughfare. And there was Isobel's car, parked neatly at the gate.

His foot found the brake almost involuntarily, and he swung jerkily into the kerb, narrowly avoiding a bicycle that was parked there. But the shock of seeing her car, of knowing that Isobel had come back, was so shattering that he needed a few minutes to recover his scattered senses.

When had she decided to return to Newcastle? he wondered. When had she changed her mind about making a life for herself so far from all the people and places she knew and loved? And why hadn't she told him?

The answer was obvious, of course. As his heartbeat

slowed and the trickle of perspiration that had dampened his temples dried, he realised he had no grounds for thinking she'd changed her mind. Quite the opposite, in fact. It wasn't a coincidence that Isobel had chosen to visit Michelle this weekend when everyone no doubt assumed he was away with his wife and her father. Isobel's sister could have told her. Elizabeth was bound to have mentioned the cruise at the golf club. The last thing she'd be expecting was for him to turn up.

He blew out a breath. Now what? Could he really walk up to Michelle's door and ask to speak to her? Would she be prepared to speak to him?

Of course, Michelle might not let him in. And, judging by the cars parked in the drive, her husband was home as well. Not that he was daunted by the thought of facing Phil Chambers. On the contrary, he had the feeling that only another man might understand the torment he was going through.

A spatter of rain wet the windscreen of the Mercedes, and he expelled an impatient sigh. He couldn't sit here contemplating his alternatives indefinitely. Already the people who lived in the house nearby were peering out of the window, speculating as to his intentions.

Dammit, he was going to have to take a chance on her not rejecting him outright, he decided at last. He had to convince her that seeing her with Luke Herrington had made him realise how much she meant to him. Only if he saw her again would he know whether he was wasting his time.

Despite the obvious disapproval of the neighbours, Jared decided to leave the car where it was. He told himself it was because there were already too many cars parked around the Chambers' house as it was, but in fact he felt less conspicuous on foot.

He was wearing a long overcoat over black jeans and a purple tee shirt, and he pushed his hands into the coat's pockets to hold the sides together after locking the car. It was cold, damn cold, and the wind whistling between the houses didn't help. But, once again, his body heat was rising. He felt like a schoolboy, he thought mockingly, preparing to ask for a first date.

The rain blurred his vision, and he took off his glasses and rubbed them on his sleeve. But as he put them on again he saw that the front door of the Chambers' house was opening, and his pulse accelerated as Isobel and Michelle came out.

He was approximately fifty yards from the gate when Isobel saw him. He knew the moment she recognised him, because she half turned around, and he was afraid she was going to dart back into the house. Michelle hadn't seen him yet, and, judging by the fact that she was closing the door behind her, the two women were going out together. Shopping, probably, Jared speculated. He just wanted to stop and stare at Isobel, but he knew if they reached her car before he did, his chance would be lost.

But that didn't stop him gazing at her, drinking in the delightful picture she made in a long, loose-fitting coat he hadn't seen before. It was a deep blue and complemented the silky darkness of her hair. She looked well, he thought enviously, half resenting the connotations that implied. She was making a life for herself without him, and he had no real right to interfere with that.

Except…

Except that he *needed* her, he acknowledged, in a moment of self-revelation. He needed her, and if that was selfish then so be it, but he was going to do everything in his power to get her back. Elizabeth didn't need him, she'd proved that in a hundred different ways, and three years was surely a long enough penance for the sin of not caring enough.

He was well aware that if he and Elizabeth got a divorce he'd have to leave Goldman-Lewis. Howard would probably never forgive him for abandoning his daughter, and, unless Elizabeth chose to tell her father about the abortion, that would be another cross he'd have to bear. But it was a price he was prepared to pay for his freedom. Being with Isobel was the only thing that mattered to him and he was a fool for not realising it before now.

Something about Isobel's attitude must have communicated itself to her friend because Michelle frowned and turned to look in his direction. Her face changed when she saw him, whatever she'd been saying to Isobel was silenced, and they both gazed at him with guarded eyes when he halted at the foot of the drive.

'What do you want—?' Michelle started, but Jared looked only at Isobel.

'Hi,' he said, aware that his voice was gravelly with emotion. 'Can we talk?'

'You've got a nerve!' protested Michelle fiercely, stepping in front of Isobel as if there was some danger of him using force to gain his own ends.

'It's all right, Michelle.' Isobel's face had paled slightly at his appearance, but now she moved round the other woman to fix him with an unfriendly stare. 'She's right,' she added tersely. 'You have got a nerve coming here. Aren't you supposed to be cruising the Mediterranean with your wife?'

'Is that what you thought?' Jared's glasses were becoming smeared with rain again, and he pulled them off to gaze at her with hungry eyes. He was aware of Michelle getting ready to answer the question and hurried on, regardless, 'No. I've been in London; working. I just got back last night.'

'But Elizabeth—?'

'She's still away,' said Jared impatiently, not wanting to get into a discussion of his wife's whereabouts with Michelle waiting to pounce like a rabid dog. 'Look, I mean it, Belle. I would like to talk to you—alone.'

'How did you know I was here?'

Despite her friend's frustration, Isobel was evidently curious enough to ask the question, and Jared took some heart from that. 'I didn't—' he began earnestly, only to have Michelle break in again.

'If you believe that, you'll believe anything,' she said disparagingly. 'Why else do you think he's turned up?' She grimaced. 'Like the proverbial bad penny!'

Jared ignored her. 'I didn't know you were here,' he insisted, clenching his teeth when once again Michelle insisted on having her say.

'Who told you?' she demanded. 'Was it Isobel's sister? I'm surprised she's even speaking to you after—'

'No one told me.' Jared kept his temper with an effort, but, realising he had to convince Michelle of that, he turned to look at her instead. 'Can you honestly see Marion Rimmer telling me anything?'

Michelle scowled. 'So what are you saying? That you were coming to see me?' Her scepticism was evident.

'Obviously,' replied Jared flatly. 'I don't know anyone else in Cunningham Grove. You can believe it or not, I don't particularly care, but I was going to ask you if—if Isobel was—all right.'

Well, in a manner of speaking, he defended himself silently, watching Michelle's expression as she absorbed his words. Then Isobel spoke again, and he forgot all about her companion, his eyes devouring the delicate beauty of her face.

'I—' she began, and then halted for a moment. 'As you can see, I'm perfectly all right. I—appreciate your concern, but it really wasn't necessary.'

'It is necessary.' Jared spoke urgently, and then, afraid he was jeopardising his case, he forced himself to calm down. 'Belle, please—I really do want to speak with you.'

'Well, she doesn't want to talk to you,' retorted Michelle, urging her friend towards the Peugeot that was parked in the drive, and Jared's hands balled into impotent fists in his pockets.

'Wait—' To his astonishment, he saw that Isobel was holding back now. But, although he knew a moment's exultation, her next words dashed his fledgling hopes. 'You're wasting your time, Jared. I thought I'd made that perfectly plain when—when—well, weeks ago, anyway.'

'You don't understand—'

'It's you who doesn't understand,' exclaimed Michelle impatiently. 'Tell me, what part of the word "no" don't you comprehend?'

'I suggest you keep out of this,' said Jared coldly, stung into an unwary retort, and Michelle gave Isobel a triumphant look.

'You see—' she began, and Jared closed his eyes for a moment against the smugness of her expression. Then, with a gesture of defeat, he turned away, striding back towards his car before the bitterness inside him consumed his common sense.

He had the key fob in his hand, already using the remote to deactivate the alarm, when he heard Isobel calling him. Looking back over his shoulder, he saw her hurrying towards him, but although his spirits stirred in reluctant response, he had more sense than to be fooled again.

Nevertheless, he didn't attempt to get into the car, and her footsteps slowed when she realised he wasn't about to drive away. Glancing beyond her, Jared saw to his relief that Michelle had apparently gone back into the house and he supposed he ought to be thankful for small mercies.

Isobel's cheeks were flushed when she reached him and, for a woman as slim as she was, she was surprisingly out of breath. But that wasn't his concern at the moment. Even if he desperately wanted to have the right to take care of her, he hadn't yet earned her trust.

'What do you want to say?' she asked, gazing up at him

with parted lips, and he had to steel himself against the desire to cover her mouth with his own.

'We can't talk here,' he protested, glancing up the Grove, and Isobel sighed.

'Let's get into the car, then,' she said, and Jared expelled an exasperated breath.

'You are aware that we're under observation, aren't you?' he exclaimed, his eyes darting towards the house nearby, and the colour in Isobel's cheeks deepened as she realised they were being watched by an old man in a cardigan, who was standing belligerently in the bay window.

'Oh,' she said, drawing her lower lip between her teeth. 'I see what you mean.' She hesitated. 'Do you want to come up to Michelle's?'

Jared gave her a retiring look. 'Oh, right. Let's make the odds even more uneven than they were before.'

'Michelle was only sticking up for me,' said Isobel defensively. 'She thought she was doing the right thing.'

Jared's eyes darkened. 'And she wasn't?'

'No.' Isobel swallowed. 'Yes, I think she probably was. But—well, I thought I owed you—'

'Owed me?'

'Owed you a chance to explain what you think we have to say to one another,' Isobel finished firmly. And, when his mouth took on a bitter slant, 'Don't make me regret it.'

Jared breathed heavily. 'So what do you suggest we do?' He turned one hand up to the rain. 'Not exactly the weather for walking, is it?'

'No.' Isobel hesitated. 'I suppose we could—drive somewhere else.'

'We could.' Jared waited for her to say something more, and when she didn't he walked round the car and opened the passenger door. 'D'you want to get in?'

Isobel was evidently torn, but, after a rueful glance towards the Chambers' house, she seemed to come to a decision. Folding the skirt of her coat about her legs, she stepped into the vehicle.

Jared slammed the door behind her with a feeling not unlike amazement. When he'd walked away from her and Michelle a few minutes ago, he'd had no inkling that she might change her mind and come after him, and it was hard to keep his excitement under control. But he shouldn't build his hopes up, he warned himself severely. She'd made no promises; only that she was prepared to hear what he had to say.

He got behind the wheel and put the powerful car into reverse before he spoke again. 'Where are we going?'

Isobel gave him a sidelong glance. 'Where do you suggest?'

Jared quelled the impulse to tell her where he'd like to take her, and said instead, 'Somewhere quiet, I guess.' He considered. 'How about the coast?'

'The coast?' She wasn't enthusiastic. 'Can't we go to a café or somewhere close by?'

A café? Jared suppressed a groan. 'What about a pub?' he asked unhopefully, and, after a moment's hesitation, she agreed.

It wasn't his choice, but Jared contented himself with choosing a secluded hostelry on the Chollerford road, where, at this time of the morning, they could be sure of finding a quiet corner.

He led the way into the cosy bar, where a real log fire was burning, but when he asked if Isobel wanted white wine, which was her usual tipple, she shook her head.

'Just a coffee,' she said tightly, leaving him to make the order, and when he'd done so he found she'd chosen a table near the hearth, in full view of everyone who came in.

'Aren't you going to be hot here?' he asked, and she looked up at him with cool derision in her eyes.

'Don't you mean that this table is too public for you?'

she suggested, and without another word he pulled out a plush-covered armchair and sat down. 'What did you order?'

'Well, nothing alcoholic,' he assured her, checking his watch. 'How long have I got?'

Isobel gave him a defensive look. 'That's not funny.'

'Isn't it?' Jared took a deep breath. 'No, perhaps not. Okay, so—how have you been?'

'Fine.' She was abrupt. 'And you?'

Jared's lips twisted. 'Bloody awful, if you must know.'

She stiffened. 'I don't want to hear this, Jared.'

'Don't you?' Once again he filled his lungs with air in an effort to calm his nerves. 'Sorry.'

'Jared—'

'Okay, okay.'

The bartender appeared at that moment, carrying the coffee his wife had prepared for them, and while he set the tray on the table and commented about the weather, Isobel remained silent. But as soon as the man had gone again she continued her attack.

'I don't know why you're doing this, Jared,' she protested. 'Just because Elizabeth is away, and you feel free to—'

Jared swore then. 'Is that what you think?' he demanded, interrupting her. 'Is that why you think I'm here? Because Elizabeth and her father are away?'

'Well, isn't it?'

'No, dammit, it's not.' He was indignant.

'If you say so.' But she obviously didn't believe him. Had he really treated her so badly that she hated him now?

'Do you want to hear what I have to say or not?' he asked huskily, and was heartened somewhat by the fact that when she poured herself a cup of coffee, her hand shook.

'Why not?' she said at last, and he expelled the breath he had hardly been aware he'd been holding.

'Okay...' He hesitated. 'I need to know, are you still seeing Luke Herrington?'

'Luke—?' Her eyes went wide, and she set her cup down with a distinct clatter, spilling some of the liquid into her saucer. 'Is that why you've brought me here? To ask about my relationship with Luke Herrington? I don't see what that has to do with you.'

Jared scowled. 'It's a start.'

'Not as far as I'm concerned. It's none of your damn business.' She pushed back her chair. 'And now, if you—'

'Wait!' His hand was gripping her wrist before he could prevent himself. 'Belle, please, wait. I have to know. Can't you understand that?'

'Why?'

Jared groaned. 'Because I'm leaving Elizabeth.'

A whole gamut of emotions crossed her face at that moment, but at least she was no longer trying to leave her seat. Shock; incredulity; arrant disbelief; they were all there. And the faintest glimmer of something else he dared not let himself identify in case he was wrong. 'I don't believe you.'

Jared's thumb massaged the inner curve of her wrist. 'But you want to, don't you?'

'What kind of a question is that?' Isobel pulled her wrist out of his grasp, rubbing at the place where his thumb had been as if trying to erase any trace of his touch. 'You said you'd never leave Elizabeth. How do I know you're not just saying this now because nothing else has worked?'

Jared chose his words carefully. 'I admit, I've never attempted to gain my freedom,' he agreed. 'But that was for reasons I'd rather not go into right now. And, until I met you, I didn't care one way or the other. You have to believe me. I wouldn't lie about something like this.'

Isobel was wary. 'And what's changed your mind?'

'You have.' He gave a rueful smile. 'Is that so hard to believe? You've been driving me crazy for months.'

Isobel shook her head. 'So—have you told her?'

'Not yet—'

'I thought not.' She was visibly withdrawing from him again. 'This is just a new ploy, isn't it, Jared? You've realised that telling me how much you need me isn't going to work, so you've decided to pretend that you're going to leave Elizabeth—'

'It's not pretence,' he said harshly.

'No?'

'No.'

'So do it,' said Isobel tightly, and he could see she was trembling a little now. 'If you mean what you say, do it.'

Jared pressed a balled fist against his thigh. 'I intend to.' He stared at her with impassioned eyes. 'Will—will you come back?'

Isobel's brows drew together. 'Back?' she echoed. 'Back where?'

'Back to me, for God's sake,' he snapped grimly. 'I need to know that you still feel the same.'

Isobel expelled an unsteady breath. 'We'll see.'

'See what?' He was getting frustrated. 'See whether this man Herrington can offer you more?'

It was unforgivable, and as soon as the words were out of his mouth he knew it. But he couldn't take them back, and he watched in dismay as Isobel thrust back her chair and got to her feet.

'No,' she said with revulsion. 'No, I didn't mean that.' Her hand clutched the collar of her coat. 'And as you obviously have such a distorted opinion of me, is there any point in continuing with this charade?'

CHAPTER THIRTEEN

THERE was a car parked at Isobel's gate when she arrived home from work on Friday evening, and for a moment her heart leapt into her throat. It was a sleek grey Mercedes, and, in spite of what she'd said last Saturday, the idea that Jared had come to tell her he'd left Elizabeth sprang irresistibly into her mind.

It wasn't Jared's car. The number plate was different, she saw, as she drew closer, and unless he'd changed his car in the last few days it belonged to someone else. But who?

Despite what her common sense was telling her, she found she was trembling. Parking behind it, she couldn't dislodge Jared from her thoughts, and even the slimmest chance of seeing him again turned her bones to water.

She was a fool, she thought impatiently. Jared thought he only had to crook his little finger and she'd come running. She didn't know how he'd found out she was staying with Michelle last weekend, but after what he'd said about Luke Herrington she couldn't believe his visit had been coincidental. He'd intended to see her, to spin her his latest scheme to get her back. He'd realised that nothing less than offering to leave Elizabeth was going to produce the desired effect, but she couldn't believe he'd leave his wife—and Goldman-Lewis—just for her.

Even so, she hadn't been able to help hoping against hope that he'd meant it. On the drive back to Fenham, he'd told her he was going to speak to Elizabeth as soon as she got home. She and her father were due back on Thursday afternoon, and Jared had promised to ring Isobel on Thursday evening.

Perhaps he'd thought his words would seduce her into spending the rest of the weekend with him, she reflected now, not wanting to remember how she'd spent the whole of the previous evening waiting for his call. He hadn't rung, of course, and she'd assured herself that she'd never really expected him to, but it hadn't worked any more successfully than the dismissive account of their meeting that she'd given Michelle. Her friend had known exactly how counterfeit her attitude was, and in spite of her efforts it had soured the rest of the weekend.

That was why she'd gone to see Marion on Sunday morning. She'd dreaded telling her sister about the baby, but in the event Marion had taken it in her stride. Perhaps she wouldn't have been so understanding if Isobel had still been living in the city. But she wasn't, so she could afford to be generous.

Of course, Isobel had mentioned nothing about seeing Jared. And she was glad she hadn't now that he'd proved himself so predictably false. Besides, Marion would have had her own opinion of a man who'd promised to divorce his invalid wife because of her sister. And that might have been one mistake she couldn't forgive.

Now, however, a woman was getting out of the Mercedes. She had evidently been waiting for Isobel to get home, and she turned to give the younger woman an imperious smile.

'Mrs Dorland?' she asked, as Isobel thrust open her door and got out, and Isobel's pulse quickened. She suspected she knew who the woman was now: it was her aunt Justine.

Swallowing to hide her agitation, she went towards her. 'I'm—Isobel Dorland, yes,' she said quickly, without being any more specific.

'How do you do?' The woman was polite, but she didn't offer her hand. 'I'm Mrs Dorland, too, although I doubt if you appreciate the distinction. Can we go inside?'

Isobel was taken aback by her hostility, although she supposed she shouldn't have been. After all, Robert Dorland had taken great pains to keep her existence a secret, and she'd already decided that after the baby was born she was going to make her home somewhere else. It had been a mistake coming here, another mistake, and she'd never felt it so strongly as she did at this moment.

'Why not?' she said now, briskly, and, opening the gate, she allowed her visitor to lead the way up the path.

Justine Dorland—if that was who she was—looked much younger than Isobel's mother had done. For one thing the coil of blonde hair she wore at her nape showed no trace of grey, and the suit she was wearing revealed a trim figure. High-heeled pumps completed a picture of fashionable elegance that was only enhanced by her rather sharp features. Yet as she waited for Isobel to unlock the door there was a certain agitation in her face that was at odds with her controlled appearance.

Thankfully, the fire was still smouldering in the grate, giving the room a welcoming warmth, and Isobel bustled around, adding a couple of logs to the coals and turning on lamps. Then, when she was sure the place looked as attractive as she could make it, she turned to her visitor. 'Won't you sit down?'

The older woman hesitated and then, closing the door on the twilit afternoon, she folded her gloved hands together. 'I'd rather stand,' she declared, unconsciously tilting her head. 'This isn't a social call.'

Isobel thought about keeping her coat on to hide her thickening waistline, and then changed her mind. Dammit, she had nothing to hide from this woman, she thought crossly, only trembling a little as she slipped the jacket from her shoulders and laid it over the back of a chair.

'As you like,' she said now, keeping her hands at her sides with an effort. 'What do you want?'

'What do I want?' The woman's voice was almost shrill. 'As if you didn't know.'

Isobel quivered. 'I—don't see that my being here has anything to do with you. Not now.'

'Don't you? Don't you?' The older woman was incensed. 'I don't know how you had the nerve to come here. Setting yourself up on my doorstep as if—as if I owed you something; as if I'd care about you and your—your bastard!'

Isobel swayed a little, and grasped the back of the chair where she'd lain her coat for support. In all the thoughts she'd had since she'd found her father's letters, she'd never imagined a scene like this, and, although she could appreciate the resentment Justine felt towards her, she couldn't understand her antagonism towards her unborn child.

'If that's the way you feel, I don't know what you're doing here,' she said now, through tight lips. 'I—I haven't asked you—either of you—for anything. And nor do I intend to. As—as soon as my baby's born, I'm moving away.'

Justine looked taken aback. 'Then why did you come here?'

'I don't honestly know,' admitted Isobel wearily. 'I—needed to get away. I'd—found some letters which my father had written to my mother, and I thought—stupidly, I realise that now—that he might want to meet me.'

Justine was looking more and more confused. 'What does that have to do with your coming here? I don't care what kind of a relationship your parents had. But I have to say it sounds as if your mother's situation was not so much different from your own. Evidently you've had as little communication with your father as your child's going to have with his.'

Isobel blinked incredulously. 'You know nothing about my baby's father,' she retorted hotly.

'Oh, I think I know more than you,' replied the older woman coldly, and Isobel's lips parted.

'You—know—Jared?' she whispered, wondering if she'd made a terrible mistake. Could the woman possibly be some relation of Elizabeth's?

'Who's Jared?' the woman was asking now, and Isobel experienced a momentary pang of relief.

'Who's Jared?' she echoed. 'I thought you said you knew him.'

'I don't know anyone called Jared, and if this is some clever attempt to divert—'

'Jared's my baby's father,' broke in Isobel fiercely. 'And I don't know what the hell you're talking about.'

Now Justine—if it was Justine, and Isobel was having serious doubts—stared at her with wary eyes. 'Is that what he told you?' she whispered. 'Was that the name he used?'

Isobel couldn't take much more of this and, sinking down onto the arm of the nearby chair, she shook her head. 'That is his name,' she insisted. 'I know it's his name. I've known him and—and—well, I know his family.'

'His family?'

Justine seemed appalled, and Isobel wanted to scream with frustration. 'Yes,' she said. 'Yes. And I don't honestly know what it has to do with you.'

'I'm his wife,' cried the older woman harshly. 'And his name's not Jared. It's Robert; Robert Dorland!'

Isobel was glad she was sitting down. 'You're crazy,' she said. 'That's *my* father's name.'

'Your father!' Justine stumbled to a chair. 'You're lying!'

Isobel spread her hands. 'I'm sorry. I know it must come as quite a shock to you. I never intended to tell you like this, but you didn't give me much choice.'

Justine fumbled a tissue out of her pocket and pressed it to her lips. If anything, she looked paler than the younger woman felt at that moment, and Isobel knew a reluctant sense of sympathy for her. It must have been quite a shock to learn that her husband had a daughter older than their own children.

'Would you like some tea?' she asked, getting to her feet again, but Justine only shook her head, staring at her across the folds of the tissue as if she couldn't believe her eyes.

'Who are you?' she asked at last. 'Your name's not really Dorland, is it?'

Isobel caught her lower lip between her teeth. 'It is, actually,' she replied after a moment. 'Isobel Dorland, as I said before.'

Justine's hands dropped into her lap. 'You're *George's* daughter?' she asked faintly.

'No.' Isobel decided there was no point in lying about it now. 'I'm Robert's daughter. George and his wife adopted me twenty-six years ago.'

Justine was patently amazed. 'I had no idea.'

'Nor did I.' Isobel couldn't keep the bitterness out of her voice. 'Not until my mother—my adoptive mother—died and I found the letters he'd written to her and my father twenty-six years ago. Apparently he and—and my biological mother—met—only briefly. When she was killed soon after I was born, he arranged for the adoption.'

'My God!'

Justine was horrified, and, realising she had to say something in her father's defence, Isobel went on. 'He—he told my parents that he hadn't known anything about me until my mother died. He also said that as you couldn't have children yourself, it wouldn't be fair to—to—tell you—'

'That's—incredible!'

'I know. I—I met your daughter the other day.' Isobel grimaced. 'But of course you know that, don't you, Mrs Dorland? That's why you're here.'

Justine seemed to be trying to make some sense of what

she'd heard. Shaking her head, she said, 'I have to admit that when Barbara told me you were—well—' She broke off, clearly embarrassed now. 'I thought—oh, God, you don't want to know what I thought.'

'I do.' Isobel resumed her seat again. 'Please: I've told you a little of why I'm here. Won't you at least tell me why you came? Did—did my father send you?'

'Your father?' Justine pressed her fingers to her lips. 'Oh, dear Lord, I don't know how to tell you this, but—' She made a distressed sound. 'Robert's dead, I'm afraid. He—he died—over five months ago.'

'Five months!' Isobel caught her breath. It was almost the same length of time that she'd been pregnant. Her lips twisted. 'So I'm too late.'

'I'm afraid so.' Justine's expression was sympathetic. 'I suppose I should say I'm sorry.'

Isobel shook her head. 'It's not as if I ever knew him…'

'Nevertheless…' Justine hesitated. 'Oh, God, I came here to—well, to be frank, to get rid of you. And now I find that you have more right to expect my sympathy than any of them.'

Isobel frowned. 'Any of whom?'

'Robert's women,' said Justine flatly. 'I hate to tell you this, my dear, but your mother was not my husband's only indiscretion.'

'And you thought that I—?'

'You must forgive me.' Justine was contrite. 'I've become so bitter in recent years. I had thought that as he got older… But, no. In that particular, at least, Robert never changed.'

Isobel could only stare at her. 'You *knew* he saw other women?'

Justine nodded.

'But—' Isobel was stunned. 'Why didn't you—?'

'Leave him?' Justine shrugged now. 'I loved him. And so long as he always came back to me…'

Isobel swallowed. 'Were there any other—any other children?'

'Not that I know of.' Justine gazed into space. 'There have been other claims over the years, of course. That's why I was so incensed to think that you—' She broke off, raising an apologetic hand. 'You see, the Dorlands used to be a wealthy family, and there were always women willing to allege that Robert had seduced them, and that the child they were carrying—' She broke off again, evidently overcome with emotion. Then, after regaining her composure, she continued unsteadily, 'Robert always denied their claims, and I suppose I always wanted to believe he wouldn't lie to me. His womanising—I could stand that. But I always insisted that if I ever found out he'd given some other woman the child I couldn't have…'

'But you have children,' protested Isobel, aware that she was feeling sorry for this woman. The more she learned about the man who had been her father, the less regret she felt at never having known him. But Justine…

'Our children are adopted,' confessed Justine after a moment, and Isobel knew a brief spurt of shame at the relief she felt at learning that at least some of what he'd told her parents was true. 'Barbara and Will are twins we adopted when they were six months old.' She paused, and then added with great dignity, 'I was born without a uterus. I was never able to give Robert the children which I think he so badly wanted.'

Isobel sat for some time after Justine had gone, mulling over the things the other woman had told her. Now that the need to maintain her composure was no longer necessary, she couldn't prevent the tears from streaming down her cheeks, though whether she was crying for her father or herself, she wasn't absolutely sure.

Oddly enough, there was a certain sense of relief in knowing that the decision about whether to contact her father or not had been taken out of her hands. She was sorry he was dead, even though he had played such a superficial role in her life, but the misgivings she'd had since coming here now all seemed justified and she desperately wanted to get away.

For her part, Justine had been amazingly understanding. Bearing in mind the fact that she'd been so opposed to her husband siring a child in his lifetime, she'd shown Isobel great respect. It was as if she'd recognised something of her husband in his daughter and, now that Robert was gone, she was prepared to sustain his memory in any way she could. Whether her own son and daughter would share their mother's feelings was another matter, and Isobel was not sufficiently sure of her own identity to want to find out.

Justine had explained so many things. Not least the reason why George Dorland had abandoned the family home. Apparently his father had been a womaniser, too, like his second son, and George had been disgusted when, only six weeks after their mother had died, John Dorland had brought one of the village women to live at Tregarth Hall.

In those days, the Dorlands had been the wealthiest landowners in the district, but times had changed. Farms had had to be sold to sustain an increasingly obsolete way of life, and by the time of John Dorland's death the estate had shrunk alarmingly. These days, Will ran things himself, and had done so since before his father's death, while Barbara had been in the United States for the past three months, learning advanced farming methods at a college in the mid-west.

Justine had also speculated about how Robert had found it so easy to deceive her.

She'd explained that after the rift that George's departure had created between the brothers they had never been friends, and it must have been a simple matter after their father died to allow whatever connection there had been to lapse completely. Until Justine had had reason to doubt her husband's word, she'd been more than willing to accept Robert's version of events, and by the time she'd suspected that George might have had some justification for his behaviour, it had been far too late to attempt to heal the breach.

Isobel had to accept that she'd never know what, if anything, her father had felt towards her mother. From what she'd learned, it would seem that Robert hadn't been capable of sustaining a relationship with any woman, even his wife, and she reflected that she'd been lucky to have been brought up by people who'd really cared about her.

She was glad now that she'd known none of this until after her adopted parents were dead. George Dorland had been right to keep it from her, for there was no doubt it would have hurt him terribly if she'd insisted on meeting her real father. Hurt her, too, she acknowledged, aware that Justine Dorland would not have been half as sympathetic if her husband had still been alive. And the man Isobel had sought had never existed—except in her imagination. He'd handed her over to his old housekeeper—Justine had told her that a Mrs Mattless, 'Matty', had worked at the Hall years ago—and that was the last he'd seen of her.

During the next couple of days, Isobel came to terms with the fact that until the baby was born she would have to stay where she was. She had nowhere else to go, after all, and, much as she wanted to escape, she had responsibilities both to herself and to her unborn child.

Justine rang once, suggesting that she might like to visit Tregarth Hall, but Isobel didn't feel as if she wanted to get involved with her father's family. It wasn't as if Justine's children were her brother and sister, and, much as she appreciated the effort Justine was making, she didn't think she and the other woman could ever be friends.

CHAPTER FOURTEEN

JARED stood at the window, staring out at the lights that were slowly appearing in the wing opposite. It wasn't yet five o'clock, but the afternoon had been dull and overcast, and the twinkling lights gave a superficial warmth to the stark bulk of the hospital buildings.

Within the private ward where he was standing there was warmth, too, but precious little comfort. The man in the iron-railed bed was still alive, but only just, his vital organs monitored by the bank of machines to which he was attached by a clutch of tubes and cables.

However, at this moment, Jared's thoughts were not on the unconscious man behind him. He was thinking about Isobel; about the effect Howard's illness would have on their relationship—if they still had a relationship, he reflected grimly—and how difficult it was going to be for him to ask Elizabeth for a divorce now.

God, was it only a little over a week since he'd seen Isobel? It seemed like a lifetime, the events that had come between then and now responsible for his present state of despair.

He'd promised to ring her Thursday night, to tell her that he'd spoken to Elizabeth, and that, no matter what obstacles she and her father might put in his path, he had taken the first steps towards gaining his freedom.

But he hadn't rung. How could he have? On Thursday night he'd been at the hospital all night, keeping vigil with Elizabeth while her father had had the first of the two operations he'd had since he'd been flown home from Greece.

Jared groaned, and raked long fingers through his hair,

allowing his hands to rest frustratedly at the back of his neck. When the phone had rung on Wednesday evening, he'd practically flung himself across the room to answer it. He'd had some crazy notion that it might be Isobel, that, knowing Elizabeth was still away, she'd taken the chance of calling him at home.

Why she would do such a thing when she'd made it plain that she was only prepared to judge him by his deeds, not his words, he didn't know. But hope sprang eternal, and it had only been when he'd heard his wife's hysterical voice that he'd been forced to abandon such foolishness.

The line had been bad. She had apparently been calling from the ship, and the reception had been distorted and intermittent. But the panic she had communicated to him had been unmistakable. Her father had had a heart attack, she'd said. He'd collapsed after dinner that evening, and he needed immediate treatment.

Jared's reactions had been automatic. After ascertaining that the cruise ship was returning to Mandraki, one of the smaller Greek islands and its nearest port-of-call, Jared had said he would make arrangements for an air ambulance to fly out and rendezvous with the ship there. Howard could be flown back to England at once, and Elizabeth should be ready to accompany him home.

Since then, none of them had had the opportunity for a prolonged conversation. Howard's condition had been critical, and Jared had wondered if the old man would make it. He'd also wondered what had happened to cause the attack, and he couldn't help the unwilling thought that perhaps Elizabeth had at last come clean about what she'd done.

Whatever, in recent days he'd been too concerned about the old man's health to tackle her about it. Besides, Elizabeth had seemed uncharacteristically vulnerable since her return. Even Janet, who had flown home separately with all the luggage, had been doing her best not to get in anyone's way.

It had obviously been a traumatic experience for both women, and Jared could sympathise with their feelings. It must have been frightening to find the old man in that state on a ship with only minimal medical facilities. Particularly as Elizabeth had always relied on her father so much.

So the promise Jared had made to Isobel had had to be put on hold. He intended to ring her, as soon as he had some positive news to give her, but with each day that passed, he grew more and more fearful that she might never want to speak to him again.

Jared heaved a weary sigh, half turning to look back at the man in the bed. Howard was peaceful now, but until the blocked valve that had caused his collapse had been cleared, it had been touch and go. When he'd first arrived at the hospital in Newcastle, he'd been too weak to stand major surgery, and the specialist who had taken charge of his case had explained that for the present they were only able to perform a stabilising operation.

Now, however, with the blockage removed, the prognosis was far more optimistic, and to Jared's amazement there was already talk of getting Howard out of bed and moving around again. It had apparently been proved that heart patients responded well to gentle stimulation, and Jared was looking forward to seeing the old man sitting up and taking notice.

A sound alerted him to the fact that there was some movement in the bed, and, leaving his position by the window, Jared went to the old man's side. Howard was stirring, and although Jared knew he should call the nurse on duty, he took a moment to reassure himself that he was not mistaken.

Howard looked so old, he thought, the hand lying limply on the coverlet so pale and ridged with veins. He'd aged enormously in the last few days, and Jared wished there was something he could do to ease his pain.

'Am I going to live?'

The whispered question caught Jared unawares, and, catching a breath, he dropped to a crouch beside the bed. 'What kind of a question is that?' he demanded, his voice gruff with emotion. 'Of course you are.' He covered the old man's hand with his own for a moment and then straightened. 'I'll get the nurse—'

'No—wait.' Howard's voice was weak, but determined. 'Not yet, Jared.'

Jared frowned, but, not wanting to upset him, he stayed where he was. 'How do you feel?'

'Sore,' admitted Howard ruefully. He frowned. 'Where am I?'

'Don't you remember?' Jared pulled a chair across to the bed and straddled it. 'You collapsed on board the cruise ship and—'

'I know that.' Howard was impatient and Jared remembered that the doctor who'd flown out with the air ambulance had told him that the old man had been drifting in and out of consciousness on the flight home. 'I meant—what hospital is this?'

'The County,' said Jared at once. 'They flew you into Newcastle airport.'

'Ah.' Howard seemed relieved. 'And you meant it? I am going to make it? That's the truth?'

Jared's smile was ironic. 'So they say. You just gave us all one hell of a scare, that's all.'

Howard's expression darkened. 'Liza most of all, I'll bet,' he muttered grimly. 'Dammit, Jared, why didn't you tell me?'

'Tell you?' Jared was confused. 'Tell you what?'

'About her and—and that woman, of course,' exclaimed Howard harshly. 'If I'd had some warning, it wouldn't have been such a—such a God-awful shock when I walked in there and found them together.'

'Wait a minute.' Jared was missing something here, and although he suspected that the last thing he should be doing at this moment was encouraging Howard to expend what little strength he had, he had to know what he meant. 'I don't know what the hell you're talking about.'

'It's no use, Jared.' Howard's blue eyes were wet with tears. 'You don't need to try and protect me any more. This is why you and Liza never had any children, isn't it? Why you took up with that Dorland woman whose car ran into yours all those months ago?'

Jared stared at him. 'You knew about that?'

'Not initially.' Howard expelled a weary breath. 'But when it became obvious that you and Elizabeth weren't trying to patch up your differences, I made a few enquiries of my own.'

'But it wasn't like that,' said Jared, feeling the need to set the record straight at last, but Howard wasn't really listening to him. He was too wrapped up with what he was trying to say.

'I should have realised what was going on sooner.' Howard groaned. 'I knew you weren't the kind of man to cheat on his wife without a reason. You've always been a decent man. Dammit, you even took the blame for the accident when you could have turned me down.'

'Howard—'

'No, hear me out.' The old man seemed determined to bare his soul, and there was no stopping him. 'I want you to know what a pathetic fool I've been.' He panted a little, but his determination was resolute. 'No wonder you found it so difficult to tell me the truth.'

'What truth?' asked Jared helplessly, but Howard just went on.

'I—I went to her cabin to talk to her,' he continued doggedly. 'She'd seemed so relaxed while we were away, and I thought it was the ideal opportunity to discuss what Beaumont had said.'

His breath caught then, and for a moment Jared was afraid he'd gone too far. But then, after drawing a laboured gulp of air, he added, 'They were there, both of them; Liza and that—that awful Brady woman—in bed—together—'

'Mr Kendall!'

The nurse's disapproving tones prevented any response Jared might have made, even if he could have found the words. Somehow he managed to push himself away from the chair and get to his feet. But his brain felt numb, and there was no co-ordination in his movements.

'I asked you to inform me immediately if the patient regained consciousness, Mr Kendall,' the nurse declared sharply. 'Mr Goldman is still a very sick man, and you had no right to engage him in conversation.'

Jared shook his head. 'I'm sorry,' he muttered, too dazed by what he'd learned to marshal a competent defence.

Ignoring the woman's censure, Howard spoke again. 'Blame me,' he wheezed, reaching for his son-in-law's hand and giving it a weak squeeze. 'We'll talk later. Right?'

Jared nodded, and although he was sure the nurse was regarding him a little strangely now, somehow he got himself out of the room.

But, in the corridor, he stood for several minutes, trying to come to terms with what Howard had told him. Was it true? Were Elizabeth and Janet Brady lovers? God, the idea was unbelievable, and yet it explained so much. Made sense of so many things. Not least Elizabeth's reasons for marrying him…

He found his way almost automatically to the visitors' lounge, where he'd spent so many hours in recent days, and was brought up short at the sight of his wife and Janet Brady sharing a tray of tea that one of the orderlies must have provided for them. Apart from the two women, the lounge was deserted, and he paused in the doorway, both hands braced on the lintel, waiting for them to notice him.

They were huddled over the table, he saw, and Jared felt an almost overwhelming sense of outrage at what their intimacy had achieved. How could he have failed to recognise what must have been going on for so long? he wondered bitterly. How long had Elizabeth intended to keep her sexuality a secret? Until her father was dead?

Well, she'd almost succeeded...

As if sensing the hostility he was projecting, his wife looked up at that moment and saw him. Immediately, she withdrew the hand that Janet had been holding, and, swinging her wheelchair round, came towards him with anxious eyes.

'What is it? What's wrong?' she exclaimed. 'Is it Daddy? Has he had a relapse?'

Jared lifted an indifferent shoulder. 'Do you really care?' he asked coldly.

'Of course I care.' Elizabeth searched his face with a troubled gaze. 'He's my father.'

'So he is.' Jared managed to contain his anger with an effort. 'Thank you for reminding me.'

Elizabeth gasped. 'Why are you being like this, Jared? You know I've been worried out of my mind. If Daddy is worse, for God's sake, tell me. I've just been reassuring Janet that the operation was a success.'

Jared's lips curled. 'And I'm sure Janet was pleased to hear that.'

'She was.' Elizabeth cast a nervous glance back at the other woman. 'She's very fond of Daddy, as you know.'

'Do I?' Jared's arms fell to his sides and, as if fearing he was about to touch her, Elizabeth drew back. But her husband only gave a sardonic smile at this evidence of her alarm. 'I don't know anything, do I? Don't they say it's always the husband who's the last to hear?'

'I think that's the wife,' said Elizabeth curtly, and then, as if realising what he'd said, her eyes went wide. 'I—' She swallowed hard. 'Is Daddy awake?'

'Only just,' replied Jared. And then, because he couldn't stand her pathetic attempt to normalise the situation, 'You could have killed him! Do you realise that?'

Elizabeth's lips quivered. 'He's told you, hasn't he?'

'Did you think he wouldn't?'

'I—I hoped—'

'Oh, yes?' Jared's hands balled into fists. 'I just bet you did.'

'No, you don't understand.' Elizabeth glanced over her shoulder again. 'I—hoped I'd have a chance to tell you myself.'

Jared's disbelief was obvious. 'So why didn't you?'

'Oh, God, I don't know.' Elizabeth groaned now. 'There—there just hasn't been time—'

'In four years!' Jared was contemptuous. 'Forgive me, but I don't believe you.'

'Well—what with the accident and everything—'

Jared's lips tightened. 'You had to bring that up, didn't you?'

'Well, why not?' Elizabeth sensed a weakness and went straight for it. 'I could say I didn't have any kind of a life until the accident, but I won't give you that satisfaction. All the same, I'm not sorry it happened. Do you hear me? If I hadn't crashed the car, Janet and I might never have met.'

Jared blinked. Had Elizabeth said what he thought she'd said? That *she'd* crashed the car?

But before he could find his voice to challenge her words, she went on, 'In any case, we can't talk about it now. I want to see Daddy—'

'Wait!' Jared deliberately blocked the doorway, determined to find a way to get her to repeat herself. 'Are you saying you—you were unhappy before the crash?'

Elizabeth gave him a scornful look. 'What do you think? Don't pretend you didn't know how I was feeling. You were going to leave me; I know you were.' She lowered her voice. 'After—after the abortion, you could hardly bear to look at me.'

Jared's voice was harsh. 'Do you blame me?'

'No.' For once, Elizabeth was being honest. 'But you couldn't expect me to be glad about it. Daddy would never have forgiven me if he'd found out. That was why—'

She broke off abruptly, but Jared couldn't let her stop there. He had a horrible inkling that he knew what was coming next, but he had to hear it from her lips. 'What?' he demanded, taking an involuntary step towards her. 'What?'

'Why I wished I'd killed us both, of course,' muttered Elizabeth in a tortured voice. She pressed the heels of her hands to her eyes. 'Now—now can I go and see Daddy?'

CHAPTER FIFTEEN

ISOBEL stood at the door, waving, until Michelle's car was out of sight. Then, quelling the urge to burst into tears, she turned and went back into the cottage.

The coffee cups they'd used after lunch were still on the table, and, gathering them up, Isobel carried them into the kitchen. She ran water into the bowl and added a liquid cleanser, then, plunging her hands into the suds, she started to wash up.

It had been good of her friend to come, she assured herself fiercely. It was a long way for anyone to drive, particularly as it was only two weeks since Isobel had spent that awkward weekend in Newcastle. Even thinking that Michelle had got a certain amount of satisfaction out of telling her about Howard Goldman's heart attack was pathetic. Of course her friend had taken some pride in having her feelings justified. She'd warned Isobel to be wary of Jared from the start.

Nevertheless, she wasn't altogether sorry that Michelle had gone. Keeping up a brave face over the last couple of days had drained her emotional resources completely, especially since at the beginning of the weekend she'd misunderstood Michelle's reasons for telling her what she had.

She was such a fool, she thought now, feeling the hot tears stinging her eyes. She'd thought at first that the news of Howard Goldman's illness meant that Jared had a legitimate excuse for not getting in touch with her, as he'd promised. But, according to Michelle, it was ten days since Howard had been flown home from his holiday, and it was rumoured that although he was making a good recovery, he was not expected to return to the office.

Which meant, Michelle had remarked slyly, that Jared had taken over the running of Goldman-Lewis in his absence. 'It's an ill wind, as they say,' she'd observed drily, and Isobel had realised at that moment that what Michelle was really saying was that there was no chance of Jared asking Elizabeth for a divorce now.

Finishing the dishes, Isobel dried her hands on a towel and returned to the living room. But the firelit warmth of the room offered no comfort at present, and, collecting her jacket from the hall, she let herself out of the front door.

It was a cold afternoon, but it was fine, and a watery sun was doing its best to give beauty to the stark silhouettes of the trees on the green. As she walked along, she tried to put all thoughts of Jared and his promises out of her mind, but it was impossible now to ignore the truth behind Michelle's words. He could have phoned her; he *should* have phoned her—if only to tell her what had happened—but it was two weeks now, and there'd been no communication whatsoever.

She should have expected it, she thought bitterly. After all, it was a classic case of two people, each wanting different things from a relationship. He wasn't to blame; she was. She'd always known that Elizabeth had an unbreakable hold on his loyalties, and despite what Michelle had said she knew he didn't take his responsibilities lightly.

There was a copse of trees at the end of the village and, although she would have liked to have gone further, she turned back. Twilight was approaching and she wasn't reckless enough to tackle lonely country lanes on her own, especially not after dark. Besides, she had no wish to encounter anyone she knew either. She'd done rather well so far, but she knew Tregarth Hall was in that direction, too, and that was an added deterrent.

The big car coming towards her in the fading light looked suspiciously like Justine Dorland's car, however, and, hoping she wouldn't be recognised, Isobel drew back into the shadows cast by the surrounding trees. The car slowed, and Isobel thought it was just her luck to be found here. Whatever she said, Justine was bound to think she'd had some ulterior motive for spying out the land around the Hall. She'd never believe that Isobel's thoughts had been far from Polgarron, or that talking to her new-found relatives was the last thing she wanted to do.

The car stopped, and for a few moments nothing happened. Then, realising it was up to her to make a brave face of it, Isobel plastered a smile on her lips and turned towards the vehicle. She had as much right to be here as anyone else, she told herself impatiently, and then was taken aback when the passenger door was shoved open from inside, and a harsh voice said, 'Get in.'

It was Jared's voice, and Isobel's lips parted incredulously. She'd been so sure it was Justine's car and she stared at the dark blur of his face in shocked disbelief.

'I said, get in,' he repeated, his tone sharpening almost aggressively, and Isobel caught her breath as another thought occurred to her.

Despite the lateness of the afternoon, he had evidently been able to recognise her at once, and the realisation that he must have seen her quite clearly in his headlights caused her to draw the sides of her jacket closer about her. But it was too late. She knew it. The sheepskin jacket couldn't disguise the rounded curve of her belly as the cashmere coat she'd worn in Newcastle had done, and she shivered at the anticipation of his reaction.

'What—what are you doing here?' she asked then, making no attempt to do as he'd asked, and with a muffled oath he thrust open his door and got out.

'Get in and I'll tell you,' he said, making no attempt to hide the fact that he was staring at her stomach. 'I think we have a lot to talk about, don't you?'

Isobel couldn't help it: her hand went almost automatically to the mound that pushed the sides of her jacket apart, and, as if he didn't trust himself, Jared swung open his door and got back into the Mercedes.

The passenger door was still ajar, and, realising she was only putting off the inevitable, Isobel moved almost mechanically towards the car. Without saying anything else she got in beside him, and Jared didn't speak to her as he reversed into the gateway where she had been standing and turned the car around.

'How—how did you know where I was?' she asked as he drove through the village, feeling obliged to make some attempt to normalise the situation. But all he did was turn to give her a brooding look, and she fell silent again.

They reached the cottage in record time, and this time Jared didn't hesitate before getting out of the car. Isobel had barely had time to open her door before he was swinging it wide for her, waiting with taciturn stillness for her to alight. He offered his hand, but she didn't take it, preferring instead to use the frame of the door to help her to get to her feet, and his features tightened at this obvious display of pride.

'Are—are you coming in?' she asked, knowing it would annoy him, but needing to assert her independence, and Jared slammed her door behind her.

'Try and stop me,' he replied, with harsh intensity, and her knees felt decidedly shaky as she hastened up the path.

She found her key but she had some difficulty getting it into the lock, and, despite her resistance, he took it from her. He had no problem in opening the door, and she made no attempt to hide her resentment at his high-handed behaviour.

'I'm not a child, you know,' she said tightly, only hesitating a moment before taking off her jacket. She held up her head. 'Why are you looking at me like that?'

'For God's sake, Belle!' He had closed the door and was now standing staring at her with tortured eyes. 'Don't expect me to behave as if I'm not in a state of shock. Why the hell didn't you tell me?'

Isobel trembled. She couldn't help it. Seeing him again had been traumatic enough without having to face his anger as well. 'You know why,' she answered unsteadily. 'You—you're married. You'll never leave Elizabeth, I know that.' She swallowed. 'Especially now.'

Jared shook his head. 'Is that what your friend told you?' he demanded. 'I should have known she hadn't come here to sing my praises.'

'Michelle?' Isobel's brows drew together. 'You know Michelle's been here?'

'I should do,' he said harshly, stepping away from the door. 'I've been waiting for her to leave for the past twenty-four hours.'

Isobel caught her breath. 'You've been here in the village for twenty-four hours?'

'No.' Jared's lips twisted. 'I've been staying at a hotel in Polgarth, but I've driven by here a dozen times in the past two days.'

'So why didn't you—?'

'What?' He halted in front of her and she was intensely conscious of the curve of her belly swelling between them. 'Come in?' And, at her involuntary nod, 'I wanted to see you alone. I had things to say to you. After the last occasion I tried to speak to you when she was there, I preferred to wait.' His eyes dropped significantly. 'I didn't think then that a day more or less would make any difference, and I guessed she'd be going back today.'

Isobel was terribly self-conscious. It was the first time he'd seen her like this and she couldn't help thinking that he was probably remembering the slim, moderately attractive young woman he had had an affair with. She looked nothing like that now. In black leggings and the chunky cream sweater that used to be his, she was anything but attractive, and she wished she'd had some warning of this meeting.

He, on the other hand, looked much the same as ever. His lean muscled frame had always looked good in jeans and tee shirts, and his black suede jerkin accentuated his raw masculinity. She could see why she'd fallen in love with him, why she'd always love him, and she wondered if Elizabeth had any idea how lucky she was.

'May I touch?' he asked suddenly, and Isobel was instantly aware of the intimacy of the situation. His words were disturbing and unexpected, and, as if reacting to her mood, the baby chose that moment to make its presence felt.

He must have seen it, because instead of waiting for her permission his hands spread possessively over her stomach. 'I can feel it,' he said, his eyes lifting to hers in sudden amazement, and she wondered if it was only pride in his offspring's exertions that gave his expression such bone-melting warmth.

'He—she—is very active,' said Isobel awkwardly, feeling the heat of his hands penetrating the layers of clothing that separated her skin from his. She would have drawn back then, but he wouldn't let her, and in an effort to regain some sense of her own identity, she added, 'I—I was sorry to hear about Mr Goldman. It must have been a terrible shock for—for all of you.'

'Howard's going to be okay,' said Jared almost absently, his hands still shaping the curve of her abdomen. Then, with a groan of impatience, his hands moved to her hips and he pulled her against him. 'I've missed you so much,' he muttered roughly. 'I was so afraid you wouldn't want to see me again.'

Isobel swallowed. 'What makes you think I do?' she protested, trying not to respond to the provocative pressure of his thighs. 'Michelle says you've taken over the running of Goldman-Lewis. Is that true?'

Jared closed his eyes for a moment and then, cupping her face in his hands, he said roughly, 'Whatever happens at Goldman-Lewis is nothing to do with why I'm here.'

'Isn't it?' Isobel gained strength from the fact that he hadn't given her a straight answer. 'Please don't insult my intelligence by pretending that you have any intention of leaving Elizabeth now.'

Jared stared at her, and then, taking a step back, he pulled off his glasses and massaged the cleft that had formed between his brows with his thumb and forefinger 'That's some opinion you've got of me, isn't it?' he remarked bitterly. 'Do you honestly think I'd put my position at Goldman-Lewis before us?'

'I don't know, do I?' Isobel was determined not to be diverted by his apparent vulnerability. 'Have you told Elizabeth you want a divorce?'

Jared uttered a harsh laugh. 'Oh, yes. She knows.'

'She does?' Isobel was taken aback. 'But—'

'Yes, *but*,' muttered Jared, returning his glasses to his nose and raking his hands through his hair. 'When you hear what I have to say, you may still want to send me away.'

'What are you talking about?' Isobel stared at him.

Jared shook his head. 'I don't know where to begin.' Then, glancing towards the fire, he added wearily, 'Do you mind if we sit down?'

'I—of course.'

Isobel gestured automatically towards the sofa, but although he only took up half the couch, she chose to perch on the edge of the armchair opposite.

Jared noticed, but although his expression mirrored his feelings, he didn't offer any protest. Instead, he spent the next few moments staring into the fire before saying flatly, 'Elizabeth has been having an affair. With Janet Brady.'

Isobel's jaw dropped. 'With Janet Brady?'

'Yeah.' Jared's shoulders sagged. 'Ironic, isn't it? I never suspected a thing.'

'But how did you...? When did you...?' Isobel broke off, and then added helplessly, 'Does her father know?'

'He does now,' said Jared pointedly, and Isobel caught her breath.

'Are you saying it had something to do with his heart attack?' She was appalled. 'I can hardly believe it.'

'It's true.' Jared sounded exhausted. 'He told me so himself.'

Isobel shook her head. 'So how do you feel?'

'How do I feel?' Jared shrugged. 'I don't feel anything for her except indifference. My feelings all depend on you.'

'On me?' Isobel stared at him.

'On whether you're prepared to take me back,' said Jared, leaning forward, his forearms resting on his thighs. 'I had hopes when we talked a couple of weeks ago, but since then—hell, I don't take anything for granted any more.'

Isobel hesitated. 'Do you want me back?'

He scowled. 'What kind of a question is that?'

'A perfectly reasonable one, I'd have thought,' she replied carefully. 'When you came here, you didn't know about—about this.' Her hand sought her abdomen again.

Jared blew out a breath. 'And you think that might make a difference?'

'Well—' She paused. 'It may be a silly remark in the circumstances, but you and Elizabeth didn't have any children, did you? Was that her choice or yours?'

Jared hesitated. 'We did have a child,' he said at last, heavily. 'Or, at least, we were going to. Elizabeth had an abortion three years ago. I knew nothing about it until it was over. Needless to say, if I'd known...'

'Oh, Jared!'

He bent his head. 'I told you we'd been having problems before—before the accident...'

'That was what you meant?' Isobel pressed her fingers to her lips. 'But then, of course, there was the crash, and after that I suppose you felt compelled to stay with her. Oh, Jared, it must have been terrible—'

'No.' Jared broke in then. 'Well, yes, the accident was terrible, and I did stay with her. But—I wasn't driving when we had the crash.'

'But everyone said you were—'

'It was what Howard wanted,' explained Jared flatly. 'I know it sounds crazy now, but at the time it seemed like such a little thing—'

'A little thing!' Isobel was aghast. 'You took the blame for crippling your wife!'

'No one knew she was going to be permanently paralysed by the crash. Elizabeth had been drinking. I hadn't. It wasn't until it was too late to do anything about it that I found out she'd never walk again.'

Isobel didn't know what to say. 'Didn't you—didn't you resent it?' she asked at last, and he gave her a wry look.

'Often,' he agreed. 'But Elizabeth suffered much more than I did, at least in the beginning, and our relationship—hers and mine, that is—had soured me for anyone else. Until I met you.' He sighed. 'I wanted to tell you. But until recently she'd always maintained that she didn't remember that evening at all.'

'And she did?' Isobel was struggling to understand, but it wasn't easy. She had the feeling it would take longer than a few minutes to take it all in. 'So why didn't you ring?' she protested at last, desperate to regain some semblance of normality, and with a groan of anguish Jared dropped onto his knees at her feet.

'Because I wanted to see you,' he said huskily. 'Because I wanted to tell you myself what had happened.' His hands curved over her thighs as he looked at her. 'Because I didn't know how you'd react when I told you about Elizabeth. Unfortunately someone else beat me to it.'

Isobel trembled. 'Michelle means well.'

'I'll take your word for it,' said Jared drily. Then, bending to rest his cheek against her stomach, he added thickly, 'God, Belle, how long do I have to wait? Do you forgive me? Do you want me?' He moaned softly. 'Because, God forgive me, I don't think I can live without you.'

Isobel's hands came up, almost of their own accord, and lifted his face to hers. 'We—we come as a package deal,' she murmured softly, and, taking off his glasses, she leant towards him and kissed each cheek in turn. 'Are you sure you want us both?'

'I'm sure,' said Jared fiercely, leaning over her and pressing a tender kiss to the corner of her mouth. 'You're the only woman I've ever loved.'

'Me?' Her voice was husky with emotion. 'Oh, God, Jared, you have no idea how much I've wanted to hear you say that—to see you—to share this—' She drew his hands to her stomach again. 'To share our baby with you.'

'Don't bet on it.' Jared's voice was rough. 'If I'd only known. You almost had me convinced that you didn't need me any more.'

Isobel made a rueful sound. 'I've always needed you,' she admitted unsteadily. 'But I was never sure what you wanted.'

'What I wanted?' Jared eyes sought hers in arrant disbelief. 'But surely you knew how I felt about you?'

'I thought I did.'

Jared frowned. 'What does that mean?'

'That evening—at the hotel in Polgarth—you told me you didn't know what love was.'

'Oh, God!' Jared's cool fingers caressed her jaw now. 'I was jealous that evening. I'd found you with another man, and I guess I wanted to hurt you as much as you were hurting me. I lashed out. I shouldn't have, but when you told me you never wanted to see me again, I hated myself for the mess I'd made of my life.'

'Do you mean that?'

'I mean it,' he assured her huskily. His thumb found

the corner of her mouth and traced the shape of her lips with aching tenderness. 'I'm not making excuses, but until you came along there hadn't been much affection in my life. When I was a kid, I'd been slung from one children's home to another, never knowing if the next place was going to be any better than the last. Then, later, when I realised Elizabeth had only married me to get her father off her back, I began to believe that life was only about using people. Even the accident, and its aftermath, only reinforced my opinion that there was no such thing as selfless love.' He shook his head. 'Then I met you.' His eyes darkened. 'And I treated you in exactly the same way as everyone else had treated me. I didn't want to believe that there might be something more than a sexual attraction between us. That would have meant me revising my opinion of everything I believed in and it wasn't until you went away that I realised what I'd lost.'

'Oh, Jared…' There were tears trembling on Isobel's lids now, and she grasped his hands and brought them clumsily to her lips. 'I've missed you so much. If it hadn't been for—for this, I'd probably have given in and come back to you. But I kept telling myself that I'd have your baby, and that was what kept me going.'

'Belle…' Jared got to his feet and drew her up with him. He pulled her into his arms, the mound of her belly cradled between them. 'I love you, I need you; I want you; and I never want us to be apart again.'

He kissed her then, his lips slanting tenderly across her mouth, his hands moving from her hips to the small of her back. But his touch was gentle, undemanding, as if he was afraid he might hurt the baby, and it was Isobel who had to solicit a more satisfying embrace. 'Kiss me properly,' she protested, arching her body against him until she could feel the reassuring thrust of his maleness. 'Open your mouth.'

Her tongue pressed eagerly between his lips, and although she felt his momentary withdrawal, the need he'd been stifling for so long was stronger than he knew. 'Belle...' he groaned, in a final bid for sanity, but Isobel wouldn't let him go.

'I'm not made of sugar,' she breathed, circling his ear with her tongue. 'I won't melt.'

'But—'

'But, nothing.' She looked into his eyes, her own moist with emotion. 'Don't you want to make love with me?'

'Ah, God—'

That was a question he could only answer in one way, and, giving in to his own eager longings, he covered her mouth with his again.

Now it was his tongue that surged deeply into the dark cavern of her mouth, taking possession of its yielding sweetness in the way that mimicked what he wanted to do with her body. His hands cupped her bottom, lifting her against him, and, despite the pressure of her belly, his manhood was wedged against the feminine softness of her mound.

'Do you have any idea how long I've waited to do this?' he asked, his voice muffled in the soft curve of her neck. 'Sometimes I think that was all that kept me sane. The hope that at some time in the future we'd be together again.' He drew an unsteady breath. 'And now we are.'

'Not quite,' said Isobel huskily, stepping back and taking his hand. 'Let's go upstairs.'

'Upstairs?' Jared blinked. 'Um—where are my glasses?' They'd fallen earlier, and now he started looking all around for them. 'They must be here somewhere—'

'Jared!' She gazed anxiously at him. 'Does the way I look put you off?'

'Don't be crazy!' Jared's response was harsh, but he continued to look about him. 'Where the hell are they?'

'You won't need them where we're going,' she told him firmly. 'Will you?'

Jared raked back his hair with an unsteady hand. 'Are you sure—I mean, is this wise?'

Isobel sighed. 'Is what wise?'

'Us.' A faint colour stained his cheeks. 'You.' He groaned. 'You know what I mean.'

Isobel's lips tilted. 'I don't care if it's wise or not,' she told him simply. 'I can't wait.' She paused. 'Can you?'

Jared's response was to bend and scoop her up into his arms. 'Let's say, you've just persuaded me,' he murmured, inhaling her distinctive fragrance with evident satisfaction. He nodded towards the door into the hall. 'I guess it's this way…'

Isobel's bedroom had never seemed smaller than when Jared set her on her feet and stood looking about him. His tall muscled body dwarfed the modest contours of the room, his darkness throwing the white eyelet bedspread into sharp relief.

'Do you like it?' asked Isobel softly, the confidence that had filled her downstairs dissipating with the proximity of taking off her clothes in front of him. It wasn't that she hadn't done it before, but the memory of the reflection she'd seen in her mirror that morning kept her from behaving naturally.

'I like who's in it more,' responded Jared, tossing his jacket aside and loosening the belt of his jeans. Then, noticing that she wasn't following his example, he unfastened the button at his waist but didn't go any further. 'What's wrong?'

'Nothing.'

Isobel shook her head, staring greedily at the glimpse of his stomach she could see below the hem of his tee shirt. A triangle of hair-covered skin was visible where his zip had slid partway down, impelled by the powerful swell of his erection, and she ached to go to him and slip her hand inside his jeans.

'Belle!' He could see her staring at him, and his voice was rough with feeling. 'Come here.'

Isobel trembled. 'I can't.'

'Why not?'

Her hands curved over her stomach. 'I've changed, Jared—'

'I can see that.' There was humour in his voice at first, but then, seeing her distress, he sobered. 'You look—beautiful.'

'I look ugly,' she contradicted him, looking down, and with a muffled exclamation he covered the space between them.

'Is that what this is all about?' he demanded, grasping her chin and tipping her face up to his. 'Don't you want me to see you?'

She shook her head. 'I look—grotesque.'

'I don't agree.' Taking control, he peeled the cream sweater over her head, and then smiled at the full breasts that now swelled over her lacy bra. 'You're beautiful. You'll always be beautiful to me.'

He slid the leggings over her hips and then pressed her down onto the bed so that he could pull them down her legs. When she was naked except for her bra and panties, he surveyed her with intense satisfaction. 'Beautiful, as I said.'

'Oh, Jared!' Leaning forward, she put her arms around his neck, and bestowed a kiss on his neck. 'I do love you.'

'I should hope so,' he teased her gently, releasing himself briefly to step out of his trousers and pull his tee shirt over his head. Then he joined her on the bed. 'I don't intend to let you go again.'

Her underwear was soon disposed of and then, with infinite tenderness, he bent to kiss her breasts. He suckled from each swollen nipple in turn, teasing them with his tongue and tugging on the sensitive flesh. At the same time his hands shaped the burgeoning swell of her stomach, before dipping to cup the dark curls at the apex of her legs.

Isobel arched against his hand, and his fingers slipped between the petals to find her moist sex. She was more than ready for him, and he smiled as he bent to part the curls and put his lips where his fingers had been.

'Jared...' she groaned, her rapidly beating pulse only a small part of the agitation her body was feeling. 'I want you...' She took a choking breath. 'Please...'

Jared moved over her with frustrating slowness. 'Where do you want me?' he asked huskily, depositing a trail of wet kisses from her abdomen to the curve of her nape, and she fumbled to grasp his head and bring his mouth back to hers.

'I want you—inside me,' she told him unsteadily, and, reaching down, she took his throbbing fullness into her hands.

'Okay, okay...' Jared was not proof against such outright sensuality, and, parting her legs with one hairy thigh, he eased between them. 'Take it easy,' he breathed. 'I don't want to hurt you.'

'You won't,' she assured him eagerly, and, grasping his hands, she urged him to finish what he'd started.

And, despite Jared's initial reticence, their lovemaking was as uninhibited as it had ever been. The reassurance that he loved her had freed Isobel from any restraint, and after feeling the strength of her muscles closing about him Jared was incapable of any withdrawal. He was hungry for her; they were hungry for one another; and their climax when it came was as deep and soul-shattering as either of them could have wished.

It was only afterwards when he rolled away from her that his conscience smote him. Isobel looked so pale and fragile, lying beside him, and, turning onto his side, he stroked the unfamiliar mound of her stomach with a tentative hand.

'You okay?' he asked huskily, and she turned her head to look at him with adoring eyes.

'Mmm,' she breathed. 'Heavenly. You?'

Jared allowed a wry smile to twist his mouth. 'Need

you ask?' He drew his lower lip between his teeth. 'I didn't hurt you?'

'Only in the most delicious way,' declared Isobel mischievously. Her hand sought his. 'I'm so glad you're here.'

'Me, too.' He was about to bring her fingers to his lips when something moved beneath his hand. 'Hey…' His lips parted. 'He moved again?'

Isobel smiled. 'Mmm. *She* does that all the time. She's just reminding us that she's still there.'

Jared gave a small smile, but his eyes had darkened. 'And you really don't mind?'

'About the baby?'

'Being pregnant,' said Jared huskily. He grimaced. 'You'll understand I have a special reason for asking.'

Elizabeth.

Isobel gazed at him adoringly, aware that he was listening very closely for her answer. Choosing her words with care, she said softly, 'As I said before, I thought it was all I was ever going to have of you.'

He cupped her cheek. 'I don't deserve you.' He groaned. 'After the way I behaved—'

'Hey.' She covered his hand with hers. 'I was the one who initiated our relationship, remember? And if we're placing blame on anyone for me getting pregnant, then I guess that's my fault as well. I let you—well, perhaps I secretly wanted this to happen all along.'

Jared's lips curved into a sensual smile. 'I could have insisted on taking precautions every time we made love,' he reminded her gently. 'But I have to admit, I'm glad I didn't now.'

'Are you?'

'You'd better believe it.' He gave a soft laugh. 'I can't deny I would have liked having you all to myself for a bit longer, but I'm not complaining.'

EPILOGUE

ISOBEL and Jared were married three months later at the Anglican church in Newcastle where Isobel had been christened twenty-seven years before.

The wedding, which was a quiet affair, with only Isobel's sister and her family, Michelle and Phil Chambers, and a couple of Jared's friends present, took place only two days before their son, Daniel George Kendall, was born. The baby had chosen to be over a week late, which meant that Isobel had had to be married in Michelle's hastily-altered wedding dress, which caused her friend to point out that there were advantages to being overweight, after all.

But it was a beautiful wedding, and although Isobel felt like a baby elephant, Jared assured her she was the most beautiful bride he'd ever seen. And, after all, his eyes were the only ones that mattered.

But the baby's imminent arrival meant that there was no time for a honeymoon, and Jared promised to take her and the baby away in the spring, when the weather was warmer. For the present, however, they were both content in just being together, and Marion had offered no objections when Jared had broached the subject of buying her half of the house in Jesmond Dene for himself and Isobel. It seemed that the lack of luck she'd had in selling it had worked to their advantage, and Isobel was looking forward to nursing her baby under the tree where she and her mother had spent so many happy hours when she was young.

To Isobel's surprise, Howard Goldman had attended the church service, too, though he hadn't trespassed on the family celebrations afterwards. Nevertheless, she knew his attendance had meant a lot to Jared, who still had a very genuine affection for the old man. Thankfully, Howard had made a good recovery from his heart attack, and although Jared admitted that there was still some bad feeling between him and his daughter, he was of the opinion that they each needed one another too much to remain permanently estranged.

The most remarkable thing was that Jared was still working at Goldman-Lewis. During his convalescence, Howard had sent for Jared and asked him not to consider leaving the company. He needed someone he knew, someone he could rely on, in a position of authority, and, although Jared had expected it to be a temporary appointment, the old man had little bitterness towards his ex-son-in-law.

In consequence, Jared had gradually taken over the day-to-day running of the firm, and had endeared himself still further by coaxing a talented young architect from a rival firm to join them. He had also ensured the acquisition of two new contracts, including one in the City of London, and, because he and Howard understood one another so well, he was able to keep the old man informed of everything that was going on.

So much so, that a couple of weeks before Christmas Howard had announced that he was going to take his doctor's advice and delay his return to work indefinitely. He didn't say he was going to retire, but the promise was there. If Jared was willing to remain at Goldman-Lewis, he was in no hurry to return.

Jared and Michelle had made their peace with one another, too, and although Isobel knew it would take some time before her friend completely trusted him, they were getting there. The baby's arrival had gone a long way to healing all wounds, and even Howard had made an excuse to come and see Isobel while she was in the hospital. The old man seemed to want to sustain a personal relationship with Jared and his new wife, and, as their parents were dead, neither Isobel nor her husband had any objections to him adopting the role of surrogate grandfather.

The final word on Isobel's relationship with Robert Dorland came from Marion, however. A few weeks after baby Daniel was born she came to see her sister and admitted that their mother had spoken to her about Isobel's adoption just a few days before she died.

'But she was not always coherent at that time,' she excused herself unhappily. 'I couldn't be entirely sure of what she was saying, and it seemed kinder to let sleeping dogs lie.'

Isobel didn't point out the fact that she could have mentioned something when she'd shown her the letters, but her relationship with Marion meant more to her than any lingering resentment over a man who clearly hadn't wanted her.

She confessed as much to Jared that evening, when she told him about her sister's visit. She had just fed the baby and, after putting him down for a sleep, she'd settled comfortably on Jared's lap.

'So you're not sorry that you never got to meet your real father?' he asked, nuzzling the soft curve of her nape with his lips. Since she'd had the baby, Jared thought his wife had become even more beautiful, and he loved her so much that sometimes he was horrified at the risks he'd taken with their relationship in the past.

'Well, I wouldn't say that exactly,' Isobel answered thoughtfully, smiling at the seductive brush of her husband's tongue. 'But it wasn't meant to be.'

'At least you and Justine got to know one another,' Jared remarked gently. 'And she doesn't resent you any more.'

'No.' Isobel nodded, remembering the card that had been delivered a week after the birth of their child. She suspected that Marion had taken it upon herself to inform their aunt of the baby's arrival, but she'd never actually admitted it. 'She seemed quite pleased.'

'I think that's an understatement,' said Jared drily, smoothing a silky curl of hair behind her ear. 'She wants you to go and see her. Will you?'

'Maybe. Maybe later, when Daniel's older.' Isobel gave him a doubtful look. 'Does that sound selfish? It wasn't meant to be. But it's hard to see how we could ever get along.'

'I think it's your decision to make,' declared Jared softly. 'We'll do whatever you want to do.'

'Thank you.' Isobel cupped his cheek. 'But, you know what? I don't think I'll ever regard her husband as my father. As far as I'm concerned, my mother and father were dead long before I started on that journey. For me, Robert Dorland never really existed. He was just someone I briefly thought I knew.'

'He didn't know what he was missing,' murmured Jared, his hand slipping into the collar of her soft shirt. He smiled as his fingers found what they were looking for and he bent to kiss her. 'Now, do you think I could have you all to myself for a little while?'

Robyn Donald has always lived in Northland in New Zealand, initially on her father's stud dairy farm at Warkworth, then in the Bay of Islands, an area of great natural beauty, where she lives today with her husband and an ebullient and mostly Labrador dog. She resigned her teaching position when she found she enjoyed writing romances more, and now spends any time not writing in reading, gardening, travelling and writing letters to keep up with her two adult children and her friends.

THE PATERNITY AFFAIR

by

Robyn Donald

CHAPTER ONE

OH, LORD, Kate Brown prayed silently. Oh, Lord, Oh, Lord, Oh, Lord, Oh, Lord, let this be over soon. *Please.* Beside her, her son let out an ecstatic yelp as the roller-coaster carriage swayed and dived, suspending them upside down for heart-shattering moments.

She forced her eyelids to open infinitesimally. While the world catapulted hideously around them she barked, 'Put your hands back on that bar! Now!'

'Oh, *Mummy*,' Nick protested, but obeyed.

Clamping her eyes shut again as the carriage went into another stomach-dropping spin, Kate thought wildly that his hands were long and tanned with tapered fingers—just like hers. In fact he looked so much like her that people often did a double take. Only *his* knuckles weren't white on the bar, and he didn't feel sick—his wide grin told her just how much he was enjoying himself.

Certainly he hadn't got his fearlessness—or whatever had made him wheedle until he finally got her onto the Triple-Loop Corkscrew Roller-Coaster—from her. That rash courage could have come from her parents, but she had no idea who'd bequeathed him his coaxing charm.

Not his father, she thought with a shudder. Remembering Nick's father was the worst thing to do when her stomach was already stressed to its maximum.

With the effortless ease of almost seven years' practice, she switched her mind into another channel, relaxing as the carriage steadied and slid quietly to a halt. Thank heaven it was over.

But when they were once more standing on solid ground

Nick, still fizzing, urged, 'Can we go again? Mummy, can we do it again? That was awesome.'

Never a truer word. Kate stared at him. 'Do you want to kill me?'

He grinned, blue-green eyes sparkling. 'You liked it really. I bet you did. And you'll like it much better if we go again now 'cause you'll know what's going to happen.'

'Once was quite enough, and anyway, Sea World is just about ready to close,' Kate said, steering him towards the exit. 'If you want a swim before dinner we have to go now. It gets dark early here.'

He threw her a disappointed glance, but said in a lordly tone, 'Well, all right.'

Kate laughed down at him. He beamed back, and she ruffled his black hair. As she withdrew her hand some atavistic sense, long asleep, set alarm bells clanging through her system. Turning, she met eyes—frigid iron-grey eyes—that swept her in a rapid, frightening scrutiny, then moved, inevitably, to the child at her side.

'Hello, Kate.' Patric Sutherland's voice was deadly.

Panic clutched her throat, stopped her brain. Dimly she heard Nick's startled exclamation, and then strong hands gripped her, holding her upright for a moment before settling her against a big, rock-solid body.

Enveloped in warmth, in the faint, evocative scent of male, she heard Patric say coolly, 'She'll be all right soon—she's just had a shock.'

Kate wrenched herself back from the longed-for oblivion of unconsciousness. Her deflated lungs filled on a gasping breath; she tried to pull herself away, but the arms around her remained unyielding.

Very quietly Patric said, 'Lean on me, Kate.'

'Nick,' she muttered desperately, stiffening herself against the dangerous haven of those arms.

'He's all right.'

But Nick said, 'Mummy?' with a betraying quiver.

Opening her eyes and blinking, Kate looked down at

her son, tall for a boy not yet six, and a little pale beneath his golden skin, his black hair with its red highlights setting off the blue-green eyes he shared with her.

Far too aware of the man who imprisoned her, she croaked, 'I must have been out in the sun too long.'

'I told you to wear your hat,' Nick pointed out, then added anxiously, 'Are you all right now?'

'Yes, of course.' She drew in a deep breath.

'Then why does he have to hold you up?'

'He doesn't any longer, because I'm perfectly able to stand up by myself,' she said, pulling back.

Patric released her, but kept one hand beneath her elbow, the long fingers deliberate and uncompromising. His touch, his closeness, seared through her, devastating her.

I have to get out of here!

The grimness in Patric's face might have been shock at this unwanted, unexpected meeting. Unfortunately a quick glance told her otherwise. Before she had time to react to the blaze of raw fury in his eyes, heavy lashes masked them, and when they lifted his gaze was opaque and unreadable.

'You need a drink,' he said brusquely. 'Come on, I'll get you one.'

Kate knew that look. She could object, protest, refuse, but she'd still find herself sitting in the coolness of a tea room drinking something. Patric always got his own way, and the seven or so years since she'd last seen him had chiselled more harshly a face already formidable at twenty-four. Then he'd been charismatic, irradiated by the promise of power; now it blazed forth—dominating and determined, intensely magnetic.

Someone—Fate perhaps, laughing cynically—had just walked over her grave.

Kate stretched out a hand to her son. After a swift look at the man who held her arm, Nick's hot fingers clamped onto hers. She squeezed and he squeezed back, the alarm in his face fading.

'Yes,' he said, nodding. 'That's what you need—a cup of tea.'

'All right,' she replied.

The few minutes it took to reach the café were barely enough to reinforce Kate's fragile composure. Where on earth had Patric come from? Was he living in Australia now? Here on the Gold Coast?

Impossible. Owner and managing director of one of New Zealand's most active and profitable aviation companies, he still lived in Auckland. The last newspaper article she'd read about him said that he also had a house in Aspen, Colorado, and apartments in London and New York.

Literally a jet-setter.

Once in the air-conditioned tea room, he held a chair for her, waiting until she was seated before signalling a waitress with a glance. Only Patric got such instant service, summoned by a combination of his physical presence—over six foot three of him, with broad shoulders and long legs—and something just as impressive but more intangible, the tough authority that stamped his face and bearing.

He asked, 'Tea or coffee, Kate?'

'Tea, thank you.'

'And what will you have?' Patric asked Nick.

'Orange juice or water, please,' he said politely.

Patric gave the order to the waitress, smiling at her as she tucked her pencil behind her ear. Kate had basked in that potent smile all through her adolescence; she didn't blame the waitress for blushing and simpering before hurrying off as though she'd been given a royal command.

No sign of the smile softened his angular features when he turned back to Kate. Unsparing eyes measured her, examining her face without any pretence at tact, then fell to her hand, noticing the lack of any wedding ring before flicking up again. 'Hello, Kate Brown,' he said silkily. 'The years have been kind to you—you're as beautiful as ever.'

'Thank you,' she said as she strove for a casual, friendly tone. It didn't work; all she could produce were stilted monosyllables. Repressing her churning emotions, she took a shallow breath and braced herself.

'Are you living in Australia now?' Patric asked, leaning back in his chair.

She couldn't lie, not with Nick sitting there. 'No.'

Sensing that Nick was about to break into speech, she gave him *the look*—the glare known to all children that means *not another word or there will be retribution.* Recognising it, Nick subsided into silence.

'So you're still a New Zealander?' Dark, metallic eyes were examining the mahogany highlights in her hair.

Almost seven years ago, on her eighteenth birthday—three days before he'd made love to her—he'd buried his face in her hair and told her never to cut it.

Did he remember? Yes, she thought feverishly as his gaze moved to her face, he remembered. Something brittle in her shattered, melted, dissolved.

'Yes.' And to cover the bluntness of her reply she tacked on, 'Do *you* live here?'

His beautiful, hard mouth twisted subtly. 'No. I'm over on business.'

Although beads of sweat clung stickily to her temples, and she couldn't dislodge a blockage in her chest, she managed to smile. 'It must be a pleasant place to work.'

'It depends on the business.' There was a cold, charged note in the deep voice when he asked, 'Aren't you going to introduce us?'

At first Kate's throat and mouth were too dry to get the words out. She had to swallow before she could say formally, 'This is my son, Nick. Nick, this is an old friend of mine, Mr Sutherland.'

Nick held out a hand. 'Hello, Mr Sutherland,' he said with solemn courtesy.

Patric's lean, bronzed fingers engulfed the slighter, boyish ones. Gravely he returned the greeting, and without pause asked, 'How old are you, Nick?'

'Six,' Nick said, adding before Kate could stop him, 'Well, not yet, but I will be soon. On the thirty-first of October—just five more weeks and then I'll really be six.'

Although Patric's gaze stayed on Nick, Kate didn't fool herself. Beneath the superb framework of that uncompromising face his brain was making connections. An exhausting mixture of despair and humiliation flowed through her. She was going to have to tell him, and that would effectively ruin the fantasy she'd hidden so well in the privacy of her mind that she hadn't even been aware of it until she saw Patric's ruthless, disturbing face again.

Welcome to the real world. Better late than never—but oh, it had hurt no one, that wistful little fairy story.

Patric said thoughtfully, 'You're tall for your age.'

'Yes.' Her son grinned, pleased at being the focus of Patric's attention. Nick could be reserved with strangers if he didn't like them, but he was no more immune to the charm of Patric's smile than anyone else. 'I'll soon be taller than Mummy. Mummy will be twenty-five in February next year, but Mr Frost says she looks like my sister, not my mother.'

Patric's smile was a masterpiece, establishing a men-together situation that had to appeal to a child with no visible father. 'Mr Frost is right. Who is he?'

'He's my teacher.'

This was getting too close to home. Clumsily, Kate interposed, 'What business brings you to the Gold Coast, Patric?'

His name stumbled across her tongue. For nearly seven long years it hadn't passed her lips, and saying it tore apart the barrier she'd constructed with such painful determination.

'I'm checking out a firm I'm thinking of buying,' he said pleasantly. 'What are you doing here?'

'She won a prize,' Nick told Patric importantly.

The waitress arrived then, with a tray. Kate accepted her tea gratefully, and drank some down.

But Nick hadn't finished. 'She made up a poem about lemonade, and so we got seven days in Surfers' Paradise and a free ticket to all the parks like this. We came now because it's the holidays. I have to go back to school when we get home.'

'I see,' Patric said. A rapier glance pierced Kate's meagre poise. 'Clever Kate.'

Nick visibly expanded, sitting straighter, taller. He asked, 'Have you got any boys like me, Mr Sutherland?'

Patric's expression froze. 'No,' he said, and added, 'I don't have a wife, you see. Mine died three years ago.'

Laura dead? 'I'm so sorry,' Kate said inadequately.

He said, 'It was a tragedy,' and looked again at Nick. 'Are you enjoying the theme parks?'

Nick beamed. 'Oh, yes,' he said eagerly, adding with a teasing glance at his mother, 'But Mummy doesn't like to go on the rides very much.'

'And you do?'

'I love them!' he said, with such exuberance that the people at the next table glanced at him and smiled.

Kate's heart contracted. That effortless magnetism had always surrounded her son; in his pram people used to stop and comment on what a splendid child he was. He'd gone sunnily through infancy to school, hiding his formidable intelligence and fierce will with a bright, open friendliness.

Patric's eyes lingered for a moment on Kate's hair. She just managed to stop herself from putting up a nervous hand to push the black tresses into shape, and her hand shook a little as she picked up her cup again.

He said lightly to Nick, 'I'm surprised you managed to persuade your mother onto a roller-coaster. She's always been afraid of heights.'

'I just asked and asked,' Nick told him, adding, 'Did you used to know Mummy? Is that why you came here?'

'I used to know her very well. When she was fourteen

she came with her uncle and aunt and cousins to live on the big cattle and sheep station my father owned.'

'Tatamoa, in the Poto Valley?' Nick asked knowledgeably. 'She tells me stories about that place. One day we're going to go there—when I'm bigger.'

Patric didn't look at Kate. 'Yes, that's it. Her uncle managed the station.'

'Did you live there too?'

Patric shook his black head. 'No, I lived in Auckland with my parents, because my father worked there, but we always came down for the summer holidays.'

'Did you see us on the roller-coaster?' Nick asked, with the innocent self-absorption of the very young.

'Yes. I saw you from the hotel next door, and thought it would be fun to say hello.'

Which seemed perfectly sensible to Nick. Nodding, he drank his orange juice with enthusiasm. Kate kept her eyes fixed on Nick's face while her brain struggled to process this. Patric must have waited by the exit for them, she realised with a chill of foreboding.

Tension stretched to breaking point. Determined to put an end to it, she flashed a smile in Patric's direction and improvised recklessly, 'It's time we moved on. Nice to see you again, Patric. I hope your business here goes well for you. Say goodbye, Nick.'

After a mildly exasperated glance—he was rather proud of remembering his manners—Nick said politely, 'Goodbye, Mr Sutherland. Thank you for the drink.'

'Do you have a car?' Patric asked.

She knew what was coming. 'No, but we like riding on the bus, don't we, Nick?'

'I'm sure Nick will enjoy my car.' Although Patric spoke smoothly he didn't try to hide the mockery in his eyes.

Reining in the irritation that would have revealed far too much, she said, 'Oh, we can't take you out of your way. The bus will be fine.'

'The bus will be hot and full.' His smile was subtly taunting. 'Whereas the car's in the parking building just around the corner.'

It wasn't like Patric to over-persuade. He'd never had to—people always fell in with his wishes. So why was he forcing the issue when he knew damned well that she didn't want anything more to do with him?

Nick looked from one to the other, his brows creasing slightly. 'Why can't we go with Mr Sutherland, Mummy?'

Desperation forced Kate's brain into swift, fruitful action. Collectedly she said, 'Of course we can. Thank you, it's very kind of you.'

Patric's eyes glinted with unholy appreciation of her capitulation. 'Let's go, then.'

The car was parked in the hotel basement. Large and dark green, it sat in an area ringed with notices warning people that this was a private car park.

'Cool,' Nick breathed. 'It's a Rolls Royce!' One of his intense, short-lived passions had been cars. 'Is it yours, Mr Sutherland?'

Patric opened the rear door for him. 'No, a friend lent it to me.'

Nick settled in the back and began to examine the fittings. As Patric closed the door on Kate in the front, she turned anxiously. 'Don't touch anything.'

'Not even the seat?'

'Don't you be smart with me, mister.' His grin soothed some tightly wound fear. Kate grinned back. 'Nothing else, all right?'

Patric opened the driver's door and slid behind the wheel. Kate's throat tightened. Too close—even in this huge car he was too close.

'Mummy,' Nick exclaimed, 'there's a television here!'

Kate forced a laugh. 'I'm not surprised—you could just about live in a car this size,' she said, holding her hands still in her lap.

Sitting in a vehicle was infinitely more intimate than

being across a table in a crowded café. Kate's heartbeat picked up speed. She concentrated on relaxing her taut muscles, and as the big car eased out of the parking bay she managed to say steadily, 'It's glorious weather, isn't it? I believe it's still raining at home.'

'New Zealand's having its wettest spring for decades,' Patric said.

His hands rested confidently on the wheel, long-fingered, competent—hands that could be tender, or excitingly fierce against a woman's soft skin...

The car drew up at an intersection. 'Where are you staying?' Patric asked, waiting on the lights.

'Robinson's Hotel is just this side of Cavill Avenue,' she said colourlessly.

'I know it.' He manoeuvred between two other cars, one driven by a tourist if its erratic progress was anything to judge by. 'It's a pleasant place, I believe,' he observed.

Kate's fingers clenched, loosened. 'Very pleasant.'

'How long have you been here?'

Her voice dropped. She hated lying. 'Since yesterday. I hope the weather stays like this, although Nick loved the thunderstorm we had this afternoon.'

'When storms start coming across the Gold Coast you know summer's on its way,' Patric said laconically. 'I'd like to see you again, Kate. And the boy.'

She'd been expecting some such request, bracing herself for it. Above the thick roar in her ears she heard her voice—cool, composed—say, 'I don't think that would be a good idea.'

'We have a lot to talk about.'

'We have nothing to talk about.' Denying the wild thunder of her pulses, she stared straight ahead.

'You could start by explaining why you didn't tell me almost seven years ago that you were pregnant,' he said, his deep, quiet voice edged with menace as he eased the huge car between the palms on either side of the entrance to Robinson's Hotel.

When a uniformed porter emerged, Nick pushed open the door and hopped out, looking around him with interest. Watching him carefully, Kate said huskily, 'It wouldn't have made much difference, Patric. I said then that I didn't want to continue our relationship. I'm saying it again. We have nothing in common—we never did.'

In the small, taut cocoon of silence that enclosed the front of the car, Patric said levelly, 'One of the things I always found so fascinating about you was the contrast between your intelligence and that doe-eyed, vulnerable face. I'll ring you.' Ruthlessness hardened his voice. 'My son won't grow up not knowing his father.'

White-lipped, Kate returned, 'It's not that simple, I'm afraid.' She had to force herself to continue, and all pretence of composure vanished as the short, ugly syllables dragged across her tongue. 'He's not your son.'

His long, well-cut mouth thinned into a cruel line. 'Don't lie, Kate.'

She shook her head. 'It's the truth.'

Quietly, lethally, he said, 'He was born almost exactly nine months after we made love.'

I can't bear this, she thought, pushing a shaking hand through the heavy mass of silken hair that clung to her neck and temples. But it had to be endured. In a hoarse voice she said, 'Nine months and two weeks.'

'I'm sure that's within the normal range of gestation,' he said curtly. 'You were a virgin. I remember it vividly.'

Kate opened her mouth, but he continued with icy detachment, 'And don't try telling me Nick's the son of your lover at university—you hadn't even gone to Christchurch when the boy would have been conceived.' Eyes hooded and dangerous, he added coldly, 'Besides, there was no lover.'

How did he know that?

He looked past her as Nick came up to her door. In an almost soundless voice Patric said, 'Try not to work yourself up. Nothing worthwhile is ever easy, but obstacles are made to be overcome. I'll ring you tomorrow morning. Don't make any plans for the day.'

She scrambled out. 'Goodbye, Patric,' she said unevenly, and took Nick's hand, leading him away from the Rolls towards the reception area of the apartment block.

Behind them, the car door closed with a soft, opulent thunk. Kate had to strain her ears to hear the vehicle whisper away. She didn't turn, didn't look back.

'Mummy,' Nick said, wide-eyed, 'why did we come here?'

'Oh, I just thought it might be fun to eat at the restaurant one day. Let's go and have a look at it, shall we?'

After a tour of the restaurant, and a discussion about the menu cards, they walked back into the vestibule. Kate couldn't prevent a swift glance through the large glass doors but of course the Rolls was long gone, its place taken by two taxis. 'When we get back home I want something cold to drink,' she said brightly. 'How about you?'

'A milkshake?'

'Why not?' She smiled at the porter as she and Nick went out through a side door and walked steadily beneath the palms that were the Gold Coast's signature plant, beside a wall brightened by a scarlet drape of bougainvillea, through beautifully manicured gardens.

A skateboarder shot past, slowing and stopping as they passed the entrance to a complex of pools. About fifteen, he grinned at them before stooping to adjust something on his skateboard. Kate and Nick went sedately past the tennis courts, eventually leaving the grounds through a small gate that opened onto the street behind.

'Mummy, *look*! There's a bungee jump!'

'No,' Kate said automatically. 'You're too young.'

He laughed, but stared longingly while they walked past the apparatus. His adolescence, Kate thought grimly, was going to be a nightmare, unless he found some pursuit that would safely satisfy his thirst for adventure.

Perhaps she could convince him that skateboarding was

the way to go, she thought as the noise of the boarder's wheels started up behind them again.

Reaction was setting in. Fear tasted coppery in her mouth and sweat trickled down her back. Sometimes she'd imagined meeting Patric again, but in her dreams it had been vastly different from that unnerving, violently painful experience.

Of course he assumed that he was Nick's father, but that was his problem, not hers. And when he thought it over, he'd realise she had no reason to lie. Then he'd go, and she and Nick would be safe again.

'What's the matter?' Nick asked, surprising her with his perception.

Fighting back apprehension and anger and self-pity, and a relentless, corroding grief, she said easily, 'I think I might be getting a headache.'

He looked guilty. 'Was it because you went on the roller-coaster?'

Kate laughed. 'No, darling, it wasn't. It's my stomach I have to watch out for on roller-coasters, not my head.'

'I don't,' he said smugly. He turned and watched the skateboarder surge out onto the footpath, then said in his most comforting voice, 'Never mind, we can go for a swim when we get back home and then your headache will go away.' After gazing at a vivid yellow mini-moke chugging along the road, its cargo of girls waving at every passer-by, he added thoughtfully, 'I don't s'pose Mr Sutherland has to worry about his stomach when he goes on roller-coasters.'

Kate had once watched Patric walk surely and swiftly across a narrow plank suspension bridge high above a gorge, not bothering to touch the single wire that others had clung to all the way across. He hadn't been showing off; he'd been in a hurry to get to her.

Ruthlessly suppressing the image, she said, 'I don't suppose so.'

She stepped to one side to let the skateboarder past, but

he seemed content to idle along behind them. Probably eyeing the bungee jump too. What was it with some people that made them want to terrify the wits out of themselves? Adrenalin addiction?

Nick said, 'I didn't know Mr Sutherland came to Poto when you were there. You didn't tell me about him, only about Uncle Toby and Aunt Jean and your cousins all beginning with J—Juliet and Josephine and Jenny. And the horses, and the swimming pool in the creek. Why haven't I got cousins?'

It made her heart raw to talk about those days so long ago, days perpetually hazed with summer's golden light. 'Because I didn't have any brothers and sisters.'

'I've got second cousins, though. How old were you when your mummy and daddy were killed on Mount Everest and you had to go and live with Aunt Jean and Uncle Toby and the cousins?'

'Three.'

'Younger than me,' he said. They walked on in silence until he asked casually, 'Did Mr Sutherland know *my* father?'

She'd told him his father was dead. It had weighed heavily on her conscience, but she could think of no other way to protect him from inevitable disillusion. Now, looking back on the lies she'd told Patric half an hour previously, she thought with a defeated irony that she was getting quite good at them.

Still, she'd lie her soul into hell for her son.

Aloud she said, 'The Poto Valley is a small place. He might have.'

To her great relief Nick forgot about the past in the excitement of pointing out a Harley motorcycle, all black and shiny and reeking of machismo—unlike its small, blonde, bikini-clad rider, her fine-featured face incongruous beneath the helmet.

Kate didn't delude herself that Nick had said all he had to say about Patric, but apparently he was satisfied for the moment. As they turned down the road that led to their low-rise block of apartments she could feel the pressure lift, roll from her shoulders, easing stressed tendons and muscles. Now that they had escaped Patric that simmering anxiety would soon fade.

Late that night she realised that she'd been too optimistic. Restlessness and a chilly breath of foreboding drove her to put her book down, turn off the light and slide back the door onto the balcony. Leaning against the balustrade, she stared down at the courtyard, screened from it by fronds of the ever-present palms.

Although the air was warm, a heavy stillness probably indicated a towering thunderhead somewhere close by, ready to progress regally over the Gold Coast with maximum noise and drama; the property manager had told Nick that each summer they built up inland and moved down the escarpment, across the coastal plain and out to sea.

Someone had barbecued their dinner in the courtyard; the scent of sausages and steak and seafood hung on the air. Voices, punctuated by bursts of laughter, counterpointed the hum of traffic through this favoured strip of land with its long, beautiful beaches and glamorous tourist trade.

She'd been so happy when she'd won the prize, and she and Nick had had such fun planning the trip, such fun when they finally got here. What wilful, unkind fate had brought Patric to that hotel in time to see her on a roller-coaster?

And why hadn't almost seven years given her some defences against him?

Only two hours previously, when she'd showered before bed, she'd found herself staring at her brightly lit image. The mirrors at home were so small it was years since she'd seen herself full length.

Would Patric notice the changes? Her breasts were fuller—though still not voluptuous—and the flat plane of her stomach had rounded a little. Pregnancy had added slight stretchmarks on the soft gold of her skin—faded now to thin silver lines. Would he find them ugly?

No, she'd thought, furious with herself as she'd turned away, because he wasn't ever going to see them, or get the opportunity to realise anew how long her legs were. Or that the small amount of weight she'd lost had fined her down.

Now she stared blindly into the warm, seductive night, and reiterated that she couldn't afford to surrender to the weakness that drew her to him. Although she still found Patric wildly attractive, that wasn't important. His arrival in their lives threatened Nick's safety and well-being. That afternoon she'd had to run away.

What if Patric found them again?

How could he? Thousands of tourists inhabited the apartment blocks and hotels that lined the beach.

Rapidly, frowning into the night, she went over their conversation. No, he didn't know which theme parks they hadn't yet visited. Perhaps she should start thinking of an excuse not to go to any more. Nick would be angry and upset, but that would be infinitely safer than having Patric hunt them down.

Kate drew in a deep, ragged breath and realised that her fingers were clinging to the balustrade. Stepping back, she straightened her shoulders.

Should they just go home?

No, that was overreacting. Patric was here on business; he'd have neither the time nor the ability to stand outside every theme park looking for her and Nick. Her mouth tilted in a humourless smile as she imagined him split into several Patrics, each hard and confident and authoritative, waiting impatiently outside every park. All they had to do was stay away and he'd never find them.

Patric might watch the airport at Brisbane, but they only had four days to go instead of the week she'd intimated, so they should be out of Australia and home in New Zealand before he posted anyone there.

And once they were back in New Zealand he'd never find them. New Zealand phone books were filled with K. Browns, so even if he looked in the Whangarei book he wouldn't recognise her.

Anyway, why would he think of Whangarei, a small provincial city, two hours' drive north of Auckland and more than five hours away from Poto?

Her mouth trembled. It was so unfair; she'd done nothing wrong, yet she was forced to hide.

Still, it was for Nick. And for Nick she would do anything. He was all she lived for, the only thing that made her life worthwhile.

The next day Kate organised a trip to a bird sanctuary where—to Nick's stunned delight—hundreds of brilliantly coloured lorikeets, luminously blue and red and gold, swished in to feed from trays of specially prepared food held high by hopeful tourists.

Kate took photographs of her son's absorbed, fascinated face as two, then four birds rocketed down and landed on his tray, squabbling and noisy as only parrots can be, scrambling to eat the sticky preparation. Another swooped low and landed on his shoulder, complaining vociferously as it tried to get at the syrup.

Carefully, his face oddly white beneath his cap, Nick held the tray aloft in clenched hands.

Quarrelling and pushing, the birds ate greedily until some unknown alarm signal sent them whirling and wheeling upwards in a ragged, pulsating spiral that streamed across the tops of the trees and out of sight.

'Mummy!' Nick breathed. Unable for once to speak, he gazed up at her, and then his face changed and he said, 'Hello, Mr Sutherland, did you see the birds? Did you see them on me? Did you see the one on my shoulder? I could feel its claws in my skin!'

CHAPTER TWO

In the past Kate had been threatened with death, she'd endured agony and degradation and sheer horror, but she had never known such a blast of fear as she knew then. Nick's face swung dizzily; thank God he wasn't looking at her.

Forcing her shocked features into immobility, she realised she was pressing a clenched fist to her heart, trying to contain its tumult. She dragged a breath into her labouring lungs. This was no coincidence; how could she have thought she'd escaped him?

'Hello, Patric,' she said, and was dimly proud of her steady voice.

His smile had a predatory edge. 'Hello, Kate. Yes, I saw the bird,' he told Nick. 'What did its claws feel like?'

'Little and scratchy,' Nick said, 'but it held on tight.' He beamed. 'Lots of people took my photo, and so did Mummy. I can show the class at school. And we went all around this park and saw koala bears and wombats, and birds in a high, high place like a cage.'

'An aviary,' Kate said thinly.

'Would you like something to eat and drink now that the lorikeets have gone? I know a place with a pool where birds come up to the verandah.' Patric looked down at Nick with a smile that held nothing of the hidden antagonism he'd directed at Kate.

Nick said politely, 'Yes, thank you.'

By the time Kate had got herself together it was too late; they were walking across the open space towards the gate—just like a family, some soggily sentimental part of her thought wistfully. She could protest, but it would only put off the inevitable reckoning. Better to face him.

'How did you get here?' Patric asked as they walked out of the sanctuary.

'We came in a bus,' Nick said helpfully. 'We've got a car at home, though—a Mini called Eugene.'

'I'll take you back to your apartment after we've had something to eat,' Patric said, without looking at Kate, although his steely tone was directed at her.

Nick grinned at him. 'In the Rolls Royce?' he asked.

'Not this time.' Patric's dark gaze rested on the boy's face with something like hunger.

Kate flinched; so he hadn't believed her. Now she'd have to explain exactly what had happened, and although she'd recovered from the trauma the sordid experience still sickened her. Apart from the therapist who'd helped her deal with it she'd told no one, and if asked to choose the last person in the world she'd want to reveal the truth to, she'd have picked Patric.

But she couldn't let him go on thinking that Nick was his son. And after she'd convinced him, she'd have to swear him to secrecy.

Ignoring her completely, he said, 'No, not a Rolls Royce today. My friend needed it to take his dog to the vet.'

The replacement was, however, large and opulent; judging by Nick's open appreciation, it too was something special in the car line.

Silently Kate allowed herself to be put into the front seat. Since that first icy blast of antagonism Patric hadn't looked at her. How the hell had he found them? She'd thought she'd been so clever, but he'd been even cleverer.

That was Patric—always one step ahead. At eighteen, and as green as grass, Kate had been impressed by his brilliance. Oh, she wasn't stupid, and she'd done very well at school, but everyone knew that Patric had a formidable brain.

As well as wealth, six glamorous, experienced years had

separated the son and heir to the Sutherland aviation empire from the niece of his parents' farm manager. Well and truly out of her depth, the young Kate had been awed by invitations to the homestead, moonstruck by the heady excitement of being the woman Patric wanted. Yet although the summer holidays had passed in a whirl of activity amongst the friends and visitors who flocked every year to Tatamoa, she'd been alone, lost in love.

Ignoring her aunt, who'd warned Kate that no good would come of her pursuit, as she saw it, of their employer's son—even taking no notice of kind, regal Mrs Sutherland, who had told her gently but decisively that Patric was not for her—she had danced on to an inevitable reckoning, registering nothing but her feverish, reckless dreams.

How dazed she had been when Patric told her he loved her—those three words that wove a snare about her, the delusion that dazzled and enchanted her into his bed. She'd so desperately wanted it to be true that she'd let herself believe it. It had been the sum of all her hopes, and she'd thought that nothing could ever go wrong again.

How young she'd been!

She turned to check that Nick was belted in, and for a moment met Patric's eyes, so cold they froze her heart.

No sign of love there now, she thought cynically. She didn't belong in Patric's high-flying, moneyed world, but then he didn't belong in hers either.

He took them to a pleasant, cool restaurant beside a park where water splashed over rocks into a small lakelet. Beneath the dark, feathery foliage of sheoak trees sedate ibises lifted black, bare heads and begged for food, their white bodies making them look like a sinister *corps de ballet*.

'Don't give them anything,' Patric directed Nick as the waitress showed them out onto a wide screened verandah. 'They don't need it and they can become a nuisance.'

'Like the sparrows and seagulls at home.' Nick nodded,

watching the birds with interest. 'I s'pose that's why there aren't many seagulls here—the ibises take all the food. Why do you think the birds here sing in the daytime and they don't at home?'

Kate, who'd already tried to deal with this, was impressed when Patric said briskly, 'I have no idea, but you should be able to find out. Are you interested in birds?'

Nick looked puzzled. 'I just want to know,' he said.

'The story of your life,' Kate told him drily, adding without emphasis, 'Nick has a driving curiosity.'

Patric lifted his brows slightly. The powerful face was unreadable, as were his eyes. He said with questionable pleasantness, 'It shows he's got an active mind,' before switching his attention back to Nick. 'What would you like to eat?'

Nick chose a sandwich and a milkshake.

Black brows raised, Patric looked at Kate.

'Coffee, thank you,' she said. Normally she drank tea, but an extra charge of caffeine would be welcome. A faint queasiness persuaded her to add, 'And I'll have a sandwich too.'

'Club?' he asked.

Shock silenced her for long enough to cause an awkward pause. He'd remembered her juvenile addiction to club sandwiches, she thought, almost dizzy with a suspect pleasure. Or was he trying to reinforce her memory of that long-ago summer when he'd wooed her and won her? To cover her confusion she gazed at the menu. 'I haven't had a club sandwich for years,' she said composedly, 'but it sounds lovely.'

He ordered, and asked for a jug of iced water. When it arrived Nick downed half a glass with gusto and chattered on, asking questions and answering the ones addressed to him with open ingenuousness.

Kate sat stiffly, ready to intervene if Patric should want to know things she needed to keep hidden. However, he didn't step over her unspoken boundaries, and gradually she relaxed back into the chair.

She'd forgotten his intense, crackling vitality; not purely sexual, it gave life to those enigmatic, unsettling eyes, modified the control he exerted over his features and humanised the dominant, uncompromising framework of his face. Although his mouth was beautifully moulded no one would ever call him a conventionally handsome man, yet even when he'd been barely twenty people had swivelled as he'd walked into a room, drawn by his charismatic, disturbing masculinity.

Now, Kate thought wearily, he took her breath away. Time and authority had reinforced that enviable assurance, and the whole magnetic male package was buttressed by a sexual glitter all the more compelling for being so firmly leashed. Part of it was the contrast between the colouring he'd inherited from his Spanish mother—bronze skin, black hair, and eyes of cold, dark grey—and the austere bone structure and build that had been handed down through his Scottish ancestors.

Perhaps, she thought cynically, part of that attraction was the armour of money and position.

The aviation empire left to Patric by Alex Sutherland, his father, had been founded by his grandfather, 'Black' Pat, on Tatamoa station airstrip and every summer Alex, Pilar and Patric—always accompanied by Alex's widowed sister Barbara Cusack and her son Sean, and usually by other family and friends—had spent the Christmas holidays on Tatamoa, arriving with all the drama and panache of exotic migrating birds. For the month they'd been in residence the Poto Valley had buzzed, only settling down to a quieter, more mundane life once they'd departed.

Kate took a sip of water and allowed her attention to wander as Patric and Nick began to discuss snakes. It amused her that from other tables on the big verandah other women glanced covertly at Patric. Join the throng, she thought, so caught up in her recollections that Patric's question barely impinged, and by the time she registered what he'd asked it was too late.

'In Whangarei,' Nick was saying chattily. 'In Stanner Street. I go to Whau Valley School and Mum works in a dress shop in Cameron Street. She only goes until I come home from school, but sometimes she has to work late and then I stay with Mr and Mrs Schumaker next door, or my friend Rangi MacArthur just down the road. I'm in J2, and I can read the best—'

He wasn't boasting, but Kate interrupted sharply, 'That's enough, Nick.' Too late, she thought with sick dismay. Oh, why hadn't she kept her wits about her?

Because she couldn't control a stupid, unwarranted jealousy!

Nick said reasonably, 'Mummy, you know I can—'

'I know.' Switching her gaze to Patric, she said in a voice that made her son stare at her, 'Ask *me* any questions you want answered.'

'I don't know that I'd trust you to be as veracious as Nick,' he said, leaning back in his seat and surveying her with an oblique smile. 'Why did you move to Whangarei?'

The damage was done now. Stiffly Kate said, 'I needed a place to live.'

'Why didn't you stay with your aunt and uncle?'

She looked out over the lake. 'Nick, look! There's a black swan.' Waiting until he was absorbed in the sight, she went on remotely, 'You probably don't remember, but they left Tatamoa after I went back to university. It was exactly a week after the May holidays when you and I met for the last time. My cousins and I had all left home by then, so my aunt and uncle decided on a complete change of direction and went off to manage a motel in the Cook Islands.'

Nick transferred his absorbed attention from the swan to a woman who'd just been shown to a table. Tanned and slender, she flicked back long silver-gilt hair that dazzled above her white clothes. As she stared blankly out across the pool, ringed fingers tapped impatiently on the table. Gold chains festooned her tanned throat; more were looped around her thin wrists.

'You're staring,' Kate said in a low voice.

Nick's eyes switched from the woman to a family at the next table.

'Why didn't you go with them?' Patric asked.

'I didn't want to.' Shocked, humiliated, deeply disturbed and feeling like trash—incapable of behaving rationally—she'd been unable to tell them she was pregnant.

'You dropped out of university,' he said. 'Where did you go then?'

Astonished, she looked at him, meeting eyes as disinterested and purposeful as weapons. 'How do you know?'

'I got someone to check.' He smiled at her, showing his teeth. 'The same man who discovered that you'd lied in May, when you flung your new lover in my teeth.'

Kate cast a harried glance at Nick, but he was exchanging tentative smiles with a girl his own age at the next table.

'You stopped going to lectures in June, and disappeared.' Patric paused before finishing, 'When I discovered that, I rang your aunt and uncle, only to discover they were no longer at Tatamoa. I was told they'd gone to Australia. I assumed you'd gone with them—and that you didn't contact me because you didn't want to.' His eyes left her, settled on Nick's face. 'You should have come to me,' he said evenly.

'I didn't need to. I managed.' Her voice was distant as she forced memories back into the bitter past, refusing to let their bleakness stain the present. She even managed to keep her tone steady as she added, 'You had no connection with the—the situation I found myself in.'

'I'd have helped, Kate.' His voice roughened, sending a shiver the length of her spine. 'Why didn't you tell me?'

Tempted to ask what his brand-new wife would have thought if Kate had turned up pregnant, she bit the words back. That would be indicating he might have some claim to Nick. 'It had nothing to do with you,' she repeated.

He scrutinised her with dark impenetrable eyes. 'I despise liars,' he said levelly.

Kate drew in a deep breath, deliberately relaxing the tense muscles in her face and neck. 'That must make you feel immensely superior.'

A pulse flicked in his jaw. Glancing again at Nick to make sure he still wasn't paying attention, Kate added stubbornly, 'It's not important now, anyway. It was a long time ago and things have changed completely.'

Far from listening to them, Nick was staring with appalled fascination at one of the children in the nearby family party, a small, black-eyed blonde of three or so who'd begun a spectacular tantrum.

Patric said softly, 'You can never be free of the past, Kate, never. It casts a long shadow.'

Before she could react to what had sounded like a direct threat his smile banished her pain and her fear, and for a few seconds she was young, silly Kate Brown again, all eyes and hair and worshipful wonder, dazzled and overawed and lost in the depthless, dangerous seas of first love.

Fortunately the arrival of their orders gave her the chance to huddle into the tatters of her self-control.

'That waitress liked you, Mr Sutherland,' Nick observed when they were alone again. 'She kept looking at you.'

'I liked her too,' Patric said. 'Can you manage that big sandwich?'

'I'm hungry,' he said with gusto, eyeing his plate with every appearance of satisfaction. 'Her hair was red on the ends and black by her head.'

'She dyes it,' Kate told him.

'You don't dye your hair, do you?'

'Your mother's hair has always been that colour,' Patric said, his glance lingering on the thick, glossy tresses. 'She used to wear it longer, though.'

'When she was a little girl?'

'She was fourteen when her uncle came to work for my father,' Patrick said easily.

'When I'm fourteen I'll be grown up and I can look after you,' Nick told his mother.

'That's a lovely thought, but I'll probably be old enough to look after myself by then. You'd better start on that food, or we might have to go before you've finished.'

The thought of leaving it behind filled him with such horror that he settled into silently dismembering it.

'Excuse me?'

The strident voice with its upward intonation startled them all—except Patric, Kate noticed. He got to his feet as the woman with the silver-gilt hair arrived at their table, gold chains gleaming expensively. Nick stared at Patric, then scrambled to his feet too, wringing Kate's heart.

Ignoring Kate and Nick, the woman flashed a practised smile at Patric. 'You don't happen to have a light, do you? I seem to have lost mine.'

'No, I'm sorry,' he said, and turned his head towards the serving station. Immediately the waitress headed towards them. Patric waited until she'd got there, then asked her for matches.

The silver-gilt woman treated him to a lingering smile, thanked him, and went back to her table.

Nick eyed her thoughtfully as he sat down. '*She* liked you too,' he said. 'She's pretty. But not as pretty as you, Mummy—is she, Mr Sutherland?'

Patric took the opportunity to scrutinise Kate's face. Although his hard-edged face showed no emotion, she saw a dark glint in the depths as he said gravely, 'Nowhere near as pretty.'

Heat flared across Kate's skin. Lightly, with a meaningless smile, she returned, 'Thank you. You're remarkably handsome too.'

'Not pretty.' Horrified, Nick emphasised both words.

Unexpectedly, Kate and Patric laughed together. 'No,' Kate reassured him, 'Not at all pretty.'

For a moment she and Patric hovered on the brink of some sort of harmony, a fragile rapport that shattered when he said, 'You have a babysitting service at your apartments, I understand?'

'I believe so,' Kate replied guardedly, forestalling him by adding, 'But I have no intention of using it.'

'I'd like to see you tonight,' he said, his face as purposeful as his voice. 'Nick—'

She overrode him. 'That wouldn't be a good idea,' she said. 'Eat up, Nick.'

'Kate,' Patric said, the iron determination beneath the words sending a shiver down her spine, 'we need to talk.'

Her brain was as useless as cotton wool. Patric had no claims on either her or Nick—worse, he might well reveal her whereabouts to the one man she feared and loathed—yet she had to stiffen every muscle in her body before she could say, 'No.'

He leaned back and surveyed her, his cold eyes implacable, the stark bone structure of his face giving him an impressive force and power. 'Yes,' he contradicted. 'Don't you like your sandwich?'

She pushed the plate a little to one side, picking up her cup with a shaking hand. 'I'm not hungry,' she said, hoping the coffee would banish the slow shudders that started somewhere in her heart and were spreading through her in wintry waves.

'I'm not surprised,' he said, mockery flicking each word. 'I'd have found out eventually, Kate. New Zealand's too small for secrets to lie hidden for ever.'

This secret would, she thought grimly, even if she and Nick had to leave Whangarei, stealing away like refugees. She drank the coffee, barely tasting it; strong, hot, and laden with caffeine, it still didn't warm her.

Nothing could, she thought into the lengthening silence—not the sun, not the light that licked across Nick's dark head as he solidly masticated his way through his food.

Patric wouldn't give up. He thought Nick was his son, and he was determined to play some part in the boy's life. But once he knew the truth he wouldn't care. So she'd have to tell him the truth—or as much of it as she could tailor to this situation. And then she'd have to swear him to silence.

'I know what you're thinking,' she said bleakly, 'but it isn't so.'

His eyes branded her a liar. 'If I'd known—'

'It doesn't matter,' she said desperately. 'There's no reason for you to think that anything was your responsibility. None at all.'

He said with cool, searing irony, 'Nice try, Kate. We'll discuss this later.'

Although her nerves felt like slowly shredding tissue paper, she said, 'Nick, look, there's a pukeko.'

He swung around. 'Pukekos are a New Zealand bird,' he said after a long, considering stare.

Patric said, 'Yes, but they're also quite common here.'

Nick's brows drew into a knot. 'So how did they get here from New Zealand?' he asked. 'Or from New Zealand to here?'

Patric's mouth twisted. 'The winds usually blow from Australia to New Zealand, so I imagine that thousands of years ago a couple of very tough pukekos—one male, one female—were lifted by cyclonic winds in Australia and carried all the way across the Tasman Sea, to land in New Zealand with a huge sigh of relief.'

Nick grinned. 'Birds don't sigh. I bet they were happy, though, when they got there.'

Patric asked Kate quietly, brusquely, 'Are you all right?'

'Yes.'

'Would you like some more coffee?'

'No, thank you.' So much, she thought sickly, for caffeine as a stimulant. She poured a glass of water and drank it down while Nick finished his sandwich.

'Time to go,' she said, hoping her voice sounded cool

and casual. Although it wouldn't fool Patric, she didn't want her son worried.

'OK,' he said cheerfully, but as they left the restaurant he took her hand, an unusual enough event for her to vow that nothing—especially not Patric Sutherland—would be allowed to upset him.

In the car Patric asked, 'Back to your apartment?'

'Yes, thank you,' she said rigidly. 'How did you know where we're staying?'

For a moment she didn't think he was going to tell her. Then he said, 'You don't lie well, even by omission. I paid a passing skateboarder to follow you.'

So the young man with a blond ponytail who'd trailed her and Nick from Robinson's Hotel to their apartment building had been Patric's spy. Clever. And typical.

Although the traffic had thickened, Patric guided the car through it with skill and courtesy. He did everything well—danced superbly, played sport skilfully, and made love with such heart-shattering brilliance that the effects still lingered after all these years.

It was just as well she'd grown past that juvenile infatuation, Kate thought savagely. Otherwise she could be in real danger.

As the car drew to a halt she said with an enormous, bitter reluctance, 'I'll see you tomorrow night.'

He put on the handbrake. 'Tomorrow night—yes, all right. We'll go out to dinner. I'll call for you at seven.'

Already regretting her decision, she gave a stiff nod. It had to be done, even if telling him was going to tear her apart. But it wouldn't do that; she was much stronger than she'd been when she was eighteen.

And going to a restaurant would give them the buffer of other people, of the need to act in a civilised manner.

Patric said silkily, 'Just don't go thinking you can slip off to New Zealand tomorrow. I know enough about you now to track you down.'

Well, perhaps she deserved that. 'Say thank you to Mr Sutherland,' she told Nick.

He made his thanks, and when the car drew away said eagerly, 'Can I go with you tomorrow night?'

'No, darling.'

He was ready to object, but she said, 'Come on, we've got time for a swim before dinner,' and he forgot about it.

He'd remember later, but by then she'd have recovered a bit of her normal spirit. At the moment she was too exhausted to deal with her son in a stubborn mood.

That night she twisted sleeplessly in her bed, trying to work out some sort of strategy for the meeting.

Fate, she thought grimly, was a bitch. Why did Patric have to be at that hotel when she and Nick were on the roller-coaster? Everything had been going so well—she'd achieved a measure of serenity and centred a quietly satisfying life around her son and her work. If occasionally she thought wistfully of the hopes and dreams that single motherhood had put paid to, Nick made up for everything.

If only she'd managed to see Patric first!

Restlessness clawed at her, hummed with reckless intensity through her body. Eventually she got up and walked across to the window. Although it was well after midnight cars still purred along the roads, and lights in the surrounding high-rise buildings showed that most of the Gold Coast was still awake. She looked up into the sky.

Once Patric had told her the names of the stars, pointing out the constellations—Orion the summer hunter, riding high with Sirius at heel, the fuzzy glow of the Pleiades, the wheeling cross of the south. She'd been intrigued, so the next time they met he'd brought a pair of binoculars and shown her the coloured stars in the Jewel Box and the red glitter of Antares, and they'd discussed the likelihood of life on planets around those distant stars.

She found to her surprise that she was crying, noiseless sobs that ached in her throat. How stupid—she hadn't cried for years! Stiffening her shoulders, she blew her nose and wiped her eyes; she'd been so young, so silly, a naïve country kid from the backblocks, and she'd had to grow up in such a hurry.

Sex and pregnancy had a habit of doing that to you, she thought cynically. Very maturing.

Even though each of the years between her eighteen and his twenty-four might have been a century, she'd loved Patric with all the ardour of her young, untried heart. Fascinated throughout her teens by his dark aura, she'd always watched him shyly from a distance, but the year she'd turned sixteen she'd fallen in love as only the young can—headlong and wholly—and to her delight and surprise he'd smiled at her with narrowed, gleaming eyes.

That had been the beginning.

Those holidays he'd introduced her to kisses—gentle, tender kisses, making due allowance for her innocence, apparently unaware that beneath the pressure of his already experienced mouth she'd melted, burned, flamed into incandescence.

Or perhaps he had known, she thought now, staring down at the shifting, fractured lights through the palms. He'd made sure they were almost never alone; when they rode the station horses, when he'd taught her to water-ski on the dam, when he'd played tennis with her, other people had acted as buffers.

Yes, he'd probably been well aware of her ardent, untutored response. He'd been careful and kind—and cruel, because even then she'd known there could be no future for them. That year her aunt, worried by this unusual friendship, had told her not to get her hopes up, that Patric would eventually marry a girl from his own circle. Someone like Laura Williams, the daughter of his father's best friend.

Kate's mouth clamped into a hard, tight line.

After those holidays Patric had left for America, where he'd been doing a graduate degree in some form of business studies, and she'd grieved for a lost dream.

The first postcard had filled her with excitement and relief, and although he never wrote much more than a sentence or two, and the cards arrived infrequently, they'd kept alive a spark of hope.

The following year he'd come back for a week; their meetings had been short, but he'd kissed her with much less restraint, and she'd learned just how intense sensual excitement could be.

Then at the end of her last year at school he'd finally returned, infinitely more sophisticated after two years abroad, and set in motion the turbulent trail of events that had led them to tomorrow's meeting—and indirectly to the boy who slept so peacefully in the next room.

The babysitter turned out to be a pleasant middle-aged woman who got on with Nick immediately. She said they'd swim, they'd watch a video, and after that he'd go to bed.

Grinning, Nick teased, 'At ten o'clock.'

'At eight o'clock,' Kate said firmly.

The babysitter laughed. 'Don't worry, eight o'clock it'll be.'

Since they'd arrived home from yet another theme park, Nick had prowled around the unit, demanding more attention than usual. He wasn't used to being left behind; their social life was the sort that included children. Now he asked, 'Where are you going, Mum?'

'I don't know,' she said, 'but when Mr Sutherland comes I'll get a phone number so that if I'm needed I can come straight back home. He'll probably have a mobile, but if he doesn't he can give me the number of the restaurant.'

He looked relieved. 'All right,' he said.

The intercom rang. Kate lifted the receiver and her heart jolted as Patric's voice said, 'Kate.'

'Can we have a telephone number?' she said. 'Just in case there's an emergency.'

After giving her a number, which she copied down, he said, 'I'll come up.'

'No,' she said. 'I'll be right down.'

She hung up and stooped to kiss Nick. His arms came around her a little fiercely. 'See you,' he said valiantly.

Straightening, she smiled at him. 'I won't be late, but I expect to find you sound asleep.'

It took all of Kate's determination to get herself to the comfortable, featureless foyer. And her stretched nerves were twisted into knots by the sight of Patric, tall and hard-edged and completely in control of himself and his world.

Although she no longer loved him, she was still strongly affected by his presence, by the blazing vitality that seared through his well-cut, informal clothes and proclaimed the alpha male.

Narrowed eyes—impersonal as the dark heart of thunderstorm—surveyed her. Kate's chin came up in the slightest gesture of defiance. No doubt he was accustomed to escorting women who wore designer clothes rather than a dress bought in the shop sale. However the soft gold echoed the colour of her skin and contrasted with her blue-green eyes.

'You take my breath away,' he said quietly.

Her heart jumped. 'Thank you,' she replied, the stilted words difficult on her tongue.

'I see very little difference from the girl I remember.'

Her hair swirled around her shoulders as she shook her head. 'Outwardly, perhaps.'

An old anguish ached through her like the phantom pain from an amputated limb; she had done her grieving for the Patric of Tatamoa. This man, tempered by unknown fires, a man of steel and disciplined aggression, was a different person: compelling, magnetic—much more dangerous.

'I hope you have changed,' he said, taking her arm to guide her to the car.

Sensation shivered through her in a mixture of flame and ice. 'Why?'

Once they were in motion he said, 'If you don't change you stagnate. I was a careless young fool with nothing but my own needs and desires in mind. You, of all people, should remember that. I'm not like that now.'

'I remember you being a leader—responsible and courageous and daring,' she said simply.

'Even when I made love to you and left you pregnant?' he asked with self-derisory contempt.

She glanced from her hands to his profile, an arrogant outline against the shimmering lights of the sea front. Screwing her courage to the sticking point, she said, 'You aren't Nick's father.'

His mouth tightened into a forbidding line. 'It won't work, Kate. I know his birth date—'

She interrupted jerkily, 'Patric, I tried to tell you before—you're not his father. Why would I lie to you?'

'I intend to find out.'

In any other situation she'd have been afraid of the menacing purr beneath the words. Now it merely reinforced her decision.

He put on the indicator and waited until they were halfway across the road before saying, 'So you slept with someone else within a week or so of making love to me.'

For a moment her mouth trembled. Controlling it, she said in a hard, flat voice, 'A fortnight later, to be exact.'

'Just after you went to Christchurch.'

She hesitated. 'Just before.'

He turned the wheel, and the car headed straight for a waterfall at the front of a small apartment block on the beach side of the road. Kate cried out, but beneath and to one side of the glittering curtain of water gaped an entrance, and this was where the car was heading.

'Where is this?' she asked huskily.

'My apartment. I certainly didn't want to discuss this in public. We'll eat there.'

'No!'

But the barred screen across the parking basement was already rumbling back.

'It's all right,' Patric said silkily as they drove down, 'You'll be perfectly safe while you tell me who else you slept with all those years ago, and how you know that Nick is his son and not mine.'

When the car had halted in a designated slot he switched off the engine. Into the silence he said with barely leashed antagonism, 'And why, when we met that last time in the May holidays, although you must have known you were pregnant, you didn't bother to tell me.'

CHAPTER THREE

HER swift glance at Patric's profile tightened every sinew in Kate. Ruthlessly she repressed the unjustified fear. She'd made the decision; she'd force down the crawling revulsion and tell him.

And then, she thought with a sudden stab of pain as he opened her door, the hope she'd never been able to stifle would be shown for what it was—hope's poor relation, wishful thinking. One act of violence almost seven years ago had shattered her dreams, made even friendship impossible between Patric and her.

Together they walked across the well-lit basement and took a lift to the penthouse. Naturally, Kate thought with a struggling sense of irony, trying to keep her mind away from the disclosures to come; of course Patric would be in the penthouse! Nothing but the best for the owner and managing director of Sutherland Aviation.

The lift doors opened onto a thickly carpeted hall. Without speaking, Patric unlocked a door and led her into the apartment.

A huge sitting room stretched out before her, decorated in the soft colours fashionable in south-eastern Queensland—a ceramic tiled floor half hidden by an off-white and blue Chinese rug, leather-covered sofas and chairs, a creamy amber travertine table surrounded by apricot dining chairs in a vaguely French style, and pictures on the walls selected for their inability to offend. It looked rich and cool and impersonal, all surface and no individuality.

If everything had been chosen to contrast forcefully with the dominant, uncompromising man who closed the door behind Kate, it couldn't have been done better. Masterful, disturbing on a primal level, Patric made the luxurious room dwindle and fade around him; even the splendid sweep of the ocean through the wall of glass doors took second place to his personality.

'Sit down.' He waited until she'd taken one of the leather chairs before asking with an unyielding courtesy that shivered across Kate's exposed nerves, 'Would you like a drink?'

'No, thank you,' she said quietly, stopping her fingers from worriedly smoothing the soft suede 'But you have something.'

'I think it would be a good idea if I abstained too,' he said, dark eyes watching—watching, weighing and measuring as they roamed her face.

'Look, let's get this over and done with.' Carefully controlling the desperation that roiled beneath each word, she said, 'Nick is not your son, Patric. Please believe me.'

'Why should I?'

'I'm telling you the truth. I ask you again—why would I lie?'

'Revenge?' His voice was expressionless.

She couldn't believe her ears. 'Why would I want revenge?'

'Because I married Laura six weeks after the last time we met and exactly four and half months after I'd sworn undying love for you.'

'No,' Kate said stonily. 'I told you at Tatamoa in the May holidays that it was over. You had every right to marry Laura.'

It was the truth, yet would she have been so adamant if she hadn't been kept informed of the other woman's presence in his life?

Lifting gritty eyelids, Kate looked directly at him. 'If there was any chance you might be Nick's father I'd have contacted you. But you're not.'

'Tell me about the man you slept with so soon after you

slept with me,' he suggested levelly, those hard eyes probing, his mouth twisted.

Kate closed her eyes for a second. But she'd lied to him, made him believe this, and she had to live with her lies. Raising her lashes, she shrugged. It took a lot of effort. Forcing her voice into an unnatural steadiness, she said, 'You said you knew there wasn't any man. Why did you send someone to Christchurch to pry into my affairs?'

Violence broke shockingly through the armour of his self-control as he swore. With a white line around his mouth he demanded, 'Why the hell do you think I did? I was in love with you—I went down to Tatamoa to ask you to marry me! When you told me so easily, so calmly, so definitely that it was over, all I could think of was that making love to you had scared you, or repelled you so much you couldn't bear to be in the same room as me.'

'No!'

His eyes narrowed. 'I told you I loved you, that I'd wait for you, the day after we'd made love. Remember? I rang because my father was dying—it was only a matter of time before his heart gave out, and I had to go back to Auckland to be with him.'

'I remember,' she said, her heart shaking. She'd been so sorry for him, and yet his hasty departure had dimmed her trembling, nascent joy. 'I understood,' she added.

'Did you understand that I was going to have to work eighteen hours every day to pull Sutherland's back into shape?'

She lifted her chin. 'I didn't know it was in trouble, but I certainly accepted that your place was with your parents.'

'That's why I didn't come down to see you during that first term. I couldn't leave my parents; my mother had collapsed, and my father deteriorated when I did go out of town,' he said, the decisive voice so lacking in emotion that it sounded pitiless as stone. 'And although you seemed distant when I rang, and your letters were the sort good little girls write to their cousins, I thought it was because you were so young, and because I couldn't be with you.'

Kate's hand went out towards him; she snatched it back as though it had touched an invisible flame, but he saw. 'Of course you had to stay with your father—and your mother. It wasn't that.'

He reined in his temper. 'Then what happened to make you change your mind? I know you loved me—you wouldn't have made love with me if you hadn't. Why didn't you tell me you were pregnant that day in the May holidays?'

'Because it was nothing to do with you. The baby wasn't—isn't—yours.' Nausea clutched her. 'Anyway, none of that matters now. All that's important is that Nick is not your son. Please believe me.'

She tried to keep any note of pleading from her voice but he must have heard it, because he gave her a glance in which anger and disgust were equally blended.

He hadn't sat down. Now he rested his hands on the back of one of the dining chairs and turned to look out over the white beach, glimmering in the swift-falling dusk. Against the wide purple sea his profile was an arrogant statement of strength. In an icily sardonic voice he asked, 'How can I? The Kate I knew, the Kate I fell in love with, wouldn't have slept with another man.'

Some frozen cinder in her heart, long dead, glowed softly. Ignoring it, she reiterated bleakly, 'I'm sorry. I wish he was, but Nick isn't yours, Patric.'

His face clamped into an expression of such fury that she had to stop herself from jumping to her feet and running. 'So whose is he?' he asked roughly.

'He's the son of the man who raped me a fortnight after you left Poto—a fortnight after your father's heart attack,' she said woodenly. 'A week after I'd had a period.' The words slid over her tongue like poisoned pebbles, bitter as rue, harsh with conviction.

For several taut, charged seconds he stared at her while

her pulse thundered in her ears. And then he swore, and she cried out with horror as he lifted the chair and crashed it onto the tiles.

She knew that she couldn't tell him the whole truth.

He looked at the maltreated chair as though it was abhorrent to him, then set it precisely back in place and strode silently across to the window, moving with the loose-limbed, deadly litheness of some big predatory animal. 'Who was he? The man who raped you?'

His voice was cold, so cold…

But beneath the cold control hid raw, uncaged savagery, a feral anger that lifted every hair on her skin. Only once before had she heard him speak in that tone—when Sean Cusack, his cousin, had tried to kiss her and fondle her.

She had no desire to hear it again.

'Nobody I knew,' she said quickly, already committed, speaking more easily now that she knew he believed her. 'He was hitch-hiking to Auckland. I was in the wrong place at the wrong time.' All lies—but her story was made more believable by the fact that the basis was true.

In that same lethal, almost soundless voice, Patric asked, 'What happened to him?'

'He stole a car from the Forsythes in Poto and smashed it into a bank fifty kilometres down the road. He died.' If Patric went looking for evidence that she was telling the truth, he'd find it written up in the newspapers of the time. Forgive me, she begged that dead thief.

Patric's dark brows drew together in a frown. 'Is that why you told me you were no longer in love with me? Because you were raped?'

Her hands gripped the glove-soft leather of the chair, then loosened. She folded them in her lap and kept them still by sheer determination. Steadily, without emphasis, she said, 'Yes. I was shattered—I couldn't bear the thought of any sort of intimacy. It's a common response.' She hesitated, then added, 'And I knew you were seeing a lot of Laura. In a way it seemed meant.'

Truth, she thought bitterly, has an infinite number of facets.

He turned to face her, the arrogant framework of his face very prominent. 'How did you know I was seeing Laura?'

'Do you remember my cousin Juliet? Your father gave her a job at Sutherland Aviation in Auckland.'

Older, more sophisticated and genuinely concerned, Juliet had tried to convince Kate that, sweet though a summer flirtation might be, it meant nothing. While Kate had been enduring a term of torment at university in Christchurch, her cousin's letters had been full of Patric. And Laura.

'I remember.' Patric's voice was distant.

His next question told her nothing, except that he was once more fully in control of himself. 'Did you go to the police?' he asked conversationally.

She bit her lip. 'It was my word against his. I didn't think anyone would believe me.' Sean had told her that. Sickened by his vengeful cruelty, she'd accepted his triumphant assessment.

Not now, she thought grimly. Now she'd see him in court so fast he'd get skid marks. But then she'd been foolishly innocent, and the thought of telling anyone what had happened had filled her with shamed horror. A thought struck her, and she added hastily, 'And anyway, he was dead.' More lies.

'It never occurred to you to have an abortion?'

'I didn't realise I was pregnant until just before the May holidays.' She hesitated, then went on, 'I was often irregular. And when I did realise—I was very depressed, still in shock, still trying to deny it. I knew there was no way I could—we could—' She stopped and regained control of her tumbling thoughts. 'Refusing to see you any more seemed the only thing to do.'

Sunk into a nadir of depression, Kate hadn't even been able to grieve. Patric had been lost to her from the night she'd been raped, because it was his cousin who'd attacked her.

'I see.' He sounded detached and thoughtful, his striking face revealing no emotion.

He was possibly a little disappointed that he didn't have a son—most men wanted one—but no doubt he was also grateful that his uncomplicated life would remain that way.

'Could you take me home, please?' Kate asked, stiffening her shoulders against waves of tiredness.

He said inflexibly, 'You look exhausted. Stay and have some dinner, and then I'll take you back.'

Kate glanced at her watch—only seven-thirty. Nick would still be awake, and for once she didn't feel up to coping with him. 'I don't want…I'm not hungry, Patric.'

'I've ordered a meal,' he said. 'Eating something will make you feel better.'

Only time could do that.

For years she'd managed to ignore her intellectual acceptance of Nick's paternity; until she'd seen Patric at the theme park she hadn't realised that in some hidden, resistant part of her heart she'd always pretended he was the father of her son.

How stupid to let her heart fool her like that! Now that her delusion had been exposed to the hard light of day it had brutally turned on her, inflicting the kind of pain she'd hoped never to suffer again.

With dark, masked eyes Patric said quietly, 'Let's sit at the table.'

Somehow the normal process of dining—sitting down, unfolding the napkin, watching him ladle out soup, picking up her spoon—steadied her, reminded her that, whatever happened, life went on.

'You must have found it difficult looking after Nick on a government benefit,' Patric said. 'Did your aunt and uncle help?'

The iced avocado soup was delicious, based on real chicken stock, Kate thought vaguely, dipping her spoon into the creamy pale green liquid. 'They couldn't; for a couple of years they really struggled in Rarotonga. Anyway, they thought I was crazy keeping him. They wanted me to adopt him out.'

'Why didn't you?'

Searching for the right words, she drank some more soup. 'Several reasons,' she said eventually. 'I'd grown up in someone else's family. Oh, they tried very hard, but I always felt the odd person out. I didn't want that for Nick. But the main reason was that when he was born—he looked just like me. It would have been like giving myself away, and I couldn't do it.'

'Did you tell your aunt and uncle that you were attacked?' he asked.

She shook her head. 'What was the use? It would only have made them wretched. I didn't even tell them about the baby until after I had him.'

'You had him alone?' he asked, looking at her with glints of cold blue in his dark eyes.

'When I dropped out of university—after the May holidays—I stayed in Christchurch and kept house for two dentists. They were good to me—took me to the hospital, visited me. Before I had Nick I'd organised a flat in Whangarei, and saved up enough money to travel to get there. We arrived when he was three weeks old.'

His brows drew together in a formidable frown. 'To all intents and purposes you were alone. Who do your family think Nick's father is?'

'I've never said.'

Surprisingly, he allowed her to get away with the evasion. Perhaps he didn't recognise it. She should have been reassured, but her hand trembled as she picked up her spoon again.

'I'm sorry,' Patric said unexpectedly.

'For what?'

'For—everything.'

Kate hadn't forgotten—she doubted whether anyone

ever forgot being raped—but she had long ago come to terms with it. Proudly she said, 'I refused to make myself a victim, so I left it behind me.'

'Very wise,' he said, a disturbing note beneath the words making her look up. But there was nothing to be read in his face, no emotion visible in his unwavering eyes as he finished, 'And strong-minded.'

'Just sensible.'

When the plates were empty in front of them Patric said, 'I'll get the second course.'

Kate opened her mouth to protest, then fleetingly met eyes as opaque as polished granite and every bit as obdurate. 'You're determined to feed me, aren't you?' she said, trying to speak lightly.

'It's the least I can do after subjecting you to such an inquisition.'

Her brows pleated as he got up, collected the soup plates, and walked from the table into the kitchen. Tall, lithe, his well-knit body vibrated with a breath-catching male beauty. Something hidden and feline stirred inside her, stretched languorously, flowed through her with a smooth, primal insistence.

Desperately, Kate dragged her gaze away. Patric had opened the long doors onto a wide terrace bordered with potted palms. Fresh and familiar, a salty breeze stirred the curtains. Through the palm fronds the sand glinted in the light of a rising moon; movement and shadows indicated that people were still walking along the beach. The sound of the sea filled the room, a quiet thunder echoed by her heart.

An ache of yearning broke over her, submerged her—sweet, inexorable, merciless, a honeyed hunger leaching into her endurance. It had been so long, and her taste of loving had been so brief, snatched away by an act of callous violence…

And that's enough of that, she told herself, stiffening her spine. You have a good life, and once this interlude with Patric is over you'll be able to settle back into it. If you meet a man you can fall in love with, one who'll love Nick as much as he would a son of his own, then you might consider changing it.

'The menu says the asparagus comes from New Zealand,' Patric said, carrying a tray to the table. 'I assume you still like it?'

Kate looked down at racks of tiny lamb chops, long straight spears of asparagus, glistening darkly green under a golden veil of butter, and small, round new potatoes, white, voluptuous and tender.

'I adore it,' she said, intolerably shaken that he'd remembered. Hastily seizing on a neutral aspect, she went on, 'I didn't know we exported asparagus to Australia.'

'Along with a multitude of other things,' he said.

At once stimulated and wary, Kate soon responded to Patric's incisive comments on the latest political scandal, contradicting him and then enjoying the resultant sparring so much that for a precious time she forgot all that stood between them. In Kate's life there was little opportunity for leisurely talk of any kind, let alone a free-ranging analysis of world events, of books, ideas and films.

At length, when they'd both eaten everything on their plates, he said, 'I gather you've not finished your degree.'

She gave a quick shake of her head.

'Are you doing subjects extramurally?' he asked.

It sounded almost like an accusation. 'No,' she said, sitting up straighter.

He lifted his brows. 'Why not?'

'I don't have the money,' she said crisply, adding, 'Or the time.'

'A brain as good as yours should be exercised, and I don't imagine that working in a dress shop in Whangarei gives you much intellectual stimulation. Nor Nick's conversation, however charming he is. There are limits to a six-year-old's depth.' He paused, then added coolly, 'Unless you have someone else to talk to.'

Turbulence swirled beneath the dark voice, like an offshore rip coiling under innocently smooth water.

Kate's mouth dried. 'I read a lot—Whangarei has an excellent library. And I have friends, and very good neighbours,' she parried. 'Anna and Jacob are in their eighties, Germans who fled the Holocaust and somehow landed up in Whangarei. They adore discussions on almost anything. Anna spoils Nick and Jacob gives him a piano lesson for ten minutes every day. He taught him how to play the mouth organ too.'

'How good is Nick?'

'On the piano?' She smiled. 'Jacob says he has talent but no genius; at the moment all he's doing is enjoying himself. He can play three tunes on the mouth organ, though, so he's now convinced he's an expert.'

Patric laughed. Low and totally self-assured, it was the laugh of a man who has everything in the world he wants—or who is positive of his ability to get it. The young Kate had been dazzled by that confidence; perhaps because she'd always felt an outsider she'd been sure she needed accomplishments to pay her way.

'He obviously has a wide range of interests,' Patric observed, pouring a glass of water for her.

Her gaze lingered on his hands—lean and sinewy and graceful. And gentle, she thought suddenly. Patric's hands had been so gentle—and then they had been harsh, and she had shivered with pleasure at both the gentleness and the harshness…

Dragging her mind back from perilous memories, she said, 'He gets fascinated by something and wants to know all about it—sort of plunges into it. I'm already an expert on spiders and lizards and how mouth organs work. When Nick gets interested, he demands more and more information, soaking it up long after everyone else is bored to screaming point.'

'And at the moment it's birds.'

'Yes. We've read books from the library about birds,

and listened to bird calls, and watched birds and collected their feathers and pasted them into a notebook—you name it, we've done it. But soon he'll become absorbed in something new and it will start all over again. Sometimes I think he's got a butterfly mind.'

'Hardly,' Patric said. He'd poured wine, a good Australian red, but had left it untouched. Now he drank some down. When he put the glass back on the table he tilted it, so that the liquid caught the light and flashed crimson, his dark eyes concealed by the thick fringe of lashes. 'He seems to explore deeply as well as widely. I remember my grandmother telling me that "Black" Pat was like that. The only thing that ever kept his attention was Sutherland Aviation.' He set the glass straight on the table and looked at her with half-closed eyes. 'It will be intriguing to see what Nick grows up like. Why did you call him Nicholas?'

'It was my father's name,' she said carefully. Nick's second name was Patrick—another instance of the delusion she'd cherished. And if Nick had inherited anything from 'Black Pat' Sutherland it had not descended through Patric.

'I'd like to have known your father. Do you and Nick look like him?'

'No, we look like my mother.'

'She must have been a great beauty.'

Kate smiled mistily. 'I don't remember her, of course—I was only three when they died—but judging by photographs she was much better looking than I am.'

He lifted his brows. 'I find that hard to believe. Did she have your astonishing eyes?' An iron-grey glance lingered a second on her mouth.

A slow shimmer of heat smouldered through Kate. Quickly, before it flared into wildfire, she said, 'She had a glory about her, a kind of radiance that shone right through the camera lens and onto paper. I wish I'd known her.'

'Why was she climbing Mount Everest when she had a small child?' he asked, frowning.

'According to Aunt Jean, my parents intended having another baby, so my mother decided to try Everest before she did. Both she and my father were born climbers. In a way it was fitting that they died there.'

'No wonder Nick likes the thrill of roller-coasters,' Patric said sardonically.

'Those genes skipped a generation. I don't like danger.'

'Really?' His smile was tinged with mockery. 'Yet I've always thought you were incredibly dangerous—even when you were fourteen—with those huge, vulnerable eyes and that passionate mouth, and skin like pale gold silk. You scared me silly, and as you grew into your beauty it became harder and harder to remember that you were six years younger than I was. And in the end I gave up trying to.'

'I'm a very ordinary person,' she objected, trying to keep her head.

'And yet you'd say that Nick is a handsome child.'

She hesitated, then admitted, 'Well, yes, but I'm allowed to be biased—I'm his mother. To me he's perfect.'

'He's a handsome boy who looks just like you.' He watched with heavy-lashed eyes as colour burnt through her skin. 'Although he doesn't look vulnerable. He has strong bones.'

His eyelids drooped further, hiding his thoughts. The light above the table played warmly across the autocratic angles and planes of his face, emphasising sweeping cheekbones, an uncompromising jaw and the surprising beauty of his mouth. No vulnerability there, Kate thought acidly, nor any innocence; he'd probably been born sophisticated, and his face revealed nothing but disciplined power.

Disconcertingly his lashes lifted, and she realised that he'd been watching her through them.

Sensation speared through her, clean and sharp and

piercing. She felt it in her suddenly heavy breasts; it cramped her womb and tightened her skin, warning her that she was heading into hazardous waters.

Patric got to his feet, startling her afresh with his height and the width of his shoulders. 'There's pudding,' he said casually. 'A mango concoction.'

'It sounds lovely.'

Now that he knew Nick wasn't his she'd never see him again; she could allow herself a few more minutes of this perilous pleasure.

While he collected the used plates and went into the kitchen, she tried to control the high beating of her heart in her throat, the singing tide of need that surged through every cell, the swift clutch of desire in the pit of her stomach.

Sexual hunger was simply a matter of chemistry—inconvenient, meaning little.

Except that she had never felt it for another man. And had never wanted to.

That first act of love all those years ago—and the subsequent brutal assault—had somehow frozen her responses. She wasn't afraid of men, and she was thankful that she'd made love with Patric first, so she'd known the glory of fulfilled desire instead of being initiated into debasement. But until she'd seen him again and felt excitement storm through her in a wild clamour she hadn't responded physically to a man.

And instead of asking herself why, she'd gratefully accepted celibacy.

Now, as she heard Patric moving quietly about the kitchen, she wondered why she'd been content to dream the years away, to ignore any overtures that came her way, to live a sexless life.

Perhaps she should thank Patric for waking her again, she thought painfully as he came back into the room.

'Mango mousse,' he said, sliding the container in front of her.

The pale contents of the elegant bowl were decorated with an elaborate swirl of chocolate in three shades.

'Where did you get such superb food?' she asked, grateful for the opportunity to ignore her thoughts.

'One of the local restaurants does a delivery service. Would you like to serve me some?'

She spooned the delicious stuff onto a plate and handed it to him, then put out a small amount for herself. It was magnificent—not too sweet, not too rich—and the chocolate shavings added a luscious touch of contrast in texture and flavour.

'Lovely,' Kate said on a slow sigh of pleasure when the first mouthful had eased down her appreciative throat. 'My compliments to the chef.'

'I'll make sure he gets them,' Patric promised. 'Eat up before it gets too warm.'

In the clipped words she heard a sudden roughness, as though he disliked the situation, but when she looked up he smiled, and at that smile—warm, a little coaxing—she knew she'd been imagining things.

After demolishing the mousse with delicate greed, she found herself agreeing to coffee. While he prepared it she got up and walked across to the windows. The moon had risen fully and was now a great white globe in the black sky, its light washing out most of the stars.

Patric had overshadowed all other men for her. Even though she hadn't loved him in the mature way that led to adult happiness, he'd blotted out the impact of any other man.

Well, that could stop right now. Oh, she still found him sinfully, threateningly attractive, but she wasn't going to spend the rest of her life mourning a youthful romance.

Or losing herself in inchoate fantasies where he was the father of her child, instead of the real father—a man who'd raped her because she was Patric's girlfriend, because he'd hated and envied Patric all his life, a man who'd laughed at her frantic struggles until she'd managed to deliver several blows to a vulnerable spot.

Then he'd held a knife to her throat, and when it was done he'd called her trash, and gloated that if she ever saw his cousin again he'd tell Patric he'd had her—describe how she'd moaned and twisted in his arms, lie about every sordid, horrifying detail as though she'd wanted him instead of fighting him almost to a standstill.

Even now, years later, she had to breathe a residue of panic away and remind herself that Patric could lead his cousin to Nick.

When she'd decided to keep her son she'd been terrified that his father's cruelty might be hereditary; she'd tried to give Nick a happy, satisfying life, with no need to express himself in aggression and malice. And she'd succeeded. He was sunny-natured—strong-willed too, but he was learning that although loyalty to friends was a good quality, sympathy and understanding of those he didn't like so much was important too.

He would never—*never*—know who his father was and what he'd done. If she had to spend the rest of her life on the run, she'd see that Sean never found out he'd fathered a child on her. But to make sure of that she'd have to persuade Patric never to tell anyone he'd seen her again.

As Patric came into the room with a tray she said, 'Can I have your promise that what I've told you tonight won't go any further?'

He bent to set the tray down on the table between the sofa and the chair. Lamplight gleamed on the blue-black depths of his hair, washed over his arrogant nose and the square chin.

When he stood up she could see that he was angry. 'I don't usually break confidences,' he said arctically.

'I'm talking about Nick.' She paused to gather strength. 'I'm not going to tell him who his father was or the circumstances of his conception. When he's older he might find out that—that you and I saw a lot of each other that summer. He might even track you down. I don't want you to lie to him, but could you simply say that you're not his father and that you don't know who is?'

'I could do that,' he said steadily, scanning her face with opaque, impersonal eyes. 'But he's going to resent your silence.'

She bit her lip. 'I've told him his father is dead.'

'What will you do when he begins to ask more detailed questions?'

'I don't know,' she admitted, 'but that's my problem, not yours.'

'All right,' he said deliberately, 'I won't tell him you were raped.'

Stiffly Kate said, 'Thank you. And—could you not tell anyone you've seen me? I don't want any reminders of the past cluttering up my life.' She made it a command rather than a plea.

His brows knitted, then smoothed out; she met the hard impact of his eyes with what she hoped was cool self-possession.

'Of course,' he said after a noticeable pause, and added, 'Come and pour some coffee. Would you like a brandy?'

She hadn't touched the wine he'd poured for her, and apart from that once he hadn't drunk any of his, either.

'No, thank you,' she said, glad of the excuse to walk back to the sofa and sit down; her legs felt as though the stuffing had been taken from them. Carefully she poured his coffee—black and sugarless, just as he liked it—and handed it to him.

They talked quietly, trying to burnish some sort of civilised gloss on an evening that had put them both through an emotional wringer. Kate cast a covert glance at the man beside her, long legs sprawled in front of him as he drank his coffee. What was he thinking?

It was impossible to tell. Even when he'd been growing up Patric's face had told the world only what he'd wanted it to know.

CHAPTER FOUR

ON THE way back to her apartment Patric asked, 'When do you really leave for New Zealand?'

Shame tripped Kate's tongue. 'On Friday.'

He gave her a quick, slicing look. 'It's all right, Kate. I won't harass you, but I don't want to lose sight of you again. We had fun all those years ago, didn't we?'

'Yes, but...'

At her hesitation he supplied drily, 'But we're two different people now. Still, you enjoyed tonight—parts of it, anyway.'

Troubled by a shadowy foreboding, she said, 'Yes, I did.'

'Don't sound so surprised. I did too.' His voice was reflective. 'I've almost tied up my business here, and I don't have to be back in New Zealand for another couple of days. Can we at least pick up the threads of our friendship?'

Excitement warred with caution, almost banishing her fears in a hot blaze of fascination. Don't be a coward, a voice purred. What harm can it do? If nothing else it might finally end those foolish, infantile hopes and dreams you've been carrying around for so long.

And he'd promised not to tell anyone he'd met her again. Patric didn't break promises.

Yet she said, 'You can never go back, Patric—life doesn't work that way.'

'I know.' He spoke calmly, almost meditatively. 'Going back is impossible, but I would like to go forward.'

The very simplicity of his words crashed through her

defences as nothing else could have. 'Yes,' she said quietly, 'I'd like that too.'

He didn't touch her, but she felt his glance, and his voice was warm as he said, 'Thank you.'

Again that fleeting, baseless apprehension whispered across her skin.

Patric asked, 'What is it?'

He'd always had an uncanny way of seeing far more than she wanted him to. Once she'd hoped it meant that they were psychically linked; now she thought it was probably an inbuilt understanding of body language, honed by his brilliant brain into a weapon. No doubt it came in very useful in his business life.

She said, 'Someone walked over my grave.'

Through the side window she stared at tourists laughing and playing and calling to each other in a streetscape that danced and dazzled, lights and music a garish counterpoint to the wide, white beach and the limitless sea beyond the buildings and the cafés and the ubiquitous palms.

'You never used to be superstitious,' Patric said.

Her smile was tinged with bitterness. 'I never used to be a lot of things.'

The unspoken past was suddenly with them, rich with memories, each one saturated with delight and the heady potency of first love—and the pain that had followed.

'How bad was it?' Patric asked, his voice harsh.

'I managed.' Why tell him that the girl she'd been had died, that for years the only thing that had kept her going was Nick's utter dependence on her? She'd struggled free of that dreary winter of the soul. It was over, over and done with.

'I wish I'd known,' he said roughly.

'It wasn't your—'

'I'd have helped you. No woman should have to go through such trauma—and then bear and bring up a child—on her own.'

Kate squelched a debilitating hope by saying, 'Your wife might not have approved.'

Was it her imagination, or did the long fingers tense a moment on the wheel?

He said remotely, 'Laura and I didn't have a particularly close relationship.'

Stupid to feel dismissed, like an impertinent schoolgirl! Just as distantly Kate returned, 'It never occurred to me to contact you,' only realising when she'd said the words that she'd tried to hurt him as he'd hurt her.

Before he could answer, if he'd intended to, she asked lightly, 'How are your family—your mother and your aunt?' Greatly daring, she added, 'And what happened to your obnoxious cousin?'

'Sean?' He said the name as though it tasted foul. 'We don't see him any more. I haven't spoken to him for the last two years, and I have no intention of ever speaking to him again. I don't know where he is, but he won't be coming back to New Zealand.'

Thank God. Oh, thank God! Banishing the wild relief from her voice, she said, 'Your mother?'

'She's fine.' He didn't hesitate—it was impossible to think of Patric hesitating—but he paused before he said, 'She divides her time between Europe and New Zealand now, with side trips to various places.'

'It sounds a wonderful life.'

'She enjoys it.' Killing the engine beneath the sheltering portico at the apartment block, Patric said, 'Where are you planning to go tomorrow?'

'The last theme park,' she said, adding with a wry smile, 'More roller-coasters.'

His quiet laugh was suffocatingly intimate in the confines of the car. 'I like roller-coasters.'

Was he inviting himself along? Kate's heart jumped and she tried to ignore a slow, tantalising glimpse of delight. It would be perilously sweet to spend a day with him, especially as Nick would be the perfect buffer. And she no longer had to worry about Sean.

Striving to be practical, she realised also that if Patric came she wouldn't have to endure any more nail-biting, white-knuckled rides on assorted torture-machines.

But it wasn't pragmatism that persuaded her to say, 'If you don't mind spending the whole day having your stomach turned upside down, you're welcome to come too.'

'Would Nick mind?' he asked.

'Why should he?'

'Some children—boys especially, and even more so if they haven't got a father—are inclined to be possessive of their mothers.'

'Nick's not like that.' He'd had no opportunity—there had never been another man.

Patric nodded. 'What time will I pick you up?'

'The park opens at ten, so we'd better be there soon afterwards. Patric, are you sure you'd like it? Nick is a tiger for punishment, and we usually go all day. It's kids' stuff.'

'I was a kid once. I'll be here at a quarter to ten,' he said, and got out of the car.

She'd expected him to leave her at the main entrance. However, waiting for the lifts were a group of young men, obviously enjoying their first adult holiday. When she opened the door Patric strode in behind her.

They weren't rude or obnoxious, merely noisy and just too openly appreciative. Nevertheless, without saying a word, Patric made it more than clear that she was under his protection. And they accepted it, giving ground before the alpha male.

Men, Kate thought. In spite of the efforts of their mothers, and other assorted females through the ages, they still operated on primitive principles.

The babysitter was waiting inside the unit. As Kate lifted her purse from her bag, Patric handed over a banknote.

The babysitter looked at it. 'I haven't got change.'

'It's not necessary,' he said. 'Can I drive you home?'

Kate opened her mouth to object, then closed it again. She'd pay him back when the sitter had gone.

'No, thanks, I've got my car here.' She glanced from one to the other, gave them both a wide smile, and left, saying, 'He was a perfect kid, no problem at all. Goodnight.'

Awkwardly Kate closed the door behind her. 'How much was it?' she asked, fishing money from her purse.

Patric's gunmetal gaze was impossible to read. 'Humour me, Kate. You wouldn't have needed her if I hadn't pressed you to go out with me.'

'Well, no— but...'

He closed her fingers over the notes in her hand. As his touch ricocheted through her, every cell in her body burst into clamorous life. Her breath died in her throat.

Something flared in the depths of his eyes. 'I don't want your money. Buy Nick a souvenir or some new clothes.' The inflexible words were modified by a raw undercurrent that set her senses jangling. He released her hand and stepped back.

After a moment her pulses calmed down enough for her to say numbly, 'Thank you. I'll just check him.'

He was sleeping soundly, sprawled out across the sheets and blanket, the muted light from a lamp outside kindling hidden fire in his hair. Desperately trying to recover, Kate bent to touch his cheek, noting the steady rise and fall of his chest, and her heart clenched with sudden, overpowering love.

Unconsciously she passed her hand over his hair, and he stirred and said in a blurry voice, 'Mummy?'

'Yes, it's me. Go back to sleep,' she said softly.

He muttered something before relapsing into slumber. Kate waited, but he didn't move again. After straightening his sheet she turned away, only taking one step before she collided with a solid body.

'Oh!' Heat, she thought dazedly, stepping back, jerking free of Patric's swift grip on her elbows so quickly she almost tripped. Heat from his body—from her own—enveloped her.

She'd forgotten his faint male scent, so evocative that it bypassed her senses and homed straight to her emotions. Owing nothing to aftershave, it was the essence of the man who was Patric Sutherland—masculine, sexual, redolent of his energy and dynamic power and discipline, his keen mind and his effortless, understated authority.

It set her heart afire, roused her senses and magically, dangerously, switched off the insistent, cautious prompting of her brain. Drowning in an urgency of physical need, she had to get out of there fast.

So she had to walk. Now.

'Kate?' he asked quietly.

'It's all right,' she muttered.

On wobbly legs she retreated out of the room and down the lighted hallway while Patric closed the bedroom door behind him. Obeying an imperative warning, Kate headed to the front door and opened it.

'Goodnight,' she said.

'Goodnight.' His voice was cool and deep and emotionless, but when he reached her he stopped and smiled—a smile that stopped Kate's heart.

'You're even more beautiful,' he said, and touched her mouth with a lean forefinger. 'The eyes of a siren and the pride of a lioness, hair like black silk dusted with fire, and a mouth that suggests promises I'd kill to collect on.'

Desire smoked through the words, stark, relentless, overwhelming her. His smile took over her mind as she closed the door behind him and leaned back against it, stupid, unwanted tears filling her eyes as her heart thudded erratically against her breastbone.

Their day at the theme park was a time of complicated, reckless pleasure. Patric rode every ride with Nick, sealing her son's affection and respect, and answered constant questions with faultless patience and what seemed to be true interest. Even when Nick became tired and a little grumpy his tolerance didn't waver.

Amusing, protective and masterful in a low-key way, formal clothes banished for a light shirt and casual trousers, those angular, striking features not exactly softened by his good humour, he gave Nick his full attention. And because he possessed a natural talent for leadership, Nick became an enthusiastic follower. Patric's hard eyes gentled when they rested on her son's face, and he joined Nick in teasing her because she refused to terrify herself into fits.

As she made a spirited defence Kate caught herself thinking how wonderful it would be to have someone to share the responsibility. It seemed shameful, as though she'd put Patric—with his broad shoulders, his ability to conjure waitresses and his compelling authority—before Nick.

Afterwards, when her son was asleep, Kate sat down on the side of her bed, listening to the silence of the apartment. That day, beguiled by an old, sentimental dream, she'd surrendered to the magic Patric had always been able to weave about her.

But once they got on the plane to New Zealand it would be over. He was a busy man—far too busy to have time to spare for a woman who'd once jilted him and a boy without a father.

The telephone rang. Starting, Kate stared at it before reaching out to pick it up. Her fingers, she noted, were shaking. Although she'd known who it would be, her bones melted at the sound of Patric's voice.

'I hoped you wouldn't be in bed,' he said.

'I'm on my way.'

'Are you tired?'

Kate seized the excuse. 'Actually, I am,' she said, keeping her voice light. 'I thought it was steeling myself to go on those wretched rides that wears me out, but it must be the parks themselves.' She made herself finish, 'Patric, thank you so much. Nick had a glorious time.'

There was a moment's silence. 'Did you have a good time too?'

'Yes, of course.'

'But Nick comes first.'

Kate said firmly, 'He has to.'

'I understand.' His voice altered slightly as he went on, 'He's a great kid. Did we ever have that much energy?'

Her mouth curved spontaneously. 'Oh, I think so,' she said. 'When we were young.'

Quiet laughter sent shivers up her spine. 'So long ago,' he mocked. 'I remember the day we all went to Raglan for a picnic—do you?'

Her heart lurched; he'd kissed her for the very first time that day, gently, tenderly, and she'd gone up like a sky-rocket as they'd stood, wet skin against wet skin, hearts beating so intensely that their subdued thunder still resounded in her ears. It had been her first experience of the merciless power of passion.

'I remember,' she said drily. How quickly he'd accustomed her to the slow, sweet, almost chaste caresses that were all he'd allowed himself that summer.

Of course he'd had a very willing pupil. Rapidly she asked, 'Why did you ring, Patric?'

'To say goodnight,' he said, his voice indolently amused. 'And to thank you.'

She should have left it at that, but she didn't. 'What for?'

'For letting me come with you today.'

A supplicant attitude was not a natural one for Patric. Uneasily wondering whether he was up to anything, Kate said, 'We had a super time, didn't we? I hope Nick thanked you.'

'Several times—he has excellent manners. What would you like to do tomorrow? You've run out of theme parks.'

'Yes, that was the last today.'

'Would Nick like to go to a lighthouse? There's a little one just over the border in New South Wales, where the waves roar in onto the rocks with a very satisfying crash and hiss of spray. Afterwards we could go to the top of Mount Tamborine and watch the hang-gliders take off.'

'Nick would love it,' she said slowly. 'Thank you.'

'Would you like it?'

A little bewildered, she answered, 'Yes, of course.'

'Right. I'll pick you up at nine.' He waited a second, then finished easily, 'Goodnight, Kate. Dream of good things.'

She murmured an answer and hung up. If only she could separate the past from the present, but whenever he spoke in that tone—whenever he smiled at her, whenever his dark gaze rested on her face—she was once more the child who'd loved him, made love with him and lost him.

One more day, she promised herself, getting into bed. That's all. And it is wonderful for Nick to have a male companion like Patric, even if it's only for a short time.

Her son knew plenty of men, but seldom had the unadulterated attention of one for any length of time. So this was for Nick. She turned out the light and went to sleep, to dream of Patric.

Kate flushed the next morning when she recalled those dreams, but Patric's behaviour that day reassured her. Because he was Patric he was sexy and wildly attractive, but there was nothing remotely sexual—or even gallant—in his attitude. For which she was grateful, she told herself.

She wasn't in the least bit irritated that Nick thought the sun shone through those dark grey eyes. Not a bit. And certainly not jealous.

Not even when Nick's every second sentence began with *Mr Sutherland says.*

The lighthouse was glorious—a cute, white, two-storeyed affair on a headland. An island crouched offshore, and through trees they could see a long, wave-pounded beach stretching to a cluster of hazy towers that denoted another seaside resort.

'Did you notice,' Kate said, 'that once you get over the border into New South Wales there are no palms?'

Patric laughed. 'Yes, I'd noticed.'

'So did I,' Nick said loyally.

They grinned at each other, and Nick suddenly hugged them both, twining his arms around their waists. 'We look like a family,' he said with satisfaction. 'I bet those people over there think we're a proper family. I'm sorry you haven't got any children, Mr Sutherland. If you had, I could play with them. Can we go and see the waves now, Mummy?'

Shaken, Kate said, 'Yes.'

'There's no beach beneath the cliffs,' Patric told him, 'So we have to stand well back. All right?'

Nick nodded, a little in awe of the cool authority in Patric's tone. They walked across the tawny grass and stood watching the rounded waves surge in and smash themselves against the rocks in a smother of spray. The impact throbbed through the ground like the dynamo of some hidden power source.

'Look!' Nick breathed, taking a few steps towards the edge of the cliff.

'Why don't you sit against that screw pine?' Patric suggested. 'You'll be able to see the foam burst above the rocks very clearly from there.'

Obediently, Nick sat on the grass, leaning back against the trunk, and stared with wide eyes at the waves.

'Do you think he might have found the next big interest?' Patric asked.

'It looks like it.'

With his eyes fixed on the smooth, humped combers coming in, and the wild outburst of spray, Patric said, 'Laura didn't want children.'

Torn between a need to know what had happened and an immense reluctance to hear anything about his marriage, Kate hesitated before saying, 'That's a shame, if you wanted them.'

He gave her a brief, unsmiling look. Another breaker thudded into the black rocks, sending a wild fountain of spray into the air, white foam against the intense ultramarine of the sea. 'It never occurred to me that we wouldn't have them. Marrying Laura was the most spectacularly stupid thing I've ever done.'

'Then why did you do it?'

'Her father was my father's greatest friend.' His voice was cool, almost bored, but the note of distaste in the words chilled her; he turned his head so that all she could see were the angles of his profile. 'I liked her and I knew she liked me. What I didn't know was that both my father and Laura's were desperate for me to marry her.'

Kate had been sure she'd overcome her disconcerting tendency to jealousy, but even to hear him say Laura's name ate like acid into her composure. 'You don't have to tell me this,' she said, the words pinched and abrupt.

'I think I do. I'd have preferred a less public place—although perhaps it's a good thing it's not.'

She said nothing, keeping her eyes fixed on a group of girls who'd just walked by with a couple of teachers and some long-suffering parents. A few feet away Nick crouched, mesmerised.

After a moment Patric went on, 'My father wanted to see me married, settled before he died.'

'I can understand that.'

Apparently irrelevantly he said, 'He loved Tatamoa, loved farming, the whole agricultural scene. He only took over Sutherland Aviation because it would have broken ''Black'' Pat's heart to see it sold.'

Kate nodded.

Patric's voice was calm, reflective. 'He wasn't a spectacular failure—he was a hard-working, reliable, conscientious managing director—but he had little understanding of business and a tendency to trust the wrong people.

When I took over Sutherland's it was perilously close to going under. It needed radical restructuring, and I had to work with a board my father had packed with men who were sure I was heading in the wrong direction. Laura's father was on it; he was the only one who understood what I wanted to do. The others trusted him, so he had the power to bring them around.'

Kate said tightly, 'You married Laura to haul Sutherland Aviation out of the fire? Pull the other leg, Patric. That sort of thing died with the Victorians.'

His mouth thinned. 'How innocent you are, Kate.' It wasn't a compliment. 'Of course no one actually came out and stated it—the pressure was subtle. I was grieving for my father, supporting my mother as best I could, and working furiously to save several thousand jobs around the world, so I didn't immediately take in the full implications.' After a taut moment he continued, 'I married Laura because I was forced to.'

Patric—determined, resolute, strong-willed Patric—forced to do something against his will? *Marry* against his will? Kate's disbelief was mirrored in her face, in the scornful twist of her mouth.

He answered her unspoken question. 'Hard to credit, I'll agree, but one tends to want to do what one can for one's dying father. Not marry to order, however. As soon as I realised what my father was pushing for I went to see Laura.'

'And?' She remembered how Laura used to look at him.

Broad shoulders moved in the slightest of shrugs. 'She thought it an excellent idea. She was ready to settle down, she said, and we knew each other well. It would make both our fathers happy, and help mine die in peace. It would also help Sutherland Aviation when it became known that her father was backing me.'

'How sensible of her.'

Patric's laugh was low and caustic. 'I'm afraid I offended her with my reaction. I had to see you, so I came down to Tatamoa.'

Kate closed her eyes briefly.

'I was going to ask you to marry me,' he said levelly, 'But you told me you no longer wanted anything to do with me, and that you had another lover. I was so stunned I couldn't think, couldn't do anything but fight to control my instinct to snatch you up and keep you with me until you admitted that you loved me.' His words were textured by self-contempt. 'My fury and panic frightened me and shocked me. I hated losing control, so I thought I'd give you until the end of the year.

'About ten minutes after I got back to Auckland from Poto still in shock because you'd said you didn't want anything more to do with me, Laura rang. She said she'd decided to inform our parents that she was pregnant to me. If that didn't persuade me to marry her, she'd tell them she was going to have an abortion. She knew what that would do to my parents—especially my father, who'd always wanted a big family.'

In the pockets of her jeans Kate's hands clenched so tightly she could feel the pain in her knuckles. It was easier to bear than the pain in her heart. 'Was she pregnant?'

'No, and if she had been it wouldn't have been mine. We'd never slept together. We had an argument. I told her to keep away from my parents, and then I flew down to Christchurch to find you, but you'd already left the university and disappeared. While I was there my father had to be rushed into hospital—it was touch and go for thirty-six hours. A week later, when he was well enough to come home, I rang your aunt and uncle. But they'd gone too.'

'They were given a handsome payment and a week to get off the place,' she said, thin-lipped. Another wave crashed onto the black rocks, its impact reverberating through the ground as foam soared high into the air.

Patric's striking buccaneer's face hardened. 'I was told your uncle had resigned.'

'He was sacked.'

He swore beneath his breath, his voice flat and lethal. 'My father wasn't the businessman that "Black" Pat was, but he could be every bit as ruthless. That was when Laura's father told me he'd see Sutherland Aviation go down if I didn't marry her. She stayed away from my parents, but she'd convinced him that she was pregnant with my child.'

'What did your mother think of all this?' It hurt that Mrs Sutherland, whom Kate had always liked, should have allowed her son to be blackmailed into marriage.

'She wasn't happy, but I suspect she had a desperate hope that a grandchild might give my father an extra reason to live.'

He was hating this, and so was Kate. Long-dormant emotions churned through her, setting fire to her temper like sparks in the wind. How could his parents have used his love and respect to force him into a marriage he didn't want?

Watching her son, Kate said in a low, furious voice, 'They should be ashamed of themselves, all of them.'

'Laura's father lost his daughter,' Patric said unemotionally. 'My father died, leaving my mother a widow. Laura died. I think they all paid, don't you?'

'What about you?' she asked passionately. 'They betrayed you.'

'After you told me you didn't want to see me any more and then disappeared I no longer cared much,' he said smoothly. 'I knew what the crash of Sutherland Aviation would do to my father, and to the people who were working for it.'

Guilt reined in her anger. 'Their pressure must have been almost unbearable. And you loved your father.'

'Oh, yes,' he said with remote precision. 'At least he was dead before it came totally unstuck. Laura wanted a playmate, and what she got was a man driven to work day and night to rescue what I could from the wreckage my father had inadvertently left.

'She waited until after my father died to announce that she'd had a miscarriage.' He swung around and directed an oblique, unreadable glance at her. 'So that's the sad story of my marriage,' he said, bare steel ringing through each word. 'Two years later Laura drank too much one night when I was overseas and went for a swim. She drowned.'

Nobody deserved to die like that, but Laura had certainly asked for unhappiness.

'I'm sorry,' Kate said, meaning it. 'I wonder why we have to make decisions when we're in the worst possible state to see clearly.'

'To test us, perhaps.' He looked down at Nick, who was utterly absorbed in watching the waves come in. 'Seen enough?'

'He won't hear you—he's lost in wonder.' Kate took the few steps to the screw pine and bent down. 'Come on, Nick, it's time to go.'

'Oh.' He scrambled up, his face radiant. 'Mummy, where do the waves come from? How do they build up? Why do they get white tops on them? Is it steam?'

'No, it's foam, and we'll look up the answers to your other questions when we get back home,' Kate said, smiling as the wind tossed her hair about her face. Patric's story had affected her profoundly but she couldn't deal with it now.

He said, 'It looks like you have another project on your hands.'

'Are we going for a swim off that beach?' Nick asked.

'It's too rough,' Kate said firmly. 'We'll wait until we get back to the apartments. However, Mr Sutherland says he knows where there are some hang-gliders.'

They spent the afternoon on top of Mount Tamborine, watching hang-gliders launch themselves and soar across a valley the colour of light toast. Kate, a sensible distance back from the low wall that marked the drop-off, watched closely as Patric took Nick's hand and walked over to the low barrier. After a few moments she relaxed; Patric was well able to curb her son's natural desire to get too close to the cliff-edge.

She allowed herself to take in the glorious gold of the valley below the cliff, the dim blue outline of the Great Dividing Range to the west, and the scent of Australia—dry, exciting, tinged with eucalyptus and smoke.

Nick, small hand lost in Patric's, hopped with eagerness, his voice rising and falling as questions bubbled from him. Patric answered them all.

After that they had a drink at a café and drove down the winding, steep highway to the Gold Coast.

'We're going home tomorrow,' Nick said from the back. 'A part of our prize is a shuttle. It's just a bus, but it brought us down from the airport and tomorrow it will take us back. We have to be ready at three in the afternoon.'

'What time do you fly out?' Patric asked.

'Qantas leaves at exactly six o'clock.' Nick sighed, then cheered up. 'But we get back to New Zealand in the middle of the night.'

Patric nodded. 'Where are you staying in Auckland?'

'With a friend who lives in Albany,' Kate said. 'She's coming to meet us at the airport.'

'And the next day we're going on the bus to Whangarei,' Nick said importantly.

Patric glanced at Kate. 'I thought you had a car?'

'Not one I'd trust to get me to Auckland and back,' she said crisply.

'We've got an old banger,' Nick informed him with relish. 'It's called Eugene.'

'I remember—a Mini. Why Eugene?'

Kate said, 'That's what its previous owner called it.'

'Once it broke down,' Nick said. 'The radiator cracked and we had to walk everywhere 'til we could save up enough to get it fixed.'

Patric's beautiful mouth tightened fractionally. 'Then you were wise to take the bus to Auckland,' he said.

Feeling like a poor relation, Kate nodded and stared out of the window.

Nick asked, 'When are you going back, Mr Sutherland?'

'Tomorrow too,' he said, 'But not on your plane.'

At the apartments he parked the car in the visitor's slot and said curtly, 'Invite me in, Kate.'

Her hands twisted in her lap. 'I don't think that would be a very good idea,' she said, when the silence had gone on too long.

He switched the engine off. 'I'd like to see how well Nick can swim,' he said, his voice betraying that he knew he was putting her in a difficult situation.

Of course Nick demanded that he stay. Kate gave in, although she was ruffled by Patric's tactics.

'You swim too,' Nick commanded.

He shook his head. 'I haven't got any togs with me. I'll watch you swim.'

Nick didn't need to look quite so disappointed, Kate thought resentfully.

As they sat on the edge of the pool, watching Nick's black head and tanned body, sleek as a seal, while he showed off his prowess, Patric said, 'Don't be angry, Kate.'

'Using Nick like that was unfair, and you know it. It's cruel to play with children's emotions.'

He frowned. 'I hadn't thought of it like that. All right, I won't do it again.'

'Good,' she said curtly, wondering whether that meant he wanted to see more of Nick. If he did, what would she say?

No, she thought swiftly, before temptation set in, it would be too dangerous.

'Come out to dinner with me tonight,' he said indolently.

She shook her head. 'I can't. I have to pack, and tomorrow morning we're going to buy clothes.'

His expression didn't change, but black lashes drooped over eyes the colour of polished iron. 'So this is goodbye,' he said coolly.

Kate kept her eyes on Nick's burnished head. 'Yes.' She knew it had to be said, so why did the word echo through her soul with such cold, implacable finality?

'You're a coward.' Contempt crackled through his voice.

Her own temper fired. 'Because I won't go out to dinner with you? Hardly cowardice, Patric! Just common sense.'

He drawled, 'Your eyes go green as grass when you're angry. What's so sensible about denying yourself a good meal—at a restaurant, if you'd feel safer?'

Kate leaned over and called Nick. 'Come on out,' she said, 'your chin's starting to wobble.'

'Now who's using him?' Patric demanded through his teeth.

Good—he'd lost his temper too. Politely, she said, 'Nick's getting cold. And I don't use him; he's the most important person—the most important thing—in the world to me.'

Complaining, dripping, Nick dragged himself reluctantly up the steps and stood by them as they got to their feet. Still buoyed by anger, Kate said easily, 'Say goodbye to Mr Sutherland, Nick.'

He held out a slim tanned hand and said his farewells. Leashing his temper, Patric shook his hand and said goodbye. Before Kate realised what was happening he bent and took her mouth in a kiss that seared her heart. Her body sprang to life, as though she'd been waiting all these years for that kiss.

When he lifted his head she stared into molten eyes, unable to speak, unable to think, unable to do anything but react.

'Remember that, Sleeping Beauty,' he said in a low,

savage voice, 'When your bed feels empty at night.' And he turned on his heel and walked away.

'Mummy!' Nick tugged at her hand and demanded indignantly, 'Why did he do that?'

Running her tongue over her tender lips, she said huskily, 'He was saying goodbye.'

'He didn't kiss *me* goodbye,' Nick said, disgruntled. 'Where's my towel?'

'Behind you.' Kate forced herself to speak calmly, to go with him into the apartment, to behave normally, when all the time she felt as though Patric had branded her with that kiss.

It was over. They'd spent the morning shopping for clothes and presents—including a weather station Nick fell in love with and refused to be parted from—and now they were all packed and ready to go. Kate made one last round of the rooms, in case they'd overlooked anything, and after glancing at her watch checked for the third time that their passports were in the pocket in her bag. 'Come on, Nick, time to go.'

The hour-long trip up the motorway and across the huge bridge over the Brisbane River assumed a dream-like aspect. Kate answered Nick's questions, periodically looking above his head at the hot, sparse landscape outside; she organised them competently off the bus, and steered the luggage trolley across the wide terminal to check in, waiting while the clerk tapped information into her computer.

'Ah, you've both been upgraded,' she said, smiling, after a quick glance at their passports. 'You'll have a more comfortable ride back.'

'How's that?' Kate asked, frowning.

The clerk looked again at her computer screen. 'It happens,' she said lightly. 'The plane's not very full tonight so they've put some lucky people up. I'd just enjoy it if I were you.'

'We'll do that,' Kate said with a smile, accepting the boarding passes. 'Thank you.'

After watching their cases disappearing down the conveyer belt, Nick insisted on a complete tour of the light, airy, tree-shaded concourse.

For once Kate found his comments and observations tiring. Making herself relax, she tried to enter into his enthusiasm, and succeeded well enough until eventually they sat down in one of the cafés for a drink.

When Nick had half drained his glass, he said, 'Mr Sutherland lives in Auckland, doesn't he?'

'Yes.' Kate knew she sounded abrupt, so she smiled.

Nick poked his straw into the ice at the bottom of his glass. 'Will he come up to see us in Whangarei?'

You too? she thought painfully. 'I don't think he'll have time to do that, Nick.'

Nick prodded some more, his long lashes dark against his golden skin. He didn't look at her as he said in a gruff voice, 'Won't we ever see him again?'

'He's a very busy man,' Kate said gently. 'But you had a good time here, didn't you?'

'Yes.' He drew a complicated pattern on the surface of the water with his straw. 'I liked it better when Mr Sutherland was with us.'

Kate began to talk of school, of what Nick would be able to tell his classmates about his holiday, of the things Anna and Jacob next door would find particularly interesting, and with the swiftness of childhood Nick forgot that he was sad and began to enthuse again.

Listening to him remind himself of the thrill of one particular roller-coaster, Kate knew there'd be moments of wistfulness whenever he remembered Patric, although eventually even they would fade until he only recalled the pleasure.

It might even happen for her too.

Before long their flight number was called.

'Up the front,' the steward on the plane said, smiling

professionally as Kate showed him the boarding passes. 'On the right, madam.'

She walked up through the throngs of passengers, then stopped.

'May I help?' An attendant appeared from nowhere.

'I think I need to go further on,' Kate said, glancing at her pass, 'but this screen seems to tell me I shouldn't go through.'

The attendant examined the passes. 'Keep going,' she said.

Waiting by the screen was another attendant, dark-suited, as dignified as a head waiter.

'Ah, we were wondering where you were,' he said, smiling at Nick, who was looking about him with frank and obvious interest. 'This way.'

Here the seats were large, and to Nick's delight each had a small television screen mounted in the arm. Did ordinary travellers routinely get bumped up to first class?

'Here we are,' the steward said, stopping. 'Would you like to sit next to the window, sir?'

'My name's Nick,' Nick said gravely. 'Can I sit next to the window, Mummy?'

'May I,' she corrected. 'Yes, of course.'

'May I?' Nick repeated, scrambling into his seat with alacrity.

Just before she sat down she cast a glance around the rest of the section, but of course Patric's black head wasn't anywhere there. And in spite of the desk clerk's comment that the plane wasn't full, first class was.

This, she thought as she clipped the seatbelt around her, was how Patric travelled all the time. And of course he wouldn't have organised it—why should he?

She had no illusions; his kindness might indicate a streak of chivalry beneath the tough, hardened businessman façade, but once he'd discovered that Nick wasn't his son his pressing interest must have died. He'd kissed her because he was angry, but by now he'd probably put them out of his mind.

As the plane took off, and they were pampered all the way across the Tasman, Kate tried to convince herself that those days in Surfers' Paradise had provided her with some sort of closure, a feeling that all the ends had been tied up and she could now face the future unimpeded by baggage from the past.

Unfortunately her response to that kiss revealed a much more unpalatable truth. She was every bit as susceptible to Patric as she had been all those years ago. The golden glamour of his youth had been replaced by a potent male charisma, part intelligence, part dynamic power, part controlled determination. And beneath that smouldered an indefinable magnetism that called to her with a sensual promise against which she had no defence.

CHAPTER FIVE

THEY landed on an Auckland spring night—wet, of course, and chilly after the burgeoning warmth of sub-tropical Australia. Nick, who'd slept most of the way across, didn't take too kindly to being wakened. His normal sunny temperament in abeyance, he trailed alongside Kate, complaining while they waited for their luggage to emerge on the carousel.

'Darling, that's enough,' Kate finally said.

He gave her a belligerent glower. 'My eyes feel sticky.'

'It won't be long now. Just hang on in there.'

As she heaved their cases off the carousel and stacked them on the trolley Kate thought wryly that although it was politically incorrect to like being cared for, just occasionally it would be wonderful to have a strong-armed man to heft luggage about.

Of course they had to wait in the Immigration and Customs hall; two other planes had arrived just before them—one, she saw, a Sutherland Aviation jet, also from Brisbane. Patric would have been on it…

Ruthlessly wrenching her mind back from that dangerous path, she concentrated on shuffling towards the desks. Thankfully Nick had forgotten his crossness in the excitement of watching a little sniffer dog bustling around. Then at last they were through and walking into the Arrivals area.

Sally Pickering, with her shock of vivid red hair, should have stood out like a bonfire on a dark night. No doubt if she'd been there she would have.

'You can sit down here and look after our suitcases while I go to the desk and see if she's left a message,'

Kate said firmly, wheeling their trolley towards a bank of seats.

Nick's lip wobbled. 'Has she forgotten us?' he asked soberly.

'Not Sally. She'll have—'

'Mr Sutherland!' he exclaimed, his face lighting up. 'Look, there's Mr Sutherland! He'll find Sally for us!'

'Don't shout!' But Kate's heart clamoured in her breast. She followed Nick's gaze and saw Patric striding across the concourse, accompanied by a man wearing the sort of clothes you'd choose to impress the boss late at night, and a woman in tailored trousers and a silk shirt, a jacket slung across one elegant, slim shoulder.

Patric swung around. His brows drew together and he turned back to speak to the other two, who stopped and waited as he headed purposefully towards Kate and Nick.

'Good flight?' he asked, as though he'd never kissed her.

'Great, thank you,' Kate returned in her briskest tone. 'We were upgraded to first class and had a wonderful time, didn't we, Nick?'

'Cool,' he agreed, gazing worshipfully at Patric, his tired face split by a smile.

Ignoring the intrigued and speculative stares from the two people who'd met Patric—and every woman within eyesight—Kate went on, 'We won't keep you, Patric. Thank you for making our last few days in Australia such fun.'

The arrogant mouth didn't soften. 'I had fun too,' he said negligently. 'Where's the friend who was going to meet you?'

Thwarted in her attempt to make a dignified and final goodbye, Kate admitted, 'She's not here yet. But she won't be long—she's very reliable, is Sally.'

Nick sagged against her, lost in an enormous yawn.

'How about her car?' Patric asked after a grim glance at the boy. 'Or is it like Eugene, prone to breakdowns?'

Kate put her hand on her son's shoulder, holding him steady. 'It's reliable too. She's just running a little late. And if she can't make it she'll have left a message for us.'

As though her words had summoned it, a pleasant female voice said over the intercom, 'Would Ms Brown—Ms Kate Brown—please come to the Information Desk.'

Patric said abruptly, 'Stay there, I'll go. Give me your passport.' When she stared at him, he said, 'I don't think they'll believe I'm Ms Kate Brown.'

Nick gave a crow of laughter, and Kate smiled but said, 'Patric, you've got people—'

'They'll wait,' he said, holding out his hand. 'I won't be a moment.'

The previous sleepless night must have clouded her brain, because she handed over the passport and watched him make his way through the press of people to the Information Desk. It might have been his height or those wide shoulders, but it was more probably the aura of dynamic power that had them parting before him like the waters before Moses. His casual clothes, although tailored to fit him, didn't mark him out from the other men there, but it was amazing how many eyes followed his progress.

Repressing a stark pang of isolation, Kate looped her arm around her son. Warm, lax, his eyes heavy with interrupted sleep, Nick gazed silently after his hero. More passengers emerged from the Arrivals Hall, were enveloped in greetings, and disappeared through the doors into the night.

The girl on the Information Desk cheered up when Patric arrived, bestowing on him a smile that went well beyond professional goodwill. He spoke; she nodded, then peered at Kate's passport and looked across. Kate gave a wave that indicated, she hoped, that she was Kate Brown.

With another dazzled smile the woman handed over an envelope. Kate braced herself. If Sally had been called away she and Nick would have to spend the rest of the night at the airport, because she didn't have enough money to pay for a motel. Every cent of holiday money was gone, and she wasn't going to hock herself to her credit card.

'She rang it in about three hours ago,' Patric told her as he handed the envelope over.

Kate's fingers shook as she slit it open. Sally's grandmother in Wellington had had a heart attack and wasn't expected to last the night, so Sally was driving down with her brother. She was so sorry... The hasty scrawl tailed off into an indecipherable signature.

Damn, Kate thought, why hadn't she left a key to her house?

And immediately she felt mean and selfish. Sally was devoted to her grandmother, and anyway, shuttles didn't go out as far as Albany.

Oh, well, a night at the airport wasn't going to mark her or Nick for life!

'What's happened?' Patric asked, as though he had the right to.

In her crispest, most confident voice she told him. He looked down at Nick, visibly drooping. 'What will you do?'

Kate said confidently, 'Nick and I will manage.'

Patric's eyes narrowed as he surveyed her face. In response Kate straightened her shoulders and tilted her chin.

Calmly he said, 'You can come home with me.' He cut off her instant rejection. 'What time do you catch your bus tomorrow morning?'

'It leaves Auckland at eight-thirty.' Tempted, she ploughed on, 'You're very kind, Patric, but of course we can't plonk ourselves onto you like this. I promise you I can deal with—'

'I'm sure you can,' he interrupted, impatience threading the words. 'But why bother when you don't need to? I live in an apartment block on the waterfront—all you'll need to do in the morning is take the lift down and walk just over a block to the bus depot.'

Nick gave a prodigious yawn.

'You and Nick can sleep in the guest bedroom,' Patric said deliberately, divining her reservation with an accuracy that sent heat licking across her skin.

'Can we, please?' Nick asked, his voice rough with exhaustion. 'May we, I mean?'

The decision was made by Patric, who took the handle of the luggage cart and headed into the press of people.

'Hey!' Kate exclaimed, scooping Nick along with her as she set off after Patric's arrogant figure. He stopped by the two people he'd abandoned. Interesting, Kate thought angrily, to see their instant attention.

Two heads nodded while he spoke with curt rapidity. As she and Nick came up to them he said, 'I'll see you at nine tomorrow morning. Goodnight.'

Again they nodded, smiled at Kate and Nick, made brief farewells and left.

'Patric,' Kate began, following him as he picked up his suitcase and settled it onto the trolley, then wheeled it through the doors.

She'd meant to tell him he was overbearing and autocratic, and insist on managing her own affairs, but when they stepped out into the cold darkness and she felt the rain on her face and Nick's hand suddenly cling to hers she admitted defeat.

As Patric had known she would, she thought crossly, already regretting it. But what harm could a night do?

Patric commandeered a taxi and put them into it, gave the driver the address and got in himself, helping Nick put on his seatbelt. Kate fumed, 'Talk about high-handed.'

'You were going to dither,' he said levelly. 'This is the most sensible way of dealing with the situation, and you know it.'

'I don't like being bulldozed.'

'No one does. Give it a rest, Kate—you can shout at me when we don't have an audience.'

Nick was sitting very quietly—too quietly. Shamefacedly Kate said, 'Ah, well, it's rather fun being in a taxi whizzing through Auckland in the middle of the night, isn't it, Nick?'

'Yes.' His voice was uncertain, but only five minutes into the trip he relaxed sideways onto Kate, abandoning himself again to sleep.

Tensely Kate cuddled him, waiting for Patric to speak. He was probably thinking he'd gone crazy, inviting two strays home for the night, she thought gloomily.

The taxi drove steadily through rain, long needles of it flashing towards the windscreen like darts until the taxi swung off the motorway into the streets of the inner city. Slowing, the taxi turned beneath a portico.

Welcome to spring, Kate thought as the engine died.

The holiday was over, yet she didn't feel depressed. In fact, excitement sizzled with delicate, feverish precision along her nerves. While Patric and the driver organised the luggage she got out of the vehicle and reached for Nick. He was sound asleep so she had to pick him up. She managed to get him into her arms, but staggered as she straightened up.

Patric looked up; some transient emotion glittered in the dark eyes. 'Give him to me,' he commanded, striding around the end of the cab.

Kate said, 'It's all right.'

'He's too heavy. Hand him over—you won't be able to carry him all the way up.'

Reluctantly she accepted his help, looking down into her son's blissfully unconscious face with a pang as she handed him over.

'What's the matter?' Patric asked, holding the boy easily.

'It's silly—but I've always been able to carry him before.'

'He's growing up.' The few conventional words sounded like a condemnation, but as he was striding away from her towards the door she might have misheard him.

Shivering in the raw air, Kate followed him.

When he stopped he said, 'The key card's in my right-hand jacket pocket. Get it out and unlock the door, will you?'

Carefully, Kate inserted her hand into his pocket and found the card. She put it into the lock, then did the same with an interior door. The taxi driver, a suitcase in each hand, followed them in.

A smooth, discreetly luxurious and very fast lift took them all up. Kate stood with her eyes averted from the man who held her son so carefully in his arms.

'The same key,' he said when the lift stopped to reveal just one door in a carpeted vestibule. 'My front door,' Patric told her. 'The light switch is inside on the left.'

Kate used the key card again, pushed the door open and turned on the lights. They revealed a hall, complete with mirror above a modern Italian-style console table in polished dark wood. An abstract painting in moody blues and golds smouldered against pale walls, and a superb plant stood in an elegant oriental pot.

'Your bedroom's the third door to the right,' Patric said. 'It doesn't look as though anything disturbs him.'

'No.' Lifting Nick's case, Kate walked slightly ahead so that she could push the door open and switch the lights on in the bedroom.

Lamps flowered in the ceiling and on either side of two large single beds. Patric laid Nick down on one of them, and stood for a moment looking down at the sleeping child, his expression guarded. Was he regretting that Nick wasn't his son? When he looked up and saw Kate watching him his mouth tightened.

'I'll pay the cab driver and bring in your luggage,' he said.

Chilled, Kate held out the key. 'Thank you.'

In spite of the warmth of the room she shivered again, oppressed by the ghosts of dead emotions. Brushing aside their inchoate warnings, she began to untie Nick's brand-new sneakers, his pride and joy.

She was easing his jeans down his legs when Patric spoke from the door. 'Does he always sleep so soundly?' he asked quietly, setting down Kate's suitcase.

'Usually. He's extra tired tonight, of course.'

Golden light from the bedside lamps gleamed on Patric's black head, picking out with loving intensity the stark planes and angles of his face, the slightly darker bronze of his five-o'clock shadow as he said, 'The beds are already made up. The bathroom is through that door—you'll find towels in the cupboard beside the hand basin. I'll go down and bring back my case.'

Nodding, Kate deftly removed Nick's shirt, rolled him over, pulled back the bedcover and inserted him between the sheets. He mumbled something but didn't stir, apart from hunching away from the light. Kate smoothed a lock of hair from his brow and kissed his cheek.

'Thank you,' she said to Patric, who had returned by then.

'Do you want a drink, or something to eat?'

She shook her head. 'No, thank you. I think I'll go straight to bed.'

'What time do you want to be woken?'

'I'll set my alarm for seven,' she said, turning to smile uncertainly at him. 'This is very kind of you, Patric.'

He stood like a sentinel in the doorway, the hard face formidable. 'Then goodnight, Kate,' he said, and although his voice was gentle there was a metallic light in the eyes that scrutinised her face.

She had to swallow, and even then her voice was croaky with strain. 'Goodnight, Patric,' she said.

When the door closed silently behind him her breath sighed out between her lips.

Kate looked at her son, still peacefully sleeping, and the old turmoil of regret and bitterness and love welled up. No, best not to think of it; she'd made her decisions and she'd stick with them.

Nick was nothing like his father. He would grow up

respecting women, liking them too much to believe that they were all whores at heart. And Patric had no place in their lives.

Grim-faced, Kate knelt by her suitcase, opened it and took out her sponge bag and T-shirt.

The bathroom that led off the bedroom was all marble, in soft creams and rosy pinks. How much had it cost? More than her entire income for a year, she thought cynically, but it was gloriously plush. After she'd worked out how the space-age controls functioned she had a splendid shower.

While drying herself she looked at her reflection in the huge mirror, wondering at first because the steam hadn't clouded it with moisture. How had they done that? No doubt it needed expensive equipment. It didn't seem worth it, just to look at yourself.

That wide expanse of fog-free glass seemed to epitomise the enormous difference between her and Patric. Coming here had been a mistake, as had letting Patric spend time with them in Australia. She'd made more than enough mistakes where he was concerned, and as she didn't seem able to learn from the past it was just as well she wouldn't be seeing him again.

But when she lay in the luxurious bed, more comfortable than any she'd ever slept in, and listened to the muted sounds of traffic and Nick's occasional little snuffle, she wondered whether forgetting him was going to be so easy.

Perhaps she should also consider the fact that a traitor was at work inside her—the adolescent passion that had never died.

Restlessly she turned over onto her back. Was Patric just through the wall? An unbidden tide of erotic anticipation swamped her as she pictured him, long and lean and tanned, sable hair on a white pillow, a lamp illuminating with excruciating accuracy the smooth olive skin, the long-boned arms and legs, the flat stomach and narrow male hips…

He'd always been beautiful to her, so strong and confident in his masculinity, so assured—to her and every other woman, she thought acidly, recalling the revealingly envious, unspoken accolades of other women.

The reason her fixation still existed was probably because she and Patric had only made love once before her blossoming sensuality had been shattered by the nightmare experience of rape and brutality.

Perhaps, her brain suddenly said, you should have an affair with him and get him out of your system.

Forget you ever thought that, Kate commanded, turning onto her side to woo sleep with desperate fervour.

She had almost made it when she snapped awake again, remembering the plastic bag with Nick's treasured weather station in it. Frowning, she tried to recall its arrival in the apartment.

It hadn't; she'd have remembered the distinctive bag Nick had carried onto the plane and insisted on having under his seat all the way across the Tasman. She recalled Patric handing it to Nick when they'd got into the back seat of the taxi; she hadn't thought of it when she'd picked him up.

He'd be desolate if it was lost.

Perhaps it had been left at the front entrance. Moving silently, she got up and slipped out of the bedroom, down the tiled hall, its warmth telling her there was underfloor heating. At the front door she switched on the light, but no plastic bag stood there.

'What's the matter?'

She whirled. Patric stood watching her, still fully clothed, although he'd changed. He now wore jeans and a cotton shirt. Paradoxically, he looked infinitely more unapproachable in them than he had before.

Feeling crucially underdressed in her T-shirt nightgown, Kate explained.

His frown deepened. 'I don't remember seeing it, and I didn't bring it in. I'll ring the taxi company.'

Although his eyes hadn't strayed from her face, she wanted to go back into the bedroom and close the door on him and hide. Which was stupid, because her nightgown covered her thighs and shoulders quite adequately. There was no reason to feel so exposed.

Yet even her bare feet felt vaguely provocative.

'Thank you, that's a good idea,' she said, trying to sound perfectly normal—as though they had never exchanged that last searing kiss.

Because it seemed rude not to, she followed him into what was clearly an office, a large room with a huge desk and some sophisticated computer equipment gleaming and humming and blinking at her.

'Were you working?' she asked blankly.

He picked up a telephone and dialled. 'Yes. Hello, I'm reporting something left in one of your cabs.'

Kate stood while he concisely told the operator what had happened. A huge rug kept her feet pleasantly warm.

'I see,' Patric said. 'Thank you. Yes, before eight o'clock.'

Alerted by a note in his voice, Kate looked up. He was watching her while he spoke, his eyes travelling in a leisurely inspection from her toes, buried in the rug, the length of her legs and on further, finally coming to rest on her face. Heat burned through her skin, but she held his gaze, refusing to be intimidated.

He didn't take his eyes off her while he put the receiver down. 'The cab driver has already handed it in,' he said conversationally. 'Someone will deliver it before eight tomorrow morning.'

'Thank you very much,' she gabbled, and turned to flee without thought for dignity.

'Kate?' He said her name as though it was a rare jewel, as though he treasured it, held it in his hand and warmed it with his lifeblood.

She froze. 'What?'

'Do you remember the night we made love?'

Her head jerked as though he'd hit her. 'Why?' she asked huskily.

'Have you forgotten, Kate?'

She dragged in a shuddering breath. 'No, I remember.'

He moved silently, but her skin warned her. When he lifted her hair from the back of her neck, threading his fingers through the silken tangle, sifting it, letting it fall back against her sensitive skin, the unbearable expectation made her flinch.

In a voice chilled by contempt, he said, 'It's all right, I'm not going to attack you.'

'I didn't think you were,' she said, realising that he'd misunderstood her reaction. 'I—I'm not used to this, that's all.'

After a moment of silence he stepped back. Bitingly he asked, 'Is this how you've lived since Nick's birth—like a coward, refusing every challenge, retreating into the tight little community of two you've made with your son? I'm surprised, Kate. I thought you had more guts.'

'No,' she said angrily, 'I have not lived like that!' She pivoted, her eyes dark and turbulent as she fought for control.

Patric smiled cynically. 'It's safe, I suppose—until Nick wants to leave home. What will happen then?'

Between her teeth she said, 'He'll go with my blessing.'

'I doubt it,' he said unforgivably. 'Not if he's the focus of your universe.' He sounded bored and indifferent. 'You look tired. Go back to bed, Kate.'

Furious and bewildered, her stomach churning, she walked out of his office and into her bedroom. He wanted her; she knew he wanted her. And if she could have taken easy, uncomplicated pleasure in his body she'd have gone to bed with him. But she couldn't.

While she'd stood there, made captive by his hard grey eyes, she'd been stormed by a discovery that shattered the brittle armour of her composure. Its shards splintered her soul, cutting away the past years, revealing her emotions in naked, shuddering urgency.

She'd been so sure of her independence, her autonomy; now she knew that somehow she was still tied to him by bonds that had never loosened. She might no longer love Patric, but she was acutely, primally aware of him with a cell-deep intensity.

Once she'd read that women never forget, never become entirely free of the men they lose their virginity to. She'd scoffed, but now she wondered whether some elemental linkage did shackle a woman to the man who'd initiated her into the pleasure of the senses.

'Mummy! Mummy, wake up! Mr Sutherland's here and he says you should get up!'

Kate lifted a reluctant eyelid and glared at her son. 'What?'

Patric's voice, smooth and amused, snapped her eyes wide open. 'You forgot to set your alarm. It's a quarter past seven, so if your bus leaves at eight-thirty you should probably get up now.'

'I'll be right out,' she mumbled, forcing the miasma of too little sleep too late from her brain.

'You're not running late yet. I'll give Nick some breakfast.'

She lifted her face an inch from the pillow. Nick had dressed himself in one of the new shirts and the jeans she'd bought, and judging by his wet forelock and virtuous smile he'd washed his face.

'Thank you,' she muttered.

At least she'd had the sense to stay prone, so Patric wouldn't see her with her hair all over her face and her eyes full of sleep. The instant the door closed behind them she leapt out of bed, thanking heaven that she wasn't one of those unfortunate people who found waking up seriously difficult.

Fifteen minutes later, showered and dressed, her armour

of composure buckled and fastened, she followed the sound of voices to find Patric and Nick in a sophisticated kitchen and family room.

Nick had seated himself at the table and was draining a glass of orange juice as Patric set a plate before him and said, 'See how you like that muesli.'

Although she sensed a taut impatience in the dark, penetrating eyes, he smiled at Kate as though nothing had happened in his office the previous night.

Nothing had. She didn't want any sort of relationship with Patric. It was too dangerous.

Acutely self-conscious, she bent to kiss Nick's forehead and said, 'He likes most mueslis.'

'But we make our own, with rolled oats and yoghurt and apples from our apple tree,' Nick said cheerfully, returning her kiss with a hug. 'I like that best. Mum, I s'pose our lettuces and cabbages are going to be ready now, do you think?'

Kate straightened. 'Yes, although I told the MacArthurs to use any that looked as though they should be eaten.'

He nodded and picked up his spoon while Patric asked, 'The MacArthurs are the parents of Nick's best friend?'

Did he ever forget anything? His level scrutiny made Kate very thankful she'd succumbed to vanity and worn her best pair of trousers and a shirt, both the smoky dark green that enhanced her green-blue eyes. Slipping into the chair he pulled out for her, she said, 'Yes, they're Rangi's parents.'

'I haven't got a real aunt, but Aunty Ngaire is my pretend one,' Nick said. 'Rangi's in my class at school—he's my best friend and my pretend cousin.'

'Rangi's the youngest of four brothers, so Ngaire's an old hand at parenting. She and Rangi steered us through play school and kindergarten,' Kate said prosaically, accepting a glass of juice from Patric. It was superb, freshly squeezed and tasty. 'Mmm, delectable,' she breathed after the first delicious, sweetly tart sip. 'I'll bet those oranges came from Kerikeri.'

'I have a friend with an orchard there who ships me down the occasional bag. What would you like to eat? I can cook you something—or there's porridge?'

He sounded just like a good host, so she endeavoured to be the perfect guest. 'It sounds wonderful, thank you, but I'll just have some toast. Don't get up—show me where the toaster is.'

But Patric got to his feet and put in a couple of slices from a loaf he'd clearly just got out of a freezer. 'Do you drink coffee at breakfast?'

'Yes, thank you.'

It was hot and invigorating—and better still, it gave her eyes and hands something to do while she waited for the toast.

Patric was eating porridge. As she glanced at it he lifted his dark brows at her. 'My Scottish grandmother firmly believed that if you didn't eat porridge you not only risked a life of moral turpitude—don't laugh, that's the word she used!—but you'd come to a bad end. She was a good propagandist. Although,' he added smoothly, 'I must confess I only eat it in cold weather.'

If he ate porridge, who did he keep the muesli for?

'It's supposed to be extremely good for you.' Kate knew she sounded stilted, but this was altogether too cosy.

She didn't trust her reactions to him, or to the occasion. It was too easy for such moments to become fodder for dreams.

And she was finished with dreams. Her life was a constant struggle with money, bringing up a child without a father, and the understanding that she wasn't likely to find herself with either a marriage or a particularly satisfying career. She'd done her best with the meagre hand fortune had dealt her, and she would continue to play it as well as she could, but she and Patric had nothing in common beyond a long-ago summer fling.

And on her side, at least, a violent physical attraction that didn't know when to die.

'Is porridge good for boys too?' Nick demanded. 'And what does t-turpitude mean?'

Kate smiled at him. 'Porridge is good for everyone, and turpitude means excessive badness.'

He looked at Patric's plate. 'I said no thank you because I didn't know what it tasted like.'

'Would you like to try some?' Patric asked.

Nick nodded, and Patric got up and disappeared into the kitchen. He came back with a small bowl containing a tiny amount of porridge, and the two slices of toast for Kate.

'Does it have sugar in it?' Nick asked, surveying the porridge.

Patric's brows lifted. 'Only Sassenachs eat their porridge with sugar,' he said austerely, in a passable Scots accent. 'Real people have it with salt.'

Nick grinned. 'What are Sass-Sassenachs?'

'Saxons. People who live in England.'

Nick picked up his spoon. Kate spread honey on her toast and tried to ignore the man serenely eating porridge across the table.

'It tastes good,' Nick said approvingly, and demolished the rest. 'We don't live in England, we're New Zealanders. So we're not Sassenachs, are we?'

'No,' Patric and Kate said together.

Nick looked puzzled. 'Why do they have it with sugar and we don't?'

Kate hid a smile, but Patric explained the millennia-long rivalry between Saxon and Celt with clarity and conciseness. Nick nodded, taking it all in.

And again an odd frisson of loneliness, of exclusion, shivered through Kate. It was ridiculous; it was also entirely natural. All Nick's life she'd been the only person he'd had to answer questions—and yet that wasn't true. He spent long hours with Jacob and the MacArthurs, and she'd never been jealous or felt left out.

Nick asked, 'Mummy, are we Scottish?'

'No. There's a little bit of Irish in us,' she said, 'But I'm afraid most of us is plain yeoman stock from England—people who ate bacon and eggs for breakfast, not porridge.'

Clearly his heart was set on Scottish ancestry, like his idol, because he demanded, 'What about my father? Was he Scottish?'

'I don't think so,' she said quietly. 'Finish your breakfast. We have to get ready soon.'

Nick gave her an exasperated look, but set to work on the rest of his food with his usual gusto, while Kate forced toast and coffee down, joining Patric in a civilised, meaningless conversation entirely suited to two strangers who just happened to be eating breakfast together, with the almost-six-year-old son of one of them listening.

When they'd finished she offered to do the dishes, but Patric shook his head. 'There's a dishwasher.'

She got to her feet, noting that he did the same. 'What about the beds? I'll strip them—'

'That's the housekeeper's job,' he said bluntly. 'Go and get ready. Oh, the lost luggage arrived early this morning. It's on the hall table. How did you sleep?'

'Very well, thank you,' she said, turning away to stack dishes on the bench.

He said, 'I didn't. I spent a lot of my time remembering that you were asleep a few feet away.'

Shortly after eight Patric knocked on the open bedroom door. 'I'll get the bags,' he said, and picked them up with effortless ease.

Kate and Nick followed him, but he put the bags down in the hall and said, 'You've got time to look at the view from the sitting room.'

Their bedroom had looked out over the city, with the Sky Tower dominating the view, but he led them into a huge room walled with glass overlooking the harbour.

From it a deck extended, furnished with pots and tubs of pansies and bamboo and other plants. Even on a cool spring morning with rain in the offing it looked lush and tropical. In summer, Kate thought, it must be magical.

Opening a door, Patric said to Nick, 'That's where the Whitbread yachts come in, and that, of course, is the harbour bridge you'll be going over shortly. Down there's the Maritime Museum, and if you look the other way that place with the funny little towers is the Ferry Building.'

Nick followed him fearlessly over to the balustrade. Kate stood just outside the door, gazing out over the glittering panorama. Nick would get over this affection for the man he'd known such a short time. She'd have to make sure he had plenty to do, plenty to think about, for the next few weeks.

'All right?' Patric asked, frowning, his dark eyes scanning her face. 'I'd forgotten you were afraid of heights.'

'I'm not afraid where there's a balustrade,' she said quickly.

He held out his hand. 'Then come on out.'

Kate looked up sharply. He'd used to scorn those who took dares, but there had been a challenging note in his voice that fired her. Ignoring his hand, she said, 'I don't need help, thanks,' and walked past him to join Nick, who was staring at a strange craft in the basin.

'Mum, that's Xena the Warrior Princess's boat,' he told her in awestruck tones. 'On television.'

Although they didn't own a television set, Kate knew that the popular series was shot in New Zealand. 'Is it?'

'Yes.' He stared reverently at the strange-looking craft. 'When I stayed with Rangi we watched that programme. It's a Greek boat. Xena's a Greek warrior princess.'

It was easy to see, Kate thought with a clutch of wry amusement, that the boat's presence in the Viaduct Basin only increased Patric's desirability as a human being.

Nick twisted to look up at his host. 'Have you seen it sailing?' he asked.

'Several times,' Patric told him, and grinned down at Nick's impressed face. 'It looks very strange. Come on, we can't stay out here—your bus will be waiting for you.'

He took them in his car on his way to work, and because he double-parked to let them off there was no time for awkward farewells, although he insisted on carrying the bags in and up to the counter.

Kate gave him her hand and said, 'Thank you, Patric.'

'My pleasure,' he said, and lifted her hand to kiss the palm.

Her heart flipped as he released her and turned to the boy he'd thought to be his son.

Nick held out his hand, and Patric shook it with gravity and a smile. 'Take care of your mother,' he said.

Nodding, Nick blinked and fought back tears. And Patric, thank heavens, ruffled the boy's hair, and turned and strode away.

CHAPTER SIX

JUST over two weeks later Kate had to stay late at work, so she arranged with Jacob and Anna next door to collect Nick from school. As she got out of the Mini he came bursting through their front door, followed by a grave Jacob.

Radiant-faced, he shouted, 'Mr Sutherland is in Disneyland in California in America, and he's written to me. It's a postcard. Look!'

He thrust a brightly coloured picture of a pirate ship into her hands. Turning it over, Kate stared down at the bold black printing.

Patric had addressed it correctly.

Dear Nick,

I went here with friends yesterday. It rained, but we had a good time. I thought of you when we saw the rides.

Yours, Patric Sutherland.

'Who is this man?' Jacob asked a little abruptly when Nick had scooted inside to collect his school bag.

'An old friend of mine,' Kate said, her smile trembling on her lips.

He gave her a shrewd look from beneath white brows. 'Who wishes to be a new friend? Or perhaps more than a friend? Anna smells a romance.'

His wife could be heard inside, fussing over Nick. Kate summoned a determined smile. 'No. He likes Nick, and feels a little sorry for him, I think.'

'So he is kind. Nicholas said that you had seen quite a bit of him in Australia. And that you stayed at his apartment in Auckland when you came back home.'

Kate managed to laugh. 'I hope Nick also told you that he and I slept in the same room!'

'It is none of my business,' Jacob said severely. 'But Nicholas is beginning to realise that most of his friends have fathers and he wonders why he should not. Also, you need someone to take care of you.'

Kate reached up and kissed him on the cheek. 'This is the end of the century, Jacob. Women take care of themselves now.'

'Perhaps,' he said, shaking his head over the vagaries of modern life, 'But it does not seem right. You are a young, beautiful, intelligent woman, and you would make some fortunate man very happy. You deserve a man who will make you happy too. And everyone needs someone to rely on. Even I rely on my Anna! Oh, well, one will come your way one day. Just make sure you choose a good man, who loves my small friend as well as his mother.'

'Believe me,' Kate said with quiet, complete sincerity, 'that would be the most important qualification.'

'Well, not *the* most important, perhaps,' Jacob returned drily, turning as Nick came bounding towards them, closely followed by Anna. 'Off you go.'

After Nick had put his school gear away, and Kate had changed and grabbed herself a cup of tea accompanied by a quick flick through the newspaper, she began preparing dinner.

'I'll have to write to Mr Sutherland,' Nick said, putting his lunchbox on the bench.

'You don't need to answer postcards.' Suddenly angry with Patric, Kate flicked open a broad bean pod with unnecessary vigour and extracted the plump green beans.

Nick's jaw firmed. 'You always make me write to people when they send me presents,' he said. 'I should thank him for his card.'

Like children the world over, Nick had to be vigorously coaxed into writing thank-you letters. If she ignored this he'd never get around to it. So she evaded the issue by asking, 'Will you take it to school and show the class?'

'Yes.' Then he frowned. 'No,' he said after a moment's thought. 'He's my secret. Do you want me to read my book to you?'

'Yes, please.'

Settling himself on a stool on the dinette side of the narrow breakfast bar, he began to read. As she peeled potatoes and scrubbed and sliced the vegetables for chicken stir-fry, Kate thanked heaven that he'd been born a reader. He thoroughly enjoyed the occasional television programme he watched with Rangi, but he didn't seem to miss it at all.

She couldn't remember seeing any sign of a set in Patric's opulent, beautifully decorated apartment. A wall of bookshelves, yes, but nothing electronic.

Probably he had a complete room dedicated to home entertainment, she thought cynically, slicing the meat into thin strips; a room decorated in the same clever, relaxed style as the sitting room to show off state-of-the-art equipment.

Kate piled the broad beans into a small saucepan and wondered why Nick's decision not to take that postcard to school had set off alarm bells. If Patric intended to continue sending him postcards, and if they unsettled him at all, she'd soon put a stop to it.

On Saturday mornings Nick played rugby. Because Kate almost always watched him, she often collected several children whose parents couldn't make it. The following weekend, however, the game was on a field close by, so she and Nick walked there.

A benign sun shone down onto a sodden world; it would have been more sensible to stay at home and make sure the week's used clothes went through her old washing machine instead of standing on the sideline of a muddy field watching a pack of small boys scamper up and down with such scant disregard for the rules that periodically she had to stop herself from laughing.

Then Nick got the ball. Grinning, he headed for the line. Unfortunately it was the wrong line.

Kate, along with the coach and half a dozen other desperate parents, yelled, 'Go back, Nick, run the other way.'

Miraculously he heard them, and slowed, looked around, and realised his mistake. Forehead furrowed with concentration, he ran back through the other small boys, bewildering so many of the opposition that he was able to fling himself triumphantly into the mud at the correct end.

'Well done, Nick,' the coach roared. 'All right, you boys, get back to the halfway line. Turn around now, turn around.'

Laughing, Kate clapped. The woman standing next to her said, 'Oh, they're gorgeous, aren't they? Is this his first try?'

'His very first,' Kate said, inflated with pride.

'It won't be his last,' her companion prophesied sagely. 'That's my fifth son playing in the other team. Believe me, I know junior rugby. He's got good instincts, your boy, and he can run.'

She looked over Kate's shoulder and made a soft growling noise in her throat. 'Your husband?' she asked beneath her breath. 'Lucky you!'

Startled, Kate turned. Iron-grey eyes met her gaze with cool, compelling self-possession.

'Patric,' she said foolishly. 'What—what are you doing here?'

'Watching Nick score a try,' he said, smiling at the woman beside her.

It was effortless, that naked, formidable charm; Kate watched with wry comprehension as her companion succumbed without a struggle.

'Hi,' she said, dimpling. 'Your son's playing very well—in fact, he's a natural.'

From further down the line someone yelled, 'Marie!' and she grinned.

'Better go. See you.'

Beating back an incandescent flare of joy, Kate waited until they were alone before asking tersely, 'How did you find us?'

'Your next-door neighbour told me where you'd be.'

'Jacob?' Somehow she had to control this violent delight, this stunned, shivering pleasure.

'Yes.' He was watching the little boys scatter and clump across the field. 'I gather they don't tackle or scrum.'

'No, they just tag each other,' Kate told him, her brain at last beginning to work. She tried to smile naturally, to sound normal. 'I'd rather hoped he'd play soccer, but Nick's had his heart set on rugby ever since he watched Rangi's older brothers play.'

'You didn't try to change his mind?'

'Of course I did, but it was hopeless, so I gave up. I save my strength for the really important issues.'

Patric grinned. 'For a moment I thought he was going to score for the opposition.'

'That happens reasonably often, although the spectators usually manage to yell loudly enough to stop it.' Happiness unfurled on slow, heavily beating wings.

She had, she thought despairingly, waited almost seven years for this—had never stopped waiting. Oh, she'd got on with her life, but immured behind barred and locked doors in her heart—ignored, quiescent, yet expectant—had been the Kate who'd fallen in love with Patric when she was sixteen and never been able to fall out of it.

That Kate had never given up hope.

And that hidden Kate—innocent, ardent, trusting, impractical—was a real threat to the secure life she'd built so painfully.

Why hadn't Patric bowed out gracefully? That moment

of charged desire in his office had revealed that he wanted her, but was he wracked by the same powerful hunger for completion?

Or did he plan an affair? It had to be wishful thinking to hope that they might be able to breach the barrier of the disillusioned years and build something true and lasting from the debris.

Because that sort of ending only came in fairy stories, she told herself with brusque common sense. Patric was one of the richest men in New Zealand—in the Pacific Basin! He owned and headed a worldwide force in aviation. What did they have in common beyond the memory of an enchanted love affair when they had both been young enough to believe that miracles could happen?

She didn't dare risk her peace of mind. Or Nick's.

After watching in silence for some minutes, the man beside her commented, 'He has good hands for a six-year-old.'

'Some might think "he has good hands" to be pretty lukewarm praise for a player as brilliant as Nick.'

Patric laughed. 'I refuse to believe you're a foolishly doting mother.'

'Doting, certainly. Foolish—no, I hope not.'

'You've made a good job of him. He's a great kid.'

'He's happy,' she said, and gathered her strength around her like armour. 'Patric, I don't think it would be wise for you to keep up this…friendship.'

The expression on his tough face didn't alter, yet she knew her blunt statement had made him coldly, implacably angry. The Patric she'd loved had been self-controlled, but nothing like this.

Her chin lifted. She met his icy stare with courage, not backing down.

'Why?' he asked quite gently.

'Because he's happy the way things are. He doesn't need any grief in his life.'

'How will I make him unhappy?'

She was floundering, but she couldn't let him see it—he was too adept at mercilessly homing in onto weakness. 'You unsettle him,' she said, and even to her own ears it sounded lame.

'Why?'

Stiffening her already aching shoulders, she said quietly, 'He might grow to love you as the father he's never had, and I don't want his heart broken. It will be better if you don't see him or write to him.' She paused, then said deliberately, 'You have no claim to him, Patric. Accept it.'

His face hardened, and for a moment something implacable glittered in the gunmetal grey eyes. It vanished almost immediately, but it left her shaken. 'Are you threatening me?' he asked silkily.

'What with?' she asked, forcing an ironic note into the words. 'A scolding?'

'You can do better than that.' His narrowed eyes moved from her face to the swarm of boys. Without any inflection, he went on, 'As it happens, I was working on the assumption that one of the easiest ways to a doting mother's heart is through the object of that devotion. Which makes it very fortunate that I like the boy.'

Kate thought she'd misheard him. She stared at the autocratic profile while fragments of thoughts jostled for room.

Patric turned to look at her. 'Surprised?' he asked softly. 'Why, Kate? I never could leave you alone. You were like a siren, singing a song that stripped me bare of everything but the need to follow you. Hadn't you realised that it's still as strong as it ever was?'

A feverish heat clouded her mind. 'No,' she said warily. 'No, I hadn't. Realised, I mean.'

'I've had years to perfect the mask—I'm glad it works so well,' Patric said, a sardonic smile curving the long mouth. 'When you turned me down so conclusively at Tatamoa I couldn't believe that the most transcendental experience of my life had meant so little to you.'

His words stabbed her to the heart. Perhaps if she'd told him then what had happened—but she'd been shattered by the cruel ugliness of her experience. Appalled at the prospect of bearing her attacker's child and horrified by his threats, she'd been unable to face what had happened to her.

But Patric knew now. He knew, and he still wanted her.

Hard on the heels of that thought came another. Did she have the right to take the risk of falling in love again when she had Nick's well-being to consider?

Kate fixed her gaze on the ragged stream of small mud-encrusted boys as they formed into some kind of order. It took all of her determination to say, 'I'm not in the market for an affair. It would be bad for Nick—he's not accustomed to a series of temporary fathers.'

Thick black lashes drooped, half hiding Patric's eyes. She had a sense of that quick, controlled brain selecting and discarding options. After a moment he said, 'I wasn't suggesting an affair. I was thinking no further than the two of us getting to know each other again.'

Embarrassed by her mistake, she tucked a strand of hair into her beret. 'Patric—'

'I don't want any promises from you, any commitment, but you have my word that I do not treat this lightly.'

Kate turned her head away in case he should see her sudden hope. Looking blindly out onto the field, she heard the coach call something, and everyone clapped. Nick looked around, beamed when he saw her—or was it when he saw Patric?—and headed off towards the goalposts at the other end of the field.

'Kate,' Patric said unhurriedly, 'I swear to you that I've learnt a little in the past seven years—I won't abandon you again.'

'You didn't abandon me,' she protested. 'I broke it off.'

'Of course I abandoned you. As well as breaking my heart you shattered my pride, and I found it very hard to forgive you for that.' His voice was clipped, but she sensed the dark emotions curbed by his will. 'Kate, could we try again?'

The stark sincerity in his words undermined her defences. Temptation wove its glittering, seductive web around her, clinging in suffocating folds so that she couldn't think. Memories of that summer seduction—so beautiful, so precious to her—held her captive, but she had to leave them where they belonged, in the past. When she'd held Nick after his birth she'd made a promise that she'd always put his welfare above her own.

She hadn't realised the first real test of that vow would be so difficult to meet.

Tentatively she said, 'We could try, I suppose.' And was assailed by an eerie inevitability, as though this was somehow fated.

'You won't regret it,' Patric said with compelling determination, 'And neither will Nick.'

Dimly she heard the sound of a whistle, followed by both teams chanting the ritual of three cheers for each other and three for the referee. Then Nick came pounding across on muddy bare feet, his face lit with delight beneath the smears.

'Hello, Mr Sutherland,' he shouted, high on adrenalin and glory. 'Did you see my try? I was going to score at the wrong end, but I heard Mummy and I turned around and came back and I scored a try!'

Noisy, uninhibited, he vibrated with joy. Patric congratulated him, and any chance of changing her mind was gone; for better or worse she'd allowed the decision to be ratified.

When Patric suggested they drive home in his car she said, 'Nick's covered in mud. We'll walk back.'

'It's just a car,' Patric told her. Steady, thoughtful, uncompromising, his eyes held hers.

She looked at the sleek dark grey monster and prevented herself from shrugging. 'Well, if you're sure you don't mind.'

'I don't mind,' he said evenly.

Once in, he checked to make sure she and Nick both had their seatbelts on, then set the car in motion. Grinning, Nick waved to a group of his friends.

From the road her flat looked small and slightly grubby; with a very straight back and rigid shoulders Kate led them up to the front door and opened it. Cool, damp air greeted them; the sun had gone in, and without its warmth the rooms felt dull and chilly.

I am not ashamed of it, she thought defiantly. Aloud she said, 'Nick, into the bath, and make sure those knees and feet get a good scrub. Patric, which would you prefer, coffee or tea?'

'Tea, thank you,' he said promptly as Nick disappeared. 'Would you like me to make it?' He met her raised brows with a faint smile. 'I thought you might need to run the bath, or find clothes.'

Her answering smile was brittle. 'Nick is perfectly capable of running his own bath and finding his own clothes,' she said. 'Did you have a nanny when you were a child?'

Sometimes when Nick frowned she thought his brows twitched together like Patric's—the same wishful thinking that had led to her giving her son Patrick as a second name.

She was no longer in thrall to it; Patric was not Nick's father.

The past was over and done with, and this was the present—at once scary and exciting, offering a chance of happiness if only she was brave enough to reach for it.

'I had a nanny until I went away to school,' Patric said, his frown smoothing away as he watched her move around the small kitchen.

'How old were you when that happened?'

'Seven.'

She didn't say anything, but he must have recognised her outrage. 'My parents travelled a lot,' he explained.

'And although I missed them, and the nanny, I enjoyed boarding school.'

'Did you take your teddy with you?' she demanded.

He laughed. 'Yes. We all took our toys. And no, I don't believe it is as good a solution as living with a loving family. My children will stay at home, and I'll only travel when it's absolutely necessary.'

Was he trying to tell her something? No, she wouldn't head down that path, searching every throwaway comment for a hidden meaning. To the sound of the water running in the bathroom, she said, 'Children need their parents.'

And immediately wondered whether her remark amounted to an admission that Nick might be missing a father figure in his life.

Well, Patric wouldn't have time to fulfil that function. He'd be too busy to come up to Whangarei much.

Which, she thought sturdily as she measured tea into the teapot, was a good thing. A new beginning was all very well, but what exactly did he mean by it? Ruthlessly subduing the anticipation that bubbled up from some secret wellspring, she poured boiling water into the pot.

'Children do, indeed, need parents,' he said, an equivocal note in his voice sending a cold finger down Kate's spine.

Surely—no, he *knew* Nick wasn't his son!

He finished smoothly, 'Or good substitutes. You said you decided to keep Nick because you'd felt like an outsider in your family—I hadn't realised you were unhappy with your aunt and uncle.'

'I wasn't unhappy,' Kate said, lifting down two mugs and a glass, 'And it wasn't their fault that I never felt entirely at home. It could have happened in any family—there's often an odd one out.'

'An odd one out who's sure of her place, nevertheless,' he said shrewdly. 'You always looked like a gazelle in a herd of cows. They were good-looking and kind, but you were exquisite, a little fey, mysterious. I'm not surprised you felt different.'

Her heart thudded. 'They were *not* like cows, and they did their best. I'm very fond of them—we keep in close touch.'

The bath water stopped running. Kate groaned inwardly at the sound of an exuberant splash. Nick was excited, so there'd be water all over the walls and floor. Lifting her voice she said in a certain tone of voice, 'Nick, stop that!'

'OK,' he shouted, not in the least intimidated.

When he reappeared—hastily scrubbed and dressed—she and Patric had moved to the small sitting room that formed an 'L' with the dining alcove and kitchen. Kate watched her son carefully skirt a pile of library books and her heart cramped. He'd taken great pains—combing his hair back and putting on the jeans and surfing sweatshirt she'd bought him on their last day in Australia. A whiff of peppermint revealed that he'd even cleaned his teeth again.

All in Patric's honour.

'Any bruises?' she asked, making a place for him beside her on the elderly, barely comfortable suite she'd bought at a garage sale.

'A graze on my knee,' he said cheerfully. 'But it's all right; I put some sticking plaster on it.' He gave Patric a suddenly shy smile. 'I haven't got a try before,' he confided. 'That was my very first one.'

Patric said, 'It was an excellent try.'

'Did you play rugby when you were as old as me?'

Patric nodded. 'I was a forward,' he said, 'probably because I wasn't as fast as you are.'

Kate gave Nick his glass of water, and a cracker with cheese, and gradually relaxed her tense muscles as they discussed football. Patric's long legs seemed to stretch out over most of the floor; he dominated the small room, its shabbiness enlivened only by the sprigs of daphne she'd picked the previous day. Scent from the starry pink flowers floated—fresh, citrus-sharp yet sweet, the perfume of spring—on the cool air.

This was her home. She and Nick were comfortable and happy here.

The emotion that gnawed at her composure was neither dissatisfaction nor its sullen sibling, envy. No, she was worried and wary and edgy. And beneath those eminently sensible responses, slowly gathering strength, lurked a caged hunger. She recognised it, knew it well; she'd thought it long dead, but it had only needed Patric's presence to bring it back to life.

Now, looking around at the hard-won fruits of her recovery, she listened to Nick and Patric talk to each other. If she learned to love again—and if her love was rebuffed—would she cope?

Oh, yes, she'd cope. She'd found the strength to endure everything that had come her way so far. But why ask for trouble? Although she accepted his version of the events of seven years ago, this Patric Sutherland was a much tougher proposition than the golden man she'd fallen in love with.

Nick's voice—eager, thrilled—broke into her reverie. 'We could go to one of the places to eat down on the wharf,' he suggested. 'You know, Mummy, the ones we saw when we looked at the blue-water boats.' He turned back to Patric. 'Mummy liked the one from Seattle in America, but I saw one from Hamburg in Germany! All the way across the world! I liked it best.'

Patric's gaze met Kate's, his dark eyes limpidly amused. 'I thought you might like to go out to lunch.'

It was her last chance to say no, to send him out of their lives. She looked from his face to Nick's, and knew that she could not. If she ran away again, she would never forgive herself. 'That will be great,' she said, trying to hide the panicky edge in her voice. 'I'd better change into something a little more upmarket.'

Patric's dark glance slid to assess her clothes. Kate knew

that her favourite sage-green jersey enhanced the green in her eyes, and that the jeans, although old, were good quality and fitted well. Patric's expression didn't alter, but she felt his regard like a caress, and to her alarm her nipples tightened and flowered beneath the soft material of her bra.

'You look lovely just as you are,' he said quietly. 'Come on.'

Nick looked from one to the other, his brows furrowed, then asked loudly, 'Do you want me to change my clothes, Mummy?'

'No, you've already got your best clothes on,' she said, getting to her feet.

Following suit, Patric said drily, 'The possessive male.'

Standing very close to his mother, Nick asked, 'What's that?'

'You are,' Patric said, and smiled at him.

It had the usual effect. Nick returned the smile, and when Patric stood back to let Kate go ahead Nick did too. It wrung her heart. If Patric put a foot wrong this time he wouldn't have a shattered teenager to deal with; he'd have a furious mother!

Then Patric said, 'Give your mother room, Nick,' and after a moment Nick walked in front, looking over his shoulder while Patric took the key from her and locked the door.

Going down the path towards the car, she thought worriedly that Nick and she had been alone for so long that the addition of another person in their tight little twosome would mean a massive shift in the way they related to each other.

CHAPTER SEVEN

'I'M NOT surprised you come here—I remember how you loved the water,' Patric said, looking around him as they walked from the car park towards the town basin. 'This is all new, isn't it?'

'Yes. Have you been to Whangarei much?' It hurt that he should have visited the city and she hadn't known.

'I come here occasionally on business,' he said indifferently, still looking around. 'They've made a good job of it.'

Indeed the town basin, with its walks and plantings, its shops and busy restaurants, its fish and clock museums, was a thriving, bustling place.

'Mummy likes the boats,' Nick said, stopping to look down at one splendid white sloop, graceful as a heron in flight.

They always made Kate feel trapped, those yachts—big and beautiful with sleek lines, breathing adventure and freedom on wide waters. But life was a ledger of choices, opportunities taken or rejected. When she'd made the decision to keep Nick she'd accepted that she'd be giving up a lot for him; she didn't regret it.

'Yes,' Patric said quietly, and for a moment an unspoken communication flashed between them. He understood the longing for freedom, and the bonds of responsibility and love that tied her.

'I'm hungry,' Nick informed them, trying to sound pathetic.

'Then we'll go to that café,' Kate said. 'And as the sun's out and there's no wind we could sit outside.'

Struck again by a chill of alienation, Kate walked across

the sunlit pavement beside Patric, Nick running ahead. She had plenty of friends, and so did Nick, but when she thought of her life it seemed that she'd spent the past seven years lost in a fog of loneliness.

Patric had exposed her to the sun, and she was afraid of that bright light—of what it might reveal about her, of the effect it could have on her pleasant, humdrum life.

'What would you like to eat?' he asked, after he'd held out a chair for her.

She had no appetite. 'A sandwich,' she said quickly, scanning the blackboard menu. 'Tomato and cheese, or something like that. And a cup of coffee, please.'

'Nick?'

Nick said, 'Can we go inside and see what there is?'

'Of course,' Patric said. 'Do you want to come, Kate?'

'No, I'll sit here.' Her voice sounded odd—thin and distant, as though all emotion and spirit had been leached from her.

After another unsettling, too perceptive glance, Patric went inside with Nick. The sun umbrellas were furled, but the sky was now bright enough to make sitting out uncomfortable. Kate stood up and opened the one above their table, then sat down again and stared gravely across the paving, across the soft, sword-shaped leaves of the rengarenga lilies and their spikes of starry white flowers, across the masts and booms and graceful hulls of the yachts, across the busy road on the other side of the basin to the peaceful, bush-clad slopes of Parahaki beyond. Deliberately she let her mind go blank.

'You look *triste*,' Patric said.

Kate jumped. Clearly delighted with his world, Nick grinned at her, but Patric's face had set in lines of aloofness.

'I was thinking,' she said lamely.

Smiling narrowly, he said, 'I used to wonder what thoughts hid behind that haunting face. You were such a graceful, laughing thing, yet it was impossible to tell what you were feeling. You're more beautiful now, although you don't laugh nearly so much. What hasn't changed is the secrets hiding in those blue-green eyes.' He looked at Nick, busily draining a glass of water with a slice of lemon in it. 'Unlike this one,' he said obliquely. 'There's no wistfulness there.'

'He's a Scorpio, with all that that implies. And I'm not *wistful*, surely? It sounds weak and wishy-washy.'

'The wrong word,' he agreed. 'There's nothing weak about you. You might look vulnerable, but you're as strong as spun steel.'

He was wooing her with his deep, sensuous voice, with hypnotic dark eyes. Kate had to swallow before she could answer, 'I hope so.'

'I used to think you were made for journeys, as though you'd come from fairyland. And not the fairyland of little beings with gauzy wings either—you have a focused, dangerous intensity that's a warning as much as a lure.'

Sensation scudded the length of her spine, pulled her skin tight. Grabbing for an anchor of reality, she said, 'I was a silly adolescent, a nobody. And don't tell me your mother didn't point that out to you.'

'My mother comes from a culture with a rigid class system, and my father had old-fashioned ideas, although he never forgot that he'd come from farming stock.' His tone hardened. '*I* wasn't a snob.'

'No, you weren't,' she admitted.

'But?' A moment's silence until he said softly, 'Did they get to you, Kate?'

Damn the man, why didn't he let things ride?

Kate looked across at Nick, wholly concentrated on tackling a large piece of quiche. 'I don't entirely blame your parents for their feelings,' she evaded. 'It's foolish to pretend there are no social barriers in New Zealand.'

'There were—are—none between you and me,' he said curtly, and waited. When she didn't answer, he asked with latent, unspoken menace, 'What did they say, Kate?'

'Your mother was worried. She said that we—weren't suited,' she said, and gave a mirthless smile. 'I already knew that.'

He too was constrained by Nick's presence; Kate saw him reimpose control. 'She was wrong,' he said levelly. 'And so are you. It's still there, Kate—that provocative lure, the exquisite siren's song we both hear when we're together.'

Kate's brows climbed—hiding, she hoped, the sudden wild thud of her pulses. 'You're a romantic,' she said, forcing a light note into her voice. 'I wish I'd known that.'

Patric's smile was enigmatic. 'It's just as well you didn't,' he said. 'You played havoc enough with my life.'

Without missing a beat he initiated the sort of catching-up conversation that happens after many years apart. 'So your cousins are all married now?'

'And with children.' Kate had no appetite, but she took a small bite of the sandwich. 'Juliet and her husband are the closest—they own an orchard in Kerikeri.'

Patric nodded. 'My Aunt Barbara—Sean's mother—has shares in an orchard in Kerikeri. She really wanted to buy an ostrich farm, but I managed to persuade her it wasn't necessarily a brilliant investment.'

Which sounded as though Patric might now be in charge of the trust fund 'Black' Pat had set up for his daughter—or what was left of it after her husband, a good-looking weakling, had frittered away much of it by making one disastrous financial decision after another.

Kate looked at Nick and said, 'Darling, have you had enough?'

'There was a cake in there,' he said, hopefully eyeing Patric as the better bet.

Patric laughed. 'You'd better ask your mother.'

Kate would have agreed to anything that made Patric laugh. She'd loved his laugh, and she hadn't heard much of it since they'd met again. 'Of course you may have a cake,' she said. 'It's a special day—you did get a try.'

Her son's eyes gleamed. 'Can I—*may* I—have a cake every time I score a try?'

'Not every try. If you score ten tries in one game you don't get ten cakes,' she said, wondering what she'd started. Nick wasn't fiercely competitive, but when he'd made up his mind to do something he got there. Would he now score several tries every Saturday?

'Relax,' Patric said lazily, reading her mind, 'The rugby season must finish soon.'

'In a couple of weeks.'

Only when they'd disappeared inside the café did Kate close her eyes and release the breath pent in her lungs. Sean's name on Patric's lips was sacrilege.

She endured the waves of rage and pain and angry humiliation, let them wash over her without resistance, and eventually they ebbed, receded into the past. What had Sean done that had finally cut the family ties? She didn't care, provided they stayed cut.

But would Patric look at Nick differently if he knew that the boy was Sean's son?

Probably. Patric had despised his cousin, a handsome, malicious bully. And although Sean was all bluster, he'd been afraid of his younger cousin.

Halfway through that last holiday at Tatamoa he'd backed Kate into a corner at a party and tried to kiss her. Revolted and furious, she'd hit him in the solar plexus. He'd been doubled up and gasping when Patric had found them and spun him away with murder in his eyes, in his lethal voice. His excoriating summary of Sean's character, morals and behaviour had reduced his cousin to humiliated sullenness.

Years later, she'd decided that one of the reasons Sean had attacked her had been to salvage some mean remnant of pride.

Hearing his name still made her shudder, but she didn't care about him now—except for Nick's sake. However, if no one in the Sutherland family communicated with Sean, he'd never find out he had a son. Nick would be safe.

Kate's fingers tightened in her lap. A gull feathered its wings and swooped slowly over the basin, glinting silver in the spring sunlight, alien, solitary. So many decisions made in unbearable emotion—who was to say whether they'd been wrong or right? She'd done the best she could at the time, and had to live with the results.

Nick arrived back, carrying a plate with a slice of cheesecake complete with cream and dark blueberries. Beaming at his mother, he set it carefully down. 'Mr Sutherland says we can go to the playground in the park afterwards, if you want to,' he announced, and watched her closely.

'Of course I want to.' Her mouth curled into a stiff smile.

He nodded in a lordly fashion and proceeded to demolish the cheesecake. Kate flicked a glance at Patric, flushing at the sudden, savage heat that flamed within his eyes.

'How long are you going to keep me on a leash?' he asked, in an almost soundless voice.

Once again she endured a dislocating awareness. Every sense burst into action so that she drank in his colours and textures—the symmetry of bronze skin and blue-black hair, the arrogant line of his nose and chin, the beautifully chiselled mouth, the lithe, male grace that had prowled through so many dreams, so many fantasies down the years.

It wasn't just Patric she was attuned to, either, for Nick seemed to shimmer in his own radiance. Bewildered, Kate felt herself respond acutely, heart-shakingly, to the scents of coffee and salty water and growing things, to the passionate caress of the sun on her skin, to the taste of a wildfire hunger in her mouth.

Although a heavy weight seemed to have taken up residence just under her heart, a consuming, elemental tide of awareness heightened every sense—the very air sparkled and swept across her skin in a charged current.

Lust, she thought flatly. You're in lust again.

Unfortunately it wasn't plain, straightforward, uncomplicated desire. Sean's callous attack had ripped through her life with the brutal efficiency of a chainsaw, its trauma setting a barrier between her and the rest of the world. In spite of her own hard work and the best efforts of her counsellor, it was a barrier she'd never managed to overcome. She'd spent all those years hiding and not even known it.

And now she wanted Patric again, yet she had no idea how she would react if he touched her with true passion. His kiss had sent her soaring, but would other, more intense responses be tainted by that act of violence?

Heat flowed inside her, smooth as velvet, inescapable as a rip tide. It had been like this nearly seven years ago—fire and ice, a turbulent, all-consuming need that still echoed through every cell in her body.

Did she dare? Patric had made no guarantees—and of course he couldn't.

But perhaps—and for the first time she allowed herself to articulate the thought—perhaps this could be a true new beginning.

It was a gamble that would play with hearts—her own and Nick's—but it would be cowardly to give up the chance to love Patric, to build some sort of future with him.

A sparrow chose that moment to land on the edge of the table—a sophisticated, worldly sparrow, with a good eye for food and danger. Nick froze; from the corner of her eye Kate saw the small bird hop twice and pick up a crumb.

Caught in a web of thick silence, walled off by Patric's intense, devouring gaze from the laughter and noise of the people all around them, she jumped when a seagull cried—raucous, infinitely forlorn. Startled, the sparrow flew away, and reality crashed into that hushed, enchanted, sensual world.

Stunned by its power, Kate dragged her gaze away.

When Nick enthused, 'Did you see that, Mum? Did you see that, Mr Sutherland?' she could only nod and wait for her spinning heart to settle down.

After Kate had finished her coffee they set off for the playground. At first Nick couldn't resist showing off, but soon his interest in the climbing bars took over and he began to concentrate on what he was doing.

'You don't seem alarmed by his daring,' Patric remarked as Nick swung across the bars.

They were seated at a picnic table close by. Kate said, 'Fussing drives him crazy. He doesn't like pain, so he's reasonably sensible—or as sensible as a child of his age can be. Because I don't often make a fuss he's inclined to listen when I do. And I watch him like a hawk.'

'You must have found it hard at first.'

She didn't lie. 'Yes,' she said. 'Having to surrender my entire life to another person, even my own child, was a real struggle.'

His expression didn't alter. 'From high school to motherhood in one huge leap. A quick lesson in maturity,' he said.

'Oh, indeed,' she said drily. It was probably just as well that she found it difficult to remember that year.

Patric's hand tightened into a fist against the rough boards of the table. Almost immediately the long fingers straightened, but that momentary lapse of control left her obscurely comforted.

She said, 'Nick was worth it.'

'Children having children is not usually good for the parent or the child,' he said austerely. 'You've done well with Nick, but at what cost to yourself? Working in a dress shop is not the career in management you wanted.'

'Without qualifications there isn't much choice,' she said bluntly. 'Anyway, I don't plan to stay in the shop for the rest of my life. Next year I'm going to start extramural studies.' It was a decision she hadn't even realised she'd made.

'Good. What made you come to Whangarei?'

Kate fixed her eyes on her son. 'I didn't want to stay in Christchurch, and any flat I could afford in Auckland was in an area I didn't want my child to grow up in.' Besides, in Auckland there had always been the remote possibility that she might run into Sean. Or Patric. 'So I looked around for a small city. Whangarei was going through a hard time then, and there was plenty of cheap accommodation.'

'You must have been lonely.'

'I soon made friends.'

'You always had friends,' he said. 'Yet I used to think that, although you were genuinely fond of them, you kept some part of yourself detached.'

Startled, she asked, 'Was I so cold and withdrawn?'

'Far from it—it was obvious that you liked your friends.' He paused, then resumed deliberately, 'You were essentially self-contained. You still are.'

Happily swinging from the bars, Nick waved; she waved back. 'I don't know where you got that idea. No one is self-contained.'

'I watched you grow up,' he said, his voice reflective. 'You were an enchanting girl, but I thought there was something wrong with me for being so fascinated by a girl so young. Especially when she obviously wasn't in the least interested in me.'

This surprised a sardonic laugh from Kate. 'Of course I was—every girl in Poto over the age of twelve was in love with you. You must have known.'

Drily cynical, he said, 'In love with love. Or more likely in love with the Sutherland name and the Sutherland assets.'

Kate turned her head. He'd been watching Nick too, but now he parried her gaze with cool, guarded eyes. Such iron discipline must have been learned in a hard school, she thought, astounded by her anger. It was ridiculous to feel protective of Patric Sutherland.

'You don't believe that,' she scoffed.

'I've had it pointed out to me by experts,' he said, sarcasm curling through his tone, flicking against each word.

'Who?'

'My father, mainly.'

Shocked, she said, 'Why on earth—?'

'On my eighteenth birthday he took me aside and explained that as I was going to take over Sutherland Aviation I was what he called "a good catch". I told you he was old-fashioned.' He spoke levelly, without inflection. 'According to him, women would do their best to lure me into relationships, not because they were attracted to me personally but because they wanted access to my bank balance.'

Kate thought of Patric's father, a tall man with a handsome face and a quick wit. Fiercely wishing she could have just five minutes with Alex Sutherland, she said, 'How ridiculous! You had a lot more going for you than your parents' money—'

He turned his head and smiled—not a pleasant smile. 'Sweet Kate,' he said evenly. 'He was right. Although she'd have denied it, that's what Laura wanted.'

She protested, 'You can't have thought the only reason you were so popular was money!'

'It helped,' he said calmly, stating a fact. 'It always helps.'

In Kate's mind he'd been the golden man—beloved of the gods, her chosen one.

It had been hero-worship. During their exquisitely drawn-out courtship they'd talked of many things—of their hopes and aspirations, of their fears and the things they loved and hated—but now she realised that she'd known very little about the man who'd taken her virginity. Known little and understood less.

She glanced at his profile, implacable against the fresh green of the park, and as if she'd spoken he turned. Desire bridged the space between them, raw and primitive, as inexorable and dangerously seductive as lava hot from the heart of the earth.

Dry-mouthed, Kate could only stare.

He asked harshly, 'What is it, do you think? Why, after all these years, and other women, do you still have the power to drive me to the edge of insanity? When you came towards me in that theme park on the Gold Coast I literally couldn't breathe; I had to force myself to move, to go to you, and it took all of my self-control not to kiss you with years of need and hunger.'

'Other women?' she asked quickly, jealously.

His smile was cold, almost aggressive. 'Oh, yes. After Laura died I looked for you again, but you'd dropped off the face of the earth.'

He looked back at Nick, still swinging on bars, scarlet-faced now. He'd stop soon, Kate thought.

'Do you know how many Browns there are in New Zealand?' Patric asked, an emotion close to contempt chilling his voice. 'Tens of thousands. I finally accepted that you'd meant what you'd said that day in Tatamoa. It seemed ludicrous to remain faithful to someone who'd turned me down so comprehensively, so I didn't. However, I have little taste for promiscuity and I'm not careless. Have you had any other lovers?'

It was none of his business. 'No.'

His austere face hardened. 'Why?'

Nothing but the truth would do. 'Because I couldn't bear to be touched.'

His expression froze. He scrutinised her face as though he'd never seen her before. Kate braced herself, but he didn't speak. Instead he reached across the rough, weather-stained wood of the table and took her hand in his. The exquisite pleasure of it almost shattered her.

Until then she'd been able to delude herself that she had

some control over the situation, but once Patric touched her she went up in flames for him like tinder in the desert, like an unstable explosive needing only a spark to set it off.

'Can you bear that?' he asked, demanding her surrender.

She wasn't prepared to give it to him. Locked in his long fingers, hers quivered.

'Kate?'

Reluctantly she said, 'I'm not screaming.'

'Your pulse is fluttering.' With his other hand he pressed the tips of her fingers against the veins in his wrist. Beneath them his pulse thundered. In a voice that compelled belief, he said, 'It's like that for me too, Kate, so it's just as well we met again. If we hadn't, we'd both have spent a lifetime searching for each other, only to go desperate and alone into our graves.'

It was too soon, she thought confusedly, looking into a face that might have been hewn in granite.

'Mummy?'

Nick's interruption, a difficult blend of concern and demand, broke the spell. With the wildfire colour of sexual awareness still burning her cheeks, she turned to greet her son; without haste Patric let go her hand and got to his feet.

Nick looked from one to the other. 'Why were you holding his hand?' he asked, his tone balanced on the edge of belligerence. 'Is he going to be my uncle, like Jason's uncle?'

'No,' Patric said coolly, 'I am not.'

'Then why were you holding his hand? You don't hold anyone else's hand.'

Kate stood up too. 'I was holding Mr Sutherland's hand because I like to, and I think we'd better be getting back home,' she said cravenly.

Both Patric and Nick glanced at her. Clearly masculine attitudes outranked genetics, because for a second they looked oddly alike, brows drawn into a knot, both gazes straight and intent.

Then they moved, and that fleeting likeness vanished. Nick came forward and took her hand. Kate thought Patric was going to walk on the other side of her; she was relieved when he took up his position so that they had Nick in the middle.

With an understanding of male psychology she applauded, Patric distracted Nick by asking, 'Who's the wing in your team—the redheaded boy?'

'Timmy Blunt.' Nick relaxed visibly. 'He's cool.'

'I liked the way he passed to you instead of keeping the ball to himself. He plays like a grown-up.'

As she listened to them discuss the prowess of several members of the team, Kate blessed the power of rugby on New Zealand males. When Patric let drop that he had not only met the All Blacks—New Zealand's highly successful national rugby team—but was a personal friend of the captain, Nick's resentment vanished and he plied this heroic being with questions.

Unbidden, into Kate's mind once again sneaked the thought that Patric would make a wonderful father. Nick said something and Patric laughed with him, and for a moment she was torn by anguish.

Oh, he'd probably be tough, but his children would know exactly where they stood with him—and he'd be fair—and they'd never grow up doubting his love for them.

CHAPTER EIGHT

IT WAS three o'clock when they reached home; after a stealthy glance at her watch Kate asked Patric whether he'd like to come in for coffee.

'No, thank you,' he replied. 'I have a meeting in Wellington on Monday morning, and I need to get some work done for it.'

Stifling a raw disappointment, she said sedately, 'Then thank you very much for lunch and a lovely day.'

From the back came Nick's voice. 'Yes, thank you, Mr Sutherland.'

Patric didn't answer immediately; Kate's muscles tightened, but when he turned his head to smile at the boy in the back seat she relaxed. She must have imagined that second of taut silence.

'I forgot to thank you for your answer to my postcard,' he said. 'It was a great letter, and I really enjoyed reading it. I'd like to come up next Saturday. Where do you play, Nick, and what time?'

'Kamo,' Nick said, adding a little uncertainly, 'Nine o'clock, isn't it, Mummy?'

'Yes.'

'I'll pick you up,' Patric said, and then, 'What's the matter?' as Kate shook her head.

'I'm taking a carload of children,' she said.

'So what's the problem?' His voice was tinged with impatience. 'This car can pick up kids as well as your Mini. Better, in fact, because we can fit more in. What time do you usually set off?'

Kate's hackles rose; he was taking too much for granted. Without giving herself time to think, she said evenly, 'You don't need to, Patric. We'll see you at Kamo.' Keeping her voice steady and unemotional, she gave him directions to the sports ground and opened her door. 'Come on, Nick.'

Patric's brows lifted, but he made no attempt to persuade her; clearly he didn't view this as a battle worth fighting. 'If you can organise someone to stay with Nick we could go out to dinner on Saturday night.'

He had tact, because Nick would have objected to the word babysitter. As it was her son's face stiffened, and he gave her the glare that indicated hurt feelings. 'I don't want you to go out,' he said bluntly.

Kate would have liked a chance to think the invitation over, but Nick's possessive response made up her mind instantly. Ignoring him, she said, 'I'd like that. What time?'

'Shall we say six-thirty? Would that suit you?'

'Seven-thirty would be better—I have to feed Nick.' Even so, it would be much earlier, she suspected with a hidden gleam of amusement, than Patric normally ate.

He walked them up the front path, waited while Kate opened the door, smiled at her and the still simmering Nick, then said, 'I'll see you next Saturday,' and left them.

He looked like a god, Kate thought foolishly, tall and confident, striding down the narrow path with an inherent, masculine grace that spoke of strength and control and dynamic power. The car door closed softly behind him.

After a moment of indecision, Nick waved. A lean hand lifted from the wheel in a cool, impersonal response as the car drew away, leaving Kate astonished and wary and excited.

She wasn't granted the luxury of examining her feelings because Nick immediately demanded, 'Why can't *I* go to dinner with you? I had to stay behind in Australia too!'

'We'll be back late—well after your bedtime.' Kate's voice was firm. Sweet-tempered though he was, when her son set his mind on something he applied constant pressure. The only way to deal with him was a pleasant, unmoved refusal to give in.

'I'll be good,' he promised now, obviously settling in for the long haul.

Kate said cheerfully, 'I don't recollect Mr Sutherland asking you.'

This threw Nick for a second, until he thought of a clincher. 'He would've if you'd said I could come.'

'He wouldn't have, because he knows that boys your age should be in bed early. Otherwise,' she added cunningly, 'they don't grow properly. How do you think Mr Sutherland got to be as tall and big as he is? Not by staying up late when he was almost six years old, I can tell you.'

And, disregarding the hot little tremor that slithered down her spine at the thought of Patric's height and those wide shoulders, she closed the door behind them and put her bag down.

Temporarily diverted, Nick said, 'I bet he could be an All Black if he wanted to. Why do you think he isn't one, Mummy?'

Kate laughed; to small New Zealand boys an All Black was next to the angels. 'I don't know. Perhaps he wasn't good enough.'

But Nick was having none of this. 'He would be,' he said indignantly. 'P'raps he hurt his leg or something. Mummy, can I go over to Rangi's place and play with his computer?'

'We're going there for dinner tonight,' Kate reminded him. 'You'll be able to play with it then. Why don't you cut me a lettuce from the garden? The big Iceberg would be best. I'm going to make a salad to take with us. Make sure you hold the knife the way I showed you.'

Being trusted to use a knife was a big deal, and Nick took his responsibilities very seriously. Kate watched from the window as he carefully cut through the stem of the lettuce, jaw angled, black hair gleaming in the fickle spring sun. When it was done he stood up and grinned at her, filled with triumph. An inconvenient blast of maternal love shook her. Did she have the right to set off down a path that might hurt them both?

Her volatile emotions seesawed between fierce protectiveness and her long-suppressed hunger for the fulfilment—sexual, emotional and mental—that only Patric had ever been able to give her.

As Nick came towards the back door, Kate wondered whether she was trying unconsciously to revert to the girl she'd been before Sean Cusack's brutality had shattered some fundamental trust in her. Was her response to Patric a hold-over from the past, rooted in her longing to wipe out the attack?

Ah, no. She had only to recall the way Patric's touch had affected her—talk about sensual overload! The physical hunger was real and honest. For the rest—only time would tell.

'Great,' she said as Nick came carefully through the door. 'Would you like to make the dressing?'

While he measured the ingredients for the dressing she ran the lettuce under the tap.

How badly hurt would Nick be if the affair died into nothingness? Perhaps she should take no risks at all, flag away any chance of fulfilment until he'd left home.

Twelve years from now; she'd be thirty-six.

It would be simpler if she could fool herself into thinking that Patric might have marriage in mind.

Perhaps he did. Could she marry him? A feverish, compelling hunger arced through her. Only, she thought stoutly, if she was sure he loved Nick.

'It's ready,' Nick said, breaking into her depressing thoughts. He set down the jar and grinned. 'Do I have to go and wash?'

'You look pretty clean to me. How about tidying up your bedroom?' She folded an old, thin teatowel around the lettuce and set off to swing it outside.

He groaned, but asked, 'Mummy?'

She recognised that tone. 'Mmm?'

'Do you think Mr Sutherland knew these are my new shirt and trousers?'

'He might not have realised they were new,' Kate said practically, 'but I'm sure he noticed how good you looked.'

He nodded and went into his room.

The lettuce-filled cloth swished through the air, spraying drops of water across the small lawn as Kate admired the fat crimson buds on Anna's climbing rose.

Patric had chosen the right time to ask her to go out with him—taking her by surprise and demanding a quick answer. And even if Nick hadn't shown that worrying possessiveness she probably would have agreed, because she wanted to go out to dinner with him.

Oh, face facts; she wanted *much* more than that.

Damn the man, she thought crossly. Why had he seen her in that theme park and tipped her life upside down?

Nick called from the steps, 'I'm ready to go now.'

'Have you tidied your bedroom?'

'I picked up my toys,' he said virtuously.

Kate glanced at her watch. 'We've still got some time. Why don't you write a letter to thank Mr Sutherland for lunch, and I'll put it in with mine?'

'All right,' he said, disappearing back inside.

Kate crouched to smell the last exquisitely scented freesias; at the evocative, poignant perfume the past surged over her in a titanic wave of mingled joy and grief and despair.

Somehow she and Patric were linked; if she wanted freedom from that emotional tie she was going to have to follow this through. He'd been right when he'd told her she was imprisoned in the past. In many ways she'd progressed no further than the naïve eighteen-year-old who'd been seduced with ravishingly tender passion by her fairy-tale prince and then brutalised by the villain.

The experience had left her locked into a frustrated, obsessive desire. Get that out of the way and perhaps—just perhaps—she might be able to meet Patric on equal terms.

Saturday found both she and Nick prickly with anticipation. Bubbling with excitement, he sat beside her in the front of the Mini as it filled up with two other children.

When they reached the sports ground Kate's heart ached at his swift glance around the small group of parents and children. Nick gave no indication that he was disappointed not to see Patric—that wasn't his way—but his mother knew.

Five minutes after the game started she heard her name. Colour heated her skin as she turned and saw Patric. He was smiling, and his eyes gleamed with a dangerous metallic sheen.

Kate's heart leapt into her throat. 'Hello,' she said, adding inanely, 'You got here.'

'I had excellent instructions,' he said, his smile widening a fraction as he stopped beside her. 'You look like spring.'

The sunlit air danced before her eyes, lighting a slow, untamed fire within her. Forcing herself to remember that there were people—friends, interested onlookers—standing close by, she said demurely, 'Thank you. Did you have a good trip up?'

'I was surprised at the traffic, which is why I'm late. Auckland must have decided to go north for the day.'

For a second—for a fraction of a second—she tensed, overwhelmed by his size, his dominating physical impact, the way he shut out everyone else. It would be too easy to let herself lean on that masculine strength, but for all their sakes she had to keep her independence.

'Thank you for the letter,' he said. 'Nick writes very well for a six-year-old.'

Pride glowed within her. 'He does, doesn't he? His teacher says he's extremely bright.' She laughed a little.

'But never tell him that—he thinks he's pretty near perfect.'

'Most children of his age find it difficult to accept that they have faults, I suspect.' Patric's voice was amused as they both turned to the game. The tension of their last meeting dissipated in eager encouragement as the two teams of small boys tussled for supremacy on the muddy field.

The game over, and the required cheers given and received, Kate watched as Nick, crimson-cheeked and mud-streaked, rushed across. 'Hello, Mr Sutherland,' he shouted as he reached them.

'Hello, Nick. You played well.'

It was clearly an accolade of the highest order, and Nick flushed even more hotly. 'I didn't get a try.'

'No, but you stayed in position and passed the ball so that the man outside you scored. That was good team play.'

Nick nodded. 'I remembered what you told me. Sister Mary-Louise said I played well.'

'Is she your coach?'

'Yes. She's cool.' Nick jumped in the air for sheer excitement. 'She can kick the ball further than the big boys.'

While Kate collected her passengers Nick and Patric walked ahead, Nick fizzing with delight, Patric smiling and relaxed. As they came up to the car, one of the boys with her asked Kate, 'Is that Nick's father?'

These children knew the realities of modern relationships. 'No, he's a friend,' Kate said.

Patric gave her a level, enigmatic glance that shivered through to her toes. Parrying it with an impersonal smile, she unlocked the doors, saying, 'OK, in you get, and make sure you do those seatbelts up.'

'I'll see you back at the house,' Patric said.

Kate nodded and got into the car. Twenty minutes later, both boys delivered into their parents' custody, she headed for home.

'One more game to go,' Nick observed, squirming beneath the seatbelt. 'If it's warm enough we can go swimming at the beginning of next month. Do you think my old togs will fit me?'

'Probably not, so you'll be able to wear your new ones.'

Next month was November, and then—too soon—it would be Christmas. Sometimes she and Nick went up to Kerikeri to spend it with her cousin, but this year Juliet and her family were going to the South Island to spend the holiday with her sister Jenny. Anticipation, keen as a needle, stirred in the pit of Kate's stomach. What would Patric be doing this Christmas?

'I'll ask Mr Sutherland if I can come with you tonight,' Nick said casually as they swung into their small street. 'Rangi won't mind if I don't stay with him. You can ring him up and tell him.'

'It would be incredibly rude of you to break your word to Rangi,' Kate said calmly. 'And even ruder to go where you haven't been invited.'

He sent her a darkling look, and would have returned to the fray if Patric hadn't been waiting for them outside the house.

He got out of the car as they came up, and smiled down at Nick. 'Where would you like to go to lunch?' he asked, and Nick forgot about his campaign for the present.

They went to a fast-food restaurant. Sitting opposite Patric, Kate realised with a small shock that he didn't seem out of place amongst the noisy families and silent elderly couples; he had a rare ability to dominate his surroundings, mould them to fit him.

After Nick had eaten his fill they visited the Clock Museum. Apparently as intrigued as Nick with the splendid array of clocks, Patric answered her determined, curious, fascinated son's questions, patiently explaining how the clocks worked, entering into his enthusiasm—and listening when Nick told him all he'd learned about wave action.

Perhaps his attitude was a carry-over from his initial belief that Nick was his son. Or perhaps he really liked children. Kate tried very hard not to build too much on it.

When at last they came out into the sunlight Nick asked, 'Can we go to the Museum of Fishes?'

Kate glanced at her watch and shook her head. 'We have to go now.'

Nick opened his mouth to protest, then thought better of it. 'All right,' he said, adding with his best smile, 'We can go there next time, can't we?'

'We'll see,' Kate said noncommittally. She turned to Patric. 'Where are we eating tonight? I'll need to leave the phone number with Ngaire MacArthur.'

'It's a place called Seabird.'

'I haven't heard of that one,' she said. 'It must be new.'

'It's not in Whangarei,' he said calmly, 'It's in the Bay of Islands.'

An hour's drive to the north. Flustered, Kate said, 'Oh. All right.'

At five o'clock she delivered Nick, with his favourite green dinosaur and a bag of necessities, to the MacArthurs' house.

'He seems a bit down,' Ngaire said, watching him with a critical eye. 'Everything all right?'

'He wants to come too,' Kate said with a wry smile. She handed over a sheet of paper with the name of the restaurant and the number.

Ngaire's eyes widened. 'So do I,' she said with feeling. 'That place is supposed to be absolutely gorgeous—very exclusive—and the food spectacularly wonderful. Who are you going out with?'

'An old friend.'

When Ngaire looked thoughtfully at Nick, disappearing rapidly through a door with the two youngest MacArthurs, Kate added hastily, 'No.'

'Pity,' Ngaire said cheerfully. 'Oh, well, have a great

time. Nick and Rangi will. Just don't get here tomorrow morning before nine, OK?'

Kate laughed. 'I promise.'

She'd never been allowed to forget that the first time Nick had stayed with the happy, noisy, chaotic MacArthurs she'd arrived at eight next morning to pick him up. He and two of the boys had been ensconced in front of the television, eating an eclectic breakfast as they watched a video, while everyone else enjoyed their Sunday lie-in.

Ngaire gave her a swift, perceptive glance. 'Have fun,' she said. 'You deserve it. One day Nick's going to grow up and leave you, and if you haven't made yourself a life by then you'll miss him unbearably.'

Her friend's injunction hit uncomfortably close to home. 'I know.'

'Besides,' Ngaire said with ruthless practicality, 'It's not good for boys to grow up believing they're the one shining star in their mother's heaven, even if they are. It makes them arrogant and dissatisfied, because no woman is going to live up to the adoring mother who loves them unconditionally.'

But Patric—the focus of his parents' hopes and love and aspirations, their golden son—hadn't grown up arrogant and dissatisfied. Of course their love hadn't been unconditional; they'd more or less forced him to marry Laura.

Kate wondered how much persuasion had been needed; Laura had been an extraordinarily beautiful woman—lushly sophisticated even as an adolescent.

'And wives no longer love unconditionally,' Ngaire went on. 'If they get treated badly they take off—and so they should. I don't think you need to worry about Nick, though. In spite of that determined chin, he's a love. He'll be all right. Now off you go and get yourself pretty for tonight.'

Nick reappeared on a wave of children and dogs to give her a swift hug. Without a trace of regret he said, 'Yes, you have a good time, Mummy. Bye.'

Kate spent the next half-hour dithering in front of her wardrobe. The top and trousers she'd selected looked good on her, but somehow didn't seem entirely suitable for a place as chic and exclusive as Seabird.

In the end she wore them because they were the most sophisticated clothes she possessed. The soft mesh-knit top in her favourite pale green, with no sleeves and a deep vee neck, revealed a lot of skin. Dreamed up by a designer famous for his slinky, erotic clothes, it was meant to be worn without lining or bra, which was probably why it hadn't sold. After Kate had bought it in the shop's sale she'd searched until she found silk the exact shade of her skin and had carefully sewn a lining into it.

Kate pulled it over her head and settled it around her shoulders, eyeing the slight swell of her breasts beneath the material. 'It's perfectly decent,' she told her reflection in the small mirror.

Complementing the top were silk trousers—loosely fitting and with a faintly oriental air. Another reason for the ensemble not to sell—it was difficult to classify; too informal in design for the occasions its cut and superb material suggested, and youthful yet expensive. Kate had loved it on sight.

How glad she was that the boutique owner had allowed her delight with the outfit to override her commercial instincts! Otherwise Kate would have had to go out with Patric in clothes chosen for their practicality and hard-wearing qualities.

What would he think when he saw her?

Ruthlessly subduing the hot excitement that clutched her stomach, she checked herself in the mirror. She'd left her face naked except for a slick of lipgloss, slightly darker than her skin, and a hint of gentle shadow to emphasise her eyes. The tunic probably should have earrings to set it off, or a thin gold chain around her neck, but she had neither.

She tied the thick, slippery mass of her hair back with

a satin ribbon the same subtle green as her clothes. Picking up the narrow clutch that doubled as her evening bag, she slid her feet into low-heeled black pumps and set her chin.

As the doorbell pealed colour drained from her face. You fool, common sense said calmly. You should never have agreed to this.

Perhaps common sense was right, but a flame of rebellion in her ignored that dreary, sensible announcement. She'd been sensible for almost seven long years; it was past time to accept the challenges life offered.

CHAPTER NINE

ALTHOUGH informal, Patric's clothes were tailored for his lean body, their skilful cut and fine materials emphasising wide, masculine shoulders, narrow hips and long, heavily muscled legs. After a quick, intent survey of her face he said quietly, 'You look like Melusina—a very young Melusina.'

A shift of perception—subtle but irreversible—took place within Kate. Suddenly free, almost as though he had somehow managed to strike invisible, unfelt shackles from her soul, she felt light, buoyant—floating in a sea of expectation, of hope.

'Who was Melusina?' she asked, locking the door behind her.

He took her arm and walked her towards the gate, keeping position so that she stayed on the narrow concrete path while he was on the grass. 'A French water spirit. Of course she was exquisitely beautiful. She fell in love with a French noble and married him on condition that he should never see her on a Saturday.'

'So he promised faithfully never to peep on a Saturday, but he couldn't resist the temptation?'

'Naturally,' he said drily. 'And like all people who pry he suffered for it, because she wasn't human, she was a serpent. Or a mermaid—history's not exactly clear. Whatever, she fled from him, and he spent the rest of his life mourning her.'

'A mermaid has charisma,' Kate said thoughtfully, 'but I don't think I like being compared to a serpent. And you'd think these mythical characters—Melusina and Bluebeard and their ilk—would learn from each other. Nothing whets a human's curiosity more than being told not to do something—it's practically an open invitation.'

He laughed and put her into the car. Once they were heading northward through Whangarei's quiet suburbs, he said, 'They were a stupid lot. And if she was a serpent, I'm sure Melusina was an infinitely seductive and alluring serpent with no idea of her power. A siren, like you.' Beneath the deep, smoothly sensual voice prowled latent emotion, edgy with the leashed violence of desire.

An answering wildness flared into life inside her, straining against the bars that will-power and discipline imposed on her emotions and her thoughts.

Unsteadily she said, 'Thank you, I think.'

Patric smiled but his voice was satirical. 'As the Americans say, you're welcome.'

Lights swung towards the car, swished by, and dwindled into a blur of brilliant red as the vehicle purred through the night. Tension stretched between them, a stark, dancing force that pulsated with unspoken thoughts, unbidden feelings, runaway sensations.

He broke into the silence. 'Your eyes are so clear, yet they hide secrets. Seven years ago I wanted to find out what those secrets were. I still do.'

A momentary flash of fear kicked in the pit of her stomach. Swiftly, almost airily, she got out, 'Everyone has things they'd rather not talk about.'

'Of course,' he said, his voice even, almost expressionless, 'but in those days I was desperate to know what you thought and felt. I suppose I hoped understanding you would give me some power.'

'Power?' She was shocked.

'Oh, yes.' He gave her a sardonic, almost angry glance. 'Didn't you realise, Kate? I was utterly defenceless and I hated it—it had never happened to me before. I couldn't get enough of you, yet I knew you were too young to make any sort of commitment. Most of all I wanted to know whether you felt the same way about me.'

'You must have known I did,' she protested, thinking back to the transparent child she'd been.

'How could I? I knew you liked me, but you seemed to like everyone. You were always unfailingly kind—to the local kids, to anyone who stayed at Tatamoa. You gave them the gift of your smile and your interest, and left them all wanting more. Girls liked you too, although they were baffled by your refusal to join in their ploys and games. You were even kind to my contemptible cousin Sean before he tried to kiss you.'

Kate stared blindly into the dark. This was what it must be like to walk on the lip of a volcano, knowing that one slip could lead to disaster. Swallowing the coppery taste in her mouth, she said the only thing she could think of. 'That last year I was just an ordinary girl well out of her depth.'

'Hardly. Ordinary girls flirted and fluttered their eyelashes and posed elegantly in their briefest clothes. You went serenely on your way. All that summer I wondered whether it was my imagination—and hormones—that made me believe you felt more for me than for anyone else. Until we made love. I knew then—or thought I knew.'

Kate's skin tightened. What had he learned then—that she was totally, completely in love with him? That she had no defence against his experienced sexuality?

'The world stopped for me,' he said roughly. 'You blew my mind away with your sweet passion. I shouldn't have made love to you, but I didn't have the self-control to pull back. Did I frighten you so much that you couldn't bear to see me again, Kate?'

'No,' she said in a low voice. 'Of course you didn't.'

His mouth thinned. 'I couldn't think of any other reason for you to break it off.'

'I was very depressed that term at Christchurch,' she said, choosing her words carefully. Numbed by shock and an all-pervading sense of degradation, for three months she'd been lost in pain.

In her innermost heart, beneath the dreams and the desire and the heat of love, Kate had known—had understood since before their first kiss—that she wasn't fit for life as Patric's wife. Kind though his parents had been to their farm manager's niece, they certainly didn't want their son to marry her. Intelligence and common sense weren't all that were necessary in the world over which Pilar Sutherland held sway. Sophistication and the gloss of social confidence, of knowing what to do and how to do it, were every bit as important.

Sean's threats had sickened her and humiliated her. 'I'll tell Patric,' he'd taunted, his handsome, fleshy face filled with a despicable glee. 'I might let him marry you—and wouldn't that give Laura a kick in the teeth, stuck-up bitch!—but sooner or later I'll tell him that I've had you. He's a possessive bastard and he hates me, so that's going to really get him where it hurts!'

He would have done it, and she couldn't have allowed herself to be the weakness that exposed Patric to that humiliation.

Disgusted and shamed, she couldn't have gone to him carrying Sean's child in her womb.

After that last, shattering meeting with Patric she'd gone back to Christchurch because it was as far away as she could get from Tatamoa. Then, mercifully, the physical and hormonal changes of pregnancy had taken her over, driving everything but the need for survival from her mind; in the end it had simply been easier to turn her back on the whole situation and strike out unencumbered by the weight of the past.

In a toneless voice Patric said, 'I've always felt I abandoned you when I left Tatamoa the day after we'd made love.'

Had she blamed him for abandoning her? Oh, not for going to his father, no, never that! But after Patric left his cousin had come to Tatamoa, lured her to the homestead with the promise of a letter from Patric, and raped her.

Had she somehow blamed him for not protecting her?

No. Sean was responsible for his own actions.

Coughing to overcome the ache in her throat, she said, 'Your father was dying! Of course I didn't expect you to dance attendance on me. You had to go. By May I knew—I was—' Her voice splintered. She dragged in a deep, impeded breath. 'Patric, I couldn't marry you when I was pregnant with another man's child.'

Hands gripping the wheel, he steered the car around one of Northland's notorious curves. Silence enveloped them, a silence thick with old pain. Kate realised she was holding her breath. A car sprang out of the darkness; in the glare of its lights Patric's face was revealed—icily rigid, each muscle clenched as though he was in intolerable anguish. Kate flinched, then shielded her eyes as the oncoming lights flicked onto full and down again.

'Patric—'

But he'd already dipped their lights. The oncoming car gave a swift toot on the horn as it surged past them.

Kate exhaled. She should let him concentrate on his driving; it was so unlike him to forget to dip.

He said harshly, 'I would have married you, Kate. I wanted to marry you more than anything in the world. I only married Laura—' He stopped and swore, his voice hoarse with anger. 'Why didn't you tell me?' he demanded between his teeth. 'Kate, you must have known I wouldn't blame you.'

No, but how would he have dealt with the knowledge that his cousin had raped her? What would it have done to a family already agonised by the prospect of Alex Sutherland's death? Because if they'd married sooner or later Sean's malice would have spilled over and he'd have told Patric, smashing any prospect of a future for them.

Noiseless, desperate words rasped her throat. Swallowing them, forbidding them life, she said, 'I was damaged, Patric—too hurt and degraded to know what I was doing. Anyway, even without…even if nothing had happened it wouldn't have worked, you and I. I was far too young; I didn't know how to be any sort of wife, especially not for a man in your position.'

'You'd have coped.' Although his voice was level, the words were rasped by a raw undernote. 'I'd trust you to deal with anything! Look at the way you managed with Nick.'

'I had only one demanding male to deal with,' she returned, trying to lighten the atmosphere. 'The past's past. Let's leave it there.'

A scurry of rain spattered against the windscreen. For several minutes they drove without speaking, until he said with a compelling intensity, 'Kate, I want very much to leave the past where it belongs, as long as my future has you in it.'

Kate's heart stopped in her chest. She stole a sideways glance. His profile, starkly outlined against the night outside, was a silhouette of strength—straight forehead, the sweep of nose, the male beauty of his mouth and the uncompromising determination of jaw and chin. Kate had expected him to suggest an affair. Unless she was mistaken, he was offering her much more.

She stared down at her hands, knuckles gleaming white in a frozen clasp. 'I—would like that too.'

Her voice sounded oddly muted, almost shaky. Scared.

Without taking his eyes off the road, Patric found her hand and lifted it to his mouth, pressing a kiss to the palm before replacing it in her lap. 'This time I won't make the mistake of valuing money and power over you,' he said uncompromisingly.

'You didn't,' she said, trying to repress the shiver of delight that ran through her. 'You put one sort of love over another, and I understand. It would have been cruel to defy your father when he was so ill. I imagine he knew that

Sutherland Aviation needed both you and Laura's father—he must have been desperately worried.'

'That was no excuse for blackmailing me,' he said, his voice grim. 'And even less excuse for me to give in to it. I've learned my lesson, Kate. Now, tell me what you've been doing these last few years.'

Relieved, she gave him a quick rundown on her life—skipping the worst bits, making him smile by recounting several of Nick's more memorable exploits—and as the minutes slipped by and the traffic thinned out tension began to seep from her. By the time they reached the star-silvered Bay of Islands she was filled with a bright, fragile hope.

That night Patric wooed her with his attention, with his voice, with his eyes—narrowed and intent—and with his conversation.

Over the ambrosial food, in surroundings of quiet, restrained sophistication looking out onto shimmering, island-dotted waters, she finally surrendered completely to that helpless, helter-skelter, headlong tumble into love, with its terrors and its singing, piercing hunger—both physical and emotional—and the fierce elation that came from exploring Patric's keen, disciplined mind and personality.

And always, always beneath the stimulating conversation and the potent communication of eyes raced a current of need, glittering and powerful and intense, marooning her on the cusp between frustration and fulfilment.

Later, outside her unit, he walked her to the door while a slow excitement built within her. He knew Nick wasn't there…

'You've made a pretty garden,' he said.

Its scents floated around them; the wet fragrance of new-mown grass, a fugitive sweetness of flowers, some intense, spicy perfume she'd never smelt before.

'With Anna and Ngaire's help.' Her voice sounded flat,

almost strained. Without looking at him she unlocked the door.

Patric came in with her and checked out each room.

'It's perfectly safe,' Kate said on a half-laugh when they stood together in the cramped sitting room.

'I lost you once,' he said. 'I couldn't keep you safe then—I don't want the same thing to happen again.'

Without thinking she put her hand on his sleeve. 'It's over,' she said quietly, and for the first time she believed that it really was: the past had been faced, robbed of its capacity to hurt.

'Kate,' he said, and put his hands on her shoulders and bent to kiss her with a curbed passion.

Closing her eyes, Kate breathed in the scent and taste of him, the pressure of his hands, of his mouth, the reality of Patric Sutherland.

Desire coursed through her, hot and untamed and slow, and she could have cried out in rebellion when he lifted his head. Unevenly he said, 'I have to go back to Auckland tonight. I'll see you next weekend.'

Disappointed and surprised, she wondered why he'd pulled back. But she told herself they needed the breathing space. Yes, the past had been dealt with; now they needed to find the path to their future.

Yet in the following weeks that hunger grew into torment, intensifying each hour she spent with him, binding Kate with fragile, unbreakable chains until she thought the wanting would drive her crazy. Yet Patric's tenderness and restraint satisfied some long-lost part of her. She honoured him for his control; he was giving her time to overcome her natural fear about making love. It was as though they were reliving his first courtship, when she'd been barely more than a child, and he had moved from big brother to lover. So, although she relearned the strength and power of need and passion, she was content to travel slowly down the path to delight.

His tenderness when he touched her—the subtle mastery

of his hands on her skin, the fleeting, frequent caresses that were far from sexual yet set her on fire—showed that he was gentling her like a nervous filly. When they finally did make love she would be so attuned to him, to the thousand sensual signals of his body, that she wouldn't be repelled by his passion.

As spring warmed into summer he came north most weekends, and he rang several times a week, the calls becoming more intimate as they grew to know each other.

He continued to be, Kate thought, six weeks after that first dinner in the Bay of Islands as she watched him from the shelter of a sun umbrella, wonderful with her son. It didn't seem to worry him that Nick was the child of the man who had raped her—carefully, cleverly, he'd forged a friendship.

They were walking—the tall, impressive man, the lithe, quicksilver boy—along the foamy line where the waves washed onto the soft apricot sand. Occasionally Patric would crouch down level with Nick, and they'd pore over whatever took their interest. Nick had become fascinated by the idea of plants growing in the sea, so it was usually seaweed, but he was also collecting shells. When Kate saw their two heads so close together her heart shivered.

Tonight she and Patric were going out to dinner as they had most Saturdays since he'd come up the first time. Surely, she thought yearningly, he knew now that she wanted him—that she was ready for their relationship to deepen? How did you tell a man that without losing your dignity?

'You look funny,' Nick said, surprising her.

While she'd been lost in a daydream they'd come up, and were looking at her with the same quizzical expression.

'That's her mermaid smile,' Patric informed him.

Nick gave a crow of laughter. 'She hasn't got a tail.'

'Some mermaids look just like human beings,' Patric

said, his half-closed eyes sweeping Kate's legs, long and winter-pale. 'They're the dangerous ones.'

Need kicked her with exquisite precision in the pit of her stomach, drawing her down into a relentless longing. 'Don't talk about me as though I'm not here,' she said.

But Patric had seen her swift, involuntary shiver. Lashes drooping, he said in a voice roughened by a hidden hunger, 'The water's warm enough to swim in.' He held out his hand.

'Lovely.' Kate let him pull her to her feet.

He dropped his hand as soon as she was upright, but his index finger lingered across her palm.

She'd worn her togs beneath her shirt and shorts, and normally she wouldn't have been at all concerned about pulling her clothes off. However, that tiny, fleeting caress made her acutely self-conscious. Turning slightly under the pretence of supervising Nick, she stripped off her shorts; her bathing suit was old, but the dark green hugged her and she knew she looked good in it.

Without looking at Patric, she challenged Nick, 'Beat you in.'

'No, you won't,' he said, sprinting down the beach.

Kate set off after him, judging her speed so that they plunged into the surf at the same time. He loved the water, and was completely confident in it.

'Look!' he shouted, and dived down to Kate's feet, tickled her ankle and emerged, bubbling and boisterous, beside her.

'I thought you were a fish!'

He laughed. 'I caught a mermaid,' he said.

'No, only a mother,' Kate said, looking up.

At the sight of Patric, bronze shoulders gleaming in the sun, the water up to his black briefs, her brain shut down. He looked like something out of the dawn of time, she thought dazedly, all male, smoothly muscled and sleek and incredibly compelling.

'Did you see me, Mr Sutherland?' Nick's voice jarred

the silence. 'I dived down and touched Mummy's toes. I can dive off the edge of the pool, and when I'm eight she's going to show me how to dive off the boards. Mummy's the best diver in the world, except for the Olympics.'

Patric ruffled his hair. 'I know,' he said, and looked at Kate.

Who was standing there, mesmerised and mute, pulses thudding, mouth dry with apprehension and thirst as though she'd wandered in a desert these last years and now at last could see the feathery tips of palms above the burning sands. It took all of her will-power to free herself from Patric's sensual spell.

'I'm a good diver,' she managed, dragging her eyes away to gaze down at her son, 'but not that good.' And because she was exposing her emotions embarrassingly, she added, 'Come on, let's swim.'

She stayed with Nick, but Patric was never far away. Every time she looked up she met his eyes, glittering with the grey-black sheen of a gun barrel. He wasn't crudely obvious, but he used the games Nick insisted on as an excuse to touch her, addicting her further to his gentle caresses.

In the midst of a fast game of water tag Kate got caught by a larger than normal wave and tumbled over. Immediately, lean hands fastened onto her shoulders and pulled her upright, and while she stared into a face set and hard and possessive Patric bent and kissed her fiercely.

'I've run completely out of patience—I need you so much,' he muttered. 'Marry me, Kate.'

And when, thunderstruck, she couldn't answer, he said harshly, 'Please!'

Dimly her dazzled senses registered skin branded by his hands, by his mouth, and the distant sound of Nick's voice, backed by the impatient bray of a car horn on the road behind the beach. She looked into hot, resolute eyes, and flame seared across her, through her. 'Yes,' she said.

'Mummy?' Nick demanded. His wet hand slid into hers,

gripped. He said truculently, 'Did you get a mouthful of water?'

'No, I didn't. I don't breathe in when I go underwater,' she said, and managed a smile.

He glowered at her through wet, spiky lashes. 'Why did he kiss you like that?'

It was Patric who answered. 'Do you want a father, Nick?'

Nick turned his head. He stared up into Patric's controlled face, and after a long, charged moment nodded.

'Mothers and fathers kiss each other a lot,' Patric said coolly. 'I'm going to be your father from now on.'

Nick stared at him, then swivelled his eyes to Kate's face. 'Oh, all right,' he said offhandedly, reassured for the moment. 'Mr MacArthur kisses Rangi's mum all the time.' He touched Kate's arm. 'Bet you can't catch me,' he shouted, and duck-dived beneath the next wave.

Patric followed him, leaving Kate to gaze foolishly after them, her skin suddenly puckered with gooseflesh.

Leaving them to their game, she swam rapidly away from the beach, trying to work through bewilderment at the unexpected proposal. After a few minutes she heard Patric call her name, and realised she couldn't keep heading out to sea.

By the time she got back to them Patric had persuaded Nick out of the water and into his clothes. 'He was shivering,' he said, rubbing his own towel across his shoulders.

'Thank you,' she said lightly, keeping her eyes firmly away from him.

Nick peered at her. 'Dad wanted to go out to you, but I told him you were the best swimmer in the world,' he said proudly.

Kate's heart clenched. She looked at Patric, saw his smile, and had to blink to hide her tears.

'We thought Dad was what a boy of Nick's age should call his father,' he said. 'That's what Rangi calls his.'

'I know,' she said in a shaken voice, poised on a knife-edge of disintegration. When Patric took Nick up to the car, she dragged her clothes on and rubbed her face vigorously with the towel before following them. In the car she covered her eyes with sunglasses.

'Would you get me mine, please?' Patric asked. 'In the glovebox.'

She found them and handed them over, acutely conscious of the warmth of his fingers as he took them. In the back seat Nick bounced around, talking almost non-stop. None of them said a word about Patric's astounding declaration. By the time they arrived home Kate was being tormented by a mixture of shock and slow, pulsing joy.

In the house, she ordered Nick to the bathroom. 'Off you go—now, right this minute, before you shed any more sand on the floor.' Carefully avoiding Patric's eyes, she asked politely, 'Would you like to shower here?'

'No, I'll go,' he said. Ignoring Nick's hovering presence, he lifted Kate's chin. His eyes were intent, probing, and ruthless. 'Don't be late,' he commanded. 'I'll pick you up at seven.'

'I'll be ready.'

From the doorway Nick asked, 'Can't I come too?'

'No,' Kate said, glad that he gave her the excuse to pull away from Patric's too-forceful gaze. 'You have an appointment with Rangi.'

He chuckled, but insisted, 'You'll come and get me early in the morning?'

'Promise,' Kate said, at the same time as Patric's short, 'Yes.'

Nick disappeared into the hall and Patric said, 'I'd better go.'

Feeling cheated, Kate nodded. He traced the tiny frown between her eyes and said, 'It'll be all right, Kate.'

'I know,' she said. 'He'll need to be reassured over and over again, but he's happy about it.'

'Is that the only reason you're marrying me? Because Nick's happy? There'll be times when he's not, Kate.'

'I know that. We'll deal with it. And, no, that's not why I said I'd marry you.' Now she knew how a woman told a man she wanted him. Reaching up, she kissed the triangle of tanned skin at the collar of his shirt. 'No,' she repeated against his skin, tasting him, breathing out on his wet skin.

His hand lifted her chin; transfixed by the blazing sensuality in his face, she'd barely begun to respond to the swift, searing kiss when he stepped back and said, 'I'll see you later,' and while she stared after him, the sound of the taps turned on full brought her back to herself.

When she went in to check Nick's cleanliness he presented her with a scrubbed and glistening face and demanded, 'Is he really, really going to be my father?'

'Yes,' she said.

Nick gave her one of his grave, unchildlike looks. 'Good,' he said. 'He knows about boys.'

'So he should. He used to be one himself.'

Nick grinned. 'Will I grow as big as him?'

'I don't know. My father was tall, and so was my mother, so although I'm not tall myself I might have handed on a few of those genes to you.'

Nodding, Nick said, 'I'd like to be tall as Mr Sutherland.' He hesitated, then added as though trying it out for sound, 'Dad.'

'Just be the best Nick Brown you can be,' she said, adding quickly, 'Bend your head forward so I can wash the salt and sand out of your hair.'

That night, with Nick safely ensconced at the MacArthurs' place, she put on the same outfit she'd worn the night Patric had taken her to dinner in the Bay of Islands. Such a short time ago, she realised with a vague sense of surprise.

Just six elongated weeks, each followed by a weekend that had gone by so fast she could barely remember the events. Yet when Patric had moved back into her life he'd almost taken it over.

And now he'd asked her to marry him.

Sinking down onto the bed, she stared at the floor. She would have to tell him who Nick's father was; she couldn't marry him with that lie still between them. She should have told him when he'd said he wanted a future with her, but she'd been a coward.

She could not marry Patric without telling him who her son's father was. To put it in Nick's terms, it simply wasn't fair. If he was the man she thought he was, he'd accept it.

If not—then she'd manage.

Starkly she thought she'd *have* to manage.

Tonight. She had to tell him tonight.

It would be all right, she comforted herself. Patric hadn't said that he loved her, but why else would he ask her to marry him? He'd forgive her for lying to him. And he'd make sure she never had to meet Sean again—from what Patric had said, even Sean's mother had given up on him. Poor Mrs Cusack. Perhaps she might find some sort of consolation with the children Kate had every intention of giving Patric.

Yes, she'd tell him tonight.

Ignoring a craven clutch of panic, Kate dried her hair and got into her clothes, wishing she had more of a choice. It would be wonderful to select from several gorgeous designer outfits, stunning and provocative and glamorous, but her wardrobe reflected her tight budget.

At least the garments in it now suited her. Until she'd started working in the shop she'd worn mostly secondhand clothes.

Patric arrived dead on time. 'I thought we'd eat at the house I'm staying in,' he said as they drove through the small city.

Normally he stayed in a hotel. Chilled by an odd sense of exclusion, she asked, 'Where is it?'

'The Heads.'

Whangarei lay at the tidal limit of a drowned river valley, its north bank a series of volcanoes forced millions of years previously through the earth's mantle. Long dead, they'd weathered into jagged, dramatic hills known as The Heads, their rock faces and sharp outlines a formidable hurdle for the sun each morning.

Tell him now, she urged herself, after he's negotiated this set of traffic lights.

But before she could speak he said, 'You'll meet Geoff and Suse Simpson one day, but at the moment they're in England. They offered me the house whenever I wanted to stay.'

'I already know Mrs Simpson as a customer.' Kate looked determinedly out of the side window. She'd wait until they got to the house. It would be easier to confess when he wasn't concentrating on the road. 'She's nice.' She didn't mention that the owner of the shop had made it clear that Mrs Simpson was important.

'I'm glad you like her,' Patric said. 'Geoff and I went to school together.'

Geoffrey Simpson was now a very successful solicitor, working in his father's practice. His wife ran a flying school and bought most of her very elegant clothes in Auckland and Australia.

Kate knew they lived in a lovely house; she discovered that it was truly fantastic, set high above the tidal estuary so that it looked south across Bream Bay to the Hen and Chicken Islands, and on to Great Barrier Island and its rugged inner companion, Little Barrier. Glittering, compelling, limitless, the sea dazzled to the horizon.

'Impressive,' Kate said, wishing she had more sophistication. Her nerves were jangling, and her voice sounded colourless. *Tell him now.*

'The house or the view?'

She turned away from the window to glance around the huge, exquisitely furnished sitting room. Her eyes lingered on a picture, all stark angles and bold juxtapositions of colour. It was exciting, almost alarming. 'Both.'

Coward!

Patric smiled at her. 'I'll get you a drink. What would you like?'

Grateful for the respite, she chose white wine; he poured her a fragrant Riesling, grown on the stony plains of Marlborough, and whisky and water for himself. Upright in a black leather Wassily chair, Kate sipped the superb wine and tried to forget her hollow foreboding.

'You're not thinking of going back on your promise this afternoon, I hope,' Patric said conversationally, watching her from heavy-lidded eyes.

Her hand jumped, almost spilling the wine. Carefully she set the glass down. 'I was wondering whether you were regretting having asked for it,' she said, pronouncing each word with circumspection. He hadn't touched her since he'd picked her up.

'You know better, Kate.' But his eyes were hooded, a formidable control keeping them blank.

In spite of the fine tremor in her hand she picked up the glass and swallowed a large mouthful of wine. 'Nick is still thrilled. I imagine he's telling the MacArthurs all about it right now.' *Now!*

But he asked without emphasis, 'What would you have said if Nick had hated the idea?' Before she could speak he said curtly, 'That's a stupid question. Forget it.'

She had to answer. 'I don't know. I'd have tried to change his mind.' And, because that seemed a cavilling response, she added, 'He admires you enormously.'

'Fortunately for me. So now,' the cool, dark voice prompted, 'I'd like to know what your problem is. Something's eating at you.'

Clutching the glass, she said, 'Patric—I need to tell you about Nick's father.'

The whisky glass rang as he set it down on the glass side table. 'No.'

Ignoble relief flooded through her, but she couldn't accept it. White-lipped, she stammered, 'I—I have to—'

'I don't want to hear.' His voice was inflexible, obdurate. 'I don't need to know anything more than you've already told me. It doesn't matter. I have everything I've ever wanted.'

Intent, his face under such rigid control it could have been carved in stone, he came across to her and pulled her gently to her feet. He didn't say anything; instead he held her close until the comfort only he could give her worked its magic. Her fears faded and shimmered into mirages, into nothingness.

'Kate,' he said eventually.

'What?'

'Just—Kate. My Kate. For ever this time.'

But he made no effort to kiss her. Bewildered, Kate looked up into narrowed, molten eyes, and realised with a jumping heartbeat that he was going to let her take the initiative. For a second memory intruded—a memory of rough hands and jeers, of helplessness and pain and degradation—and then it flickered and died.

This was Patric. She trusted him.

'I won't break,' she said, and stood on her toes so that she could touch her lips to his hard, beautiful mouth.

Time stretched, lingered. His lips were firm and totally unresponsive.

Kate was just about to jerk away when his arms contracted and he took her mouth in a kiss stripped of everything but passion and hunger. Vaguely she thought she sensed the second his self-control broke. It was followed almost immediately by the breaching of her own barriers; without any resistance she surrendered the guarded citadel of her body and her heart.

Sensation flooded through her. As she opened her lips beneath his she wondered vaguely how her response to Patric's mouth—to his scent and corded strength, his hands—flowed sweet and languorous as honey, yet at the same time pierced her with a sharp, swift ecstasy.

He broke the kiss to speak. 'Now do you understand

how I feel about you?' His voice was guttural as he fought to master himself.

Suddenly shy, she nodded.

'Then I think we'd better stop,' he said thickly.

Bewildered, her head spinning, Kate asked, 'Why?'

He said, 'I won't rush you as I did last time.'

Her heart swelled. She didn't need to hear the words—this was indication enough that he loved her. 'That was a long time ago,' she said, tracing his straight mouth with her fingertip. His lips were a little blurred by that fierce kiss, and a trace of heat stained the high, autocratic cheekbones.

Kate's spine tingled into meltdown. In a voice that trembled, she continued, 'I'm not an eighteen-year-old girl now, Patric.'

Half-closed, gleaming eyes held hers for so long that her heartbeat surged into overdrive. The dense colour of his pupils concealed his thoughts; as she waited for his answer a remnant of practicality cooled her wildfire response. Although she had no protection, she'd more or less invited him to make love to her.

And she still had to tell him.

Gathering her courage in her hands, she said huskily, 'Patric—darling—please listen to me. This is important. Please—'

He bent and kissed the hollow beneath her ear. Mouth moving with erotic finesse on her skin, he said, 'Hush. I have no other personal commitments, Kate. Only to you and to Nick.'

And before she had time to remind herself of the reason they shouldn't make love yet, he kissed her again and she yielded, helpless against the driving force of his sensuous persuasion.

CHAPTER TEN

MAKING love with Patric was like being engulfed by a hurricane—no, like submitting to the powerful, remorseless surge of the ocean, becoming one with it. On a shuddering sigh Kate surrendered to his skilled hands, to his clever, experienced mouth, to the feverish drumming of her hunger.

How did he know that her breasts ached for the touch of his hands? When he slid his hand up under the lining of her singlet top she sighed with relief, and arched so that he could reach her more easily.

'Motherhood suits you,' he said, his voice raw as he cupped the slight curves.

Sensation shimmered through her, wild and turbulent as the sea, speeding from the skin beneath his hands to every hidden, waiting part.

Stunned, her body aflame, Kate turned her face into his throat. Delicately she tasted him again, delighting in the flavour that was Patric—as much the man as the iron-blue sheen of his eyes, the determined, confident mouth that held such heaven.

'Have you changed too?' she asked against his neck.

'Why don't you find out?' he suggested tautly. 'But not here.'

With one swift, easy movement he scooped her up and carried her along the high white hall and into a bedroom cantilevered over the hillside, suspended between the sky and the sea. Through huge windows Kate saw the moon rising, following a white moonpath across the black waters, silhouetting the stark, unambiguous shapes of the extinct volcanoes against a sky robbed of all but the brightest stars.

Patric put her down on the bed. As he pulled the ribbon free from her hair and lifted the clinging tresses so that he could kiss her nape, he asked in a tight, disciplined voice, 'Do you want me to draw the curtains?'

Almost seven years ago they'd made love in his parents' house, in the bedroom he'd slept in since a child. Curtains had covered the windows and the room had seemed a safe haven, a nest. But that wasn't what she wanted now.

'No.'

Without moving he said, 'Kate, I've got protection.'

Almost inaudibly she said, 'Patric, that's up to you. I want to give you a child.'

Blue flames in his eyes swallowed the darkness. He spread a handful of her hair across her throat, then kissed the vulnerable hollow where her pulse beat fast and high.

'I used to dream of this,' he said in a quiet, almost soundless voice. 'Of you with the moon on your face and that hair spread on my pillows, and your smile for me only. Kate, if I'd known—'

'But you didn't,' she interrupted, desperate that their coming together not be overshadowed by the past. Wary of the dimness that obscured the future, she felt secure only in this rich, glorious present. 'Patric, it's over now. The past's gone—done with, finished. We're together again.'

Raising lazy, boneless hands, she undid the top button of his shirt and then the next, her senses thrilling as his chest lifted on a sharply indrawn breath. Words lingered drowsily on her tongue. 'We've got this, and each other, and Nick—so much, my darling, so much. Isn't that enough?'

Without waiting for an answer, she kissed the skin she'd uncovered, rejoicing as his heart thundered beneath her lips. 'Patric,' she whispered, and pulled his shirt free. 'I need you so much.'

The moon's restrained light silvered the broad shoulders

that tapered to narrow waist and hips, revealed the flexion of the long muscles in his arms when he pulled her singlet top over her head and looked at her with dark, flat eyes—eyes that devoured her with the same craving that ate into her heart.

That was the moment she really believed.

'Kate,' he said through lips that barely moved. 'Kate—it's so banal to say that you're beautiful, but it's the only thing I can say. You steal my strength, scramble my brain, reduce me to a mindless collection of driving hungers, and yet I've never wanted any other woman so much.'

Leaning forward, she kissed along the line of his shoulder, feeling the skin tighten, kindle beneath her questing mouth. 'Darling,' she breathed.

'I've spent nearly seven years starving for you,' he said, his voice ragged with emotion he no longer tried to hide. 'Wherever I've been, whatever I've been doing, I've looked for you, because without you I was only half a man. You were so young, and yet you gave yourself utterly, generously. And you demanded the same from me—everything. At twenty-four I rather prided myself on my understanding of women—thought I knew what passion was all about; you showed me that it was nothing without love.'

Kate whispered, 'I know. I know, Patric. But we're together now. We don't have to hide any more.'

Deliberately, worshipfully, like participants in some ancient ceremony older than time, they looked at each other. Kate's heart lurched as she drowned in the depths of Patric's eyes.

'Sometimes I wondered if I'd dreamed you,' he said hoarsely. 'Nobody could be so sweet and sensual, so gentle yet excitingly, elementally demanding. Night after night, year after year, you've haunted me, and each time I woke to loneliness.'

Shaken, her eyes dilated, she returned, 'I understand loneliness.'

His features hardening into a bronze mask, he pulled her up and measured her waist with his hands for a breathless second before sliding them up again to cup her naked breasts. Kate shivered at the strength of his long fingers.

'Yes,' Patric said unevenly. His lips drew back in a humourless smile, and he bent his head and suckled her.

Sensation splintered through her like lightning, shattering the last remnants of her will. Her strange, wild cry echoed desolately in the silent room, as the insistent heat and tug of his mouth quickened every cell in her body.

Groaning, he lifted her to meet the demands of his avid mouth.

Inside her, struggling through the languidly erotic sensations aroused by his mouth, some darker, more urgent need began to demand fulfilment. The strength and power of his arousal summoned a primitive desire; she shivered as her feet touched the floor.

'What is it?' he asked, his voice stripped of everything but raw need.

'Just you.'

His eyes searched hers. All barriers surrendered, Kate flattened her hand over his heart and smiled at the sudden thunder beneath her palm.

'Siren,' he said on an impeded breath.

Leaning forward, Kate kissed one of the small male nipples. She measured it with her teeth, softly biting, then kissed it again. Exhilaration coursed through her when he shuddered.

'Yes,' he said, as though she'd asked a question.

Deftly he removed the sage-green trousers and the skin-coloured briefs beneath. A moment later cotton sheets cooled her as she watched the man she loved kick off the rest of his clothes and lie down beside her on the bed.

All those years ago he had been tender, gentle, his love-making a salute to her youth and innocence.

Not now. Compelled by a desire he could no longer curb, Patric made love with a fierce, wildly erotic concentration, taking Kate into realms of the senses she'd only read about.

Confidence flowered in her, because at last she knew Sean's violence hadn't frozen her natural appetite. Urged on by a taut, receptive impatience, she went with Patric into that place where the only reality was his hands and his mouth and the sound of their hearts beating above the voluptuous clamour of her body, where thought was replaced by instinct, where the slow slide of his mouth across her hipbone was worth more than all the pearls in the sea, all the security in the world.

Patric turned his head to kiss the satiny top of her thigh. His hair brushed against her, the rasp of his shaven cheek quivering through her acutely susceptible body. Without volition she lifted herself against him in silent, insistent demand.

'Not yet,' he said huskily. 'Not yet, Kate.'

But that aching torment demanded satisfaction. Drugged by delight, she'd been lying in a kind of stunned stasis; now, without haste, she ran her hands from his chest down the flat muscles of his stomach, following the line of hair that pointed the way. Her teeth found the smooth swell of muscle across his shoulder; she bit into the heated skin, then licked the small abrasion.

He muttered, 'No,' and trapped her exploring fingers in a peremptory hand.

She lifted heavy eyelids. Hunger—dominating, uncompromising—emphasised the stark framework of his face. Dark, half-closed eyes glittered; his mouth was curved in a smile that owed nothing to amusement.

An instinct old as womanhood—an inborn understanding of seduction—stirred in Kate. Clasping her hands across his back, she arched up onto his strong shaft and began to pull herself around him, enclosing him, her muscles working to embed him in the silken channel that longed for him.

Her name erupted in a predatory, goaded monosyllable,

then he surged into her, the power of his whole body behind the compulsive initial thrust.

He filled her so completely that although his caresses had ensured the softening and moisture needed to ease his entrance, she took a sharp, involuntary breath.

He said through gritted teeth, 'Kate?'

'Oh, yes,' she answered on a sigh.

Almost tentatively she clenched her inner muscles and he grated, 'Yes, like that, like that…' and began to move.

Kate's hands fastened around his shoulders, the slick, hot skin delighting her fingertips until she forgot everything but the urgent rhythm of Patric's lovemaking and her own wild response. She came apart in his arms, unravelling in a consuming tide of desire.

Gradually, inexorably, sensation heightened, intensified, gripping her in fiery bonds. Consumed by ripples of pleasure, she began to strive towards some unknown apex of experience, her body tightening as she met his thrusts and matched them.

The ripples expanded, drowning her in pleasure; gasping his name, Kate forced her eyes open, trying to find some stable point in this maelstrom of passion. He was watching her, that humourless smile etched against his face, and as she was flung deep, deep down, as the light rushed over her, as waves of rapture spun her into some other dimension, he came with her, head flung back, his voice echoing in her ears while she fell into ecstasy.

How long it lasted she never knew. Not long enough, and yet any more could have tipped her over the edge into madness.

Aftershocks still shivered through Kate as slow, merciless reality pushed its way back into the enclosure of their love. Helpless tears ached behind her eyes.

Still breathing heavily, his voice guttural and strained, Patric said, 'I hurt you.'

'I'm all right.'

But he moved over onto his side and scooped her to

face him, the dark eyes intent as they searched her face. 'What is it?' he demanded. 'How much did it hurt?'

'It didn't.' Nothing would ever hurt her again; he'd just stolen her heart from her body and banished, with his skilful, urgent, wholehearted passion, the memories of Sean's attack, finally and conclusively healing an injury she'd thought long mended.

She struggled to achieve a watery smile. 'I didn't know it could be like that,' she said, the words so filled with wonder that his expression relaxed. She turned her face into his chest, and Patric lifted a hand to quietly, rhythmically, stroke her hair.

'Neither did I,' he said, and into his voice came a sombre note. 'A total, complete submersion that for precious, unbearable moments makes me whole.'

'Yes.' Her voice trembled.

All these years, she thought dizzily, she'd been walking around in an emotional shroud. Cut off from the sensual pleasures of physical contact, she'd thought she was safe.

Patric had ripped her cloak of numbness from her, leaving her at the mercy of this ravishment that robbed her of the ability to think, to do anything other than feel. He had restored her to herself, made her whole again.

They drove home through a fresh, glistening dawn, bright, sun-sprinkled, poised on the border of spring and summer.

At the town basin they stopped to drink coffee and eat fresh-baked rolls. Neither said much. Relaxed, although her muscles protested now and then, Kate could only look at Patric, her mouth still tender from his kisses, her heart so full no words seemed adequate.

Inserting the key into her door, he said, 'I have to go to Australia this afternoon, but I'll be home on Wednesday—I'll come up then and we'll make plans. Until then—keep safe, my darling. You hold my heart in your keeping.' He bent and dropped a quick, hard kiss on her lips. 'And give your notice in at the shop,' he instructed.

The sun gleamed blue-black on his head, across the skin she'd kissed the night before. 'Yes, sir,' Kate said smartly.

His brows shot up. 'Did I sound too autocratic? Blame the way you look at me—as though I'm the sum of your hopes. It makes me feel like a king.' When Kate blushed he laughed, low and tender, with a note of passion beneath the amusement. 'Stop that or I'll never get away. Miss me.'

'Of course I'll miss you,' she said, resisting the temptation to cling. 'Travel safely, and come back to me.'

'Nothing,' he said, making the words a vow, '*nothing* will keep me from you. I swear it.'

She watched him stride down the path and get into the car. He lifted a hand and drove away, the big vehicle purring down the suburban street.

Hugging herself, so happy she couldn't bear it, Kate floated inside. In the small mirror in the bathroom she thought she saw her dreams dancing around her in a golden haze, drawing her along into a future she had never hoped for.

There'd be a period of adjustment; Patric still saw her as the schoolgirl—innocent and untouched—he'd once known. But they'd deal with it. A smile curved her lips; last night had begun that process! There was nothing they couldn't do together. And he was already on the way to loving Nick for himself, with the kind of solid love that nothing could jeopardise.

Nothing but Sean.

Appalled, her smile dying, she stared at her reflection. Making love to Patric had driven everything from her mind—she hadn't even thought about telling him after that. This incandescent happiness was built on a lie.

She should have insisted on revealing the truth before they made love, before they took the chance that might lead to another child. Now she'd have to wait until he came home from Australia, because there was no way she'd blurt it out over the telephone. Guilt plucked at her as she turned the water on and undressed.

At nine, she picked Nick up, refusing a cup of coffee with Ngaire, who was still wandering gloomily around in her dressing gown.

'Not that I have time to drink coffee, I suppose, if I'm going to get to church,' Ngaire grumbled. 'Nick was fine. And I don't need to ask if you had a good time—you look like someone who's just discovered the meaning of life.'

Kate blushed, ready to tell her, then closed her mouth on the words. Patric might reject—no, of course he wouldn't.

Her friend grinned. 'Oho! All right, I won't ask, but I want to know all the details when you're ready to tell me.' Slyly she added, 'Nick said your Patric is going to be his new father.'

'We've got a few things to straighten out first,' Kate said, longing to tell her, furious with herself for not confessing when she'd had the chance.

Ngaire laughed. 'I hope it works out for you, girl. You deserve to be happy.'

They'd barely got out of the gate before Nick demanded, 'Where is he? Where's Mr Sutherland—Dad?'

Kate explained.

'He didn't tell me,' he said, scowling to hide his hurt.

'He didn't tell me until this morning, either. He has work to do in Australia.'

'I thought he was going to be my father and live with us,' Nick said.

'We'll be living with him in Auckland, but you know fathers don't stay at home all the time. Mr MacArthur goes off to work.'

'Yes, but not on the weekend,' Nick protested.

'Mr MacArthur works in an office. Patric has to travel a lot, and that means he can't always stay home.'

Stubbornly he reiterated, 'He should've told me.'

Although rather silent for the rest of the day, Nick woke up the next morning his usual sunny self, and set off for school chattering about swimming and his ambition to dive.

Monday passed in a kind of a daze for Kate. She knew she was happy, yet she couldn't feel that essential lightness, an inner conviction. A life with Patric and Nick was spread before her, the gold of bliss woven through with crimson threads of passion, but she stood like an impostor before it. So much to look forward to, yet she was unable to believe it—because she hadn't told Patric the one thing he should know.

He rang that night from Australia.

'Is everything all right?' Kate asked, eyeing Nick who was hopping up and down impatiently.

'Why?'

'You sound tired.'

He paused, before telling her drily, 'I'm clearing up a mess of Sean's.'

The name was like a foul miasma. 'Oh,' she said over a sick foreboding. 'I thought you didn't see him?'

'I don't.' Patric allowed a note of exasperation to show. 'It's under control. Normally I wouldn't have anything to do with him, but his mother asked me to tidy this up. I hadn't realised they still keep in contact—but at least Aunt Barbara has the sense not to welcome him back into the fold. And I have to do this—he's been using my name.' Abruptly he changed the subject. 'Is Nick there?'

'Yes.' And because she felt ill she asked, 'Would you like to say hello?'

'Very much.'

Handing over the receiver, Kate poured herself a glass of water. The tightness in her throat eased when she drank it, but sudden, unexpected terror still smirched her happiness.

After several minutes Nick said importantly, 'All right, I'll get her.' He held the receiver out. 'He wants to talk to you,' he informed her unnecessarily.

Patric said, 'Kate, I have to go now. I'll try to ring you

again this time tomorrow night, so I can talk to Nick as well, but I'll see you on Wednesday anyway.' He stopped, and she could hear voices in the room with him. Quickly he finished, 'Take care.'

'You too,' she said, and replaced the receiver, cross with whoever had interrupted because they'd denied her a proper farewell.

Her pulse-rate was soon back to normal, though it took a while for the lingering nausea to clear. She was overreacting. Sean couldn't harm her or Nick.

But this time she'd tell Patric whether he wanted to hear or not.

Tense, worried, she waited until Patric rang again on Tuesday night, a hurried, unsatisfactory call this time that left her even more restless than ever.

Wooing sleep, she picked up a library book and tried to read. The words danced before her eyes, mocking her. Eventually she closed the book and looked around her bedroom. It was small, as were all the rooms in the unit, and the wallpaper had faded in the harsh Northland sun so that each tiny sprig of flowers looked like a dagger pointing downwards. The curtains were ones she'd made when she first came to Whangarei; her inexperience showed in puckered hems and uneven lengths, but she'd never been able to afford to replace them.

When she was with Patric she was sure they could overcome anything Fate threw in their path. Now, in her own surroundings, the cheap bedspread and secondhand furniture ample evidence of her poverty, she was afraid. She didn't know how to be a wife to someone like Patric. Oh, she was excellent mistress material, but a *wife*—she had never presided at a dinner party in her life! She had nothing in common with the sophisticated people he moved among. She probably wouldn't even like them.

His mother wouldn't welcome her.

And there was always Sean. And Patric's response to the truth.

Kate didn't sleep that night.

The following day she had to work until four-thirty, so Nick went home with Rangi after school. As she drove into the carport she thought that if—no, *when*—when she lived in Auckland she'd miss Ngaire very much, but Whangarei was only two hours away—they'd be able to see each other frequently.

Arms filled with bags of groceries, she set off for the back door.

Once inside she began to sort and store their contents, trying to enjoy the sound of a lovesick thrush coming through the open door. The day was cool and cloudy, with drizzly showers wafting between the hills, and every bird in Whangarei seemed to have caught the mating urge.

She never knew what made her realise she wasn't alone—perhaps some alteration in the texture of the air, or some hidden instinct warning her of danger. If so, it came far too late. By the time she'd turned towards the open back door Sean Cusack was inside.

Fear kicked in her stomach, stimulating a rush of adrenalin. Without thinking, she yanked out the kitchen drawer and snatched up her carving knife. 'If you come any further I'll see what damage I can do with this,' she said hoarsely.

'Oh, brave girl,' he jeered, his large, too-pale eyes salaciously flicking the length of her body, 'but you don't have to worry—I'm not going to touch you.'

'Get out.' Thank God Nick was at the MacArthurs'.

'Is that a nice way to greet a member of the family?' he drawled. 'God, I laughed when I realised my noble cousin was seeing you again. You should be careful when you talk on telephones, you know—there's always the possibility someone might be listening on an extension! Naturally, I hopped onto a plane and followed Patric home, all eagerness to find out exactly what was going on. My poor, silly mother told me he'd been paying a lot of visits to Whangarei, so I looked you up, and there you were in the phone book! Does Patric know that your brat could be mine?'

Stone-faced, Kate held the knife in front of her, but he must have seen something in her expression because he gave a long, soft whistle and the handsome, fleshy face crumpled into laughter.

'He *is* mine, isn't he? And you've told Patric he's his. I should have stuck with you, pretty Kate—you certainly know how to organise things to your advantage.'

'Get out,' she said steadily.

'Not on your life, darling.' His voice was gleeful. 'So he doesn't know that you slept with me.'

'You can be thankful that he *doesn't* know you raped me,' she said evenly.

A momentary unease drained some of the colour from his skin. 'You wanted it,' he said viciously. 'You loved it—you only kicked up a fuss because you thought he might marry you, and you knew I had no money.'

Her skin crawled. 'You raped me,' she repeated, watching him intently, determined to make sure he never touched her again.

'Try telling my cousin that and see if he believes you. He's always been jealous because I'm better-looking than him. Anyway,' he sneered, 'it wasn't as if you were a virgin.'

This man couldn't hurt her—she wasn't even afraid of him. All he'd had of her was the unwilling use of her body. His brutality hadn't even been directed at her—he'd raped her because she was Patric's lover; it was Patric he hated and envied, and it was Patric and Nick she had to protect.

'Anyway, he doesn't care about you,' he said, the words bursting bitterly from him. 'He thinks the kid's his—that's why he's marrying you. Once you're hitched he'll ignore you just like he did Laura.'

'Go away, Sean,' Kate said with disdain. 'You can't make any more trouble. You're nothing.'

Scarlet-faced, he stared belligerently at her. Then he caught himself up; his colour faded, and the glitter in his eyes transmuted into calculation. Incredulously, she realised that he was laughing.

'Oh, this is rich. This is brilliantly rich. My arrogant, stuck-up cousin will just hate bringing up another man's bastard—especially mine,' he said, gasping with enjoyment. 'You know, I think—I really think—that it's my cousinly duty to tell Patric. What a shame. We'll see how high he holds his head up then.'

'Tell him if you dare,' she said icily. 'And he already knows my son is not his.'

'Oh, I dare. After all, it only comes down to your word against mine—and he's not trusting where women are concerned, whereas I'm family.'

Even though he was threatening her, Kate could discern his pathetic pride in being related to the Sutherlands. 'Why would he believe your lies? As for my son—Patric knows he isn't his,' Kate repeated bluntly.

'Of course, if I tell him that will put an end to your little scheme to marry well.' Sean was watching her eagerly, slyness marring his regular features. 'However, it would give me great pleasure to watch him acting as father to my son, so perhaps I won't tell him just yet.' He paused, heavily underscoring his next words. 'If you make it worth my while not to.'

'Pay you off?' She didn't try to hide her disgust. 'You must be mad.'

Anger flamed in his eyes. 'No, you snooty-faced little bitch, I'm not mad. If you want to keep your hands on my big cousin and his spectacular bank account you can bloody well pay me.'

Lip curling, she said, 'I have no money.'

He flung back his head and laughed. 'I can get all the money I need from Patric—he has this stupid sense of family honour. But money isn't the only way to pay off a man, you know. I enjoyed our interlude together last time—I'd enjoy taking you to bed even more if you were Patric's wife. Especially as I know you'd hate it. Just what sacrifices are you prepared to make for your son, Kate?'

Kate masked her agony with burning disdain. 'I wouldn't sleep—' she said, then cried out, for Patric came through the door and she saw murder in his face.

Sean swung around. His swaggering bravado left him, crumpling before the black fury in Patric's eyes.

'No!' Kate shouted, dropping the knife and racing forward.

With terrifying speed and ferocity Patric hit Sean in the mouth, and then again, seeming not to realise that Kate was clinging to his arm, pleading, 'No, Patric, no, no, no,' as Sean fell backwards across the floor and lay still, blood trickling from a cut lip.

Patric's eyes were polished and fathomless, wiped clean of emotion. Fighting down her despair, Kate managed to say clearly, 'He's not worth it. He's trash, rubbish, a nothing. He's not worth it, Patric.'

Very gently he put her aside. 'Get up,' he said to his cousin, controlled menace icing each word.

Sean scrambled to his feet and backed up against the bench. His eyes darted from Patric's implacable face to Kate's and back again. He didn't speak.

In a quiet, conversational tone, Patric said, 'Get out of here and don't ever come back. If I see you within a hundred miles of Kate or the boy I'll have you put in prison for stalking.'

Sean waited until he was well out of the door before shouting, 'I hope you enjoy bringing up my son, Patric.'

Kate forced breath into her aching lungs, closed for a second the eyes that were stretched too wide.

'Why didn't you tell me?' Patric asked with deadly composure.

'At first I couldn't bear to. I knew you despised him, and for some reason it was—it was worse that it was Sean, and not some anonymous, dead rapist.' Her voice sounded thin, remote. She waited, and when he said nothing she went on without hope, 'It made it personal. I'm not making sense, am I? But that's how I felt, and I hoped…'

'What did you hope? That you'd never have to tell me?'

She searched his face, but saw nothing there to give her confidence. In an exhausted voice she said, 'Yes. You said…you said you never saw Sean, so I thought Nick was safe.' And, knowing he wouldn't believe her, she added, 'When you asked me to marry you, I knew I'd have to tell you, but I didn't know how you'd react. I was a coward.' She hadn't known it then, but she hadn't trusted him enough. Lamely, she finished, 'I did try, but when you said you didn't want to know I was relieved and glad. I should have insisted on telling you then. I'm so sorry, Patric.'

Patric looked down at his bruised knuckles, stained with the blood from Sean's split lip. Numbly Kate turned the tap on over the sink and handed him a paper towel. When he'd washed his hands and wiped the water from them he flexed the long fingers.

Kate asked, 'Was he right? Did you think I was lying—that Nick is yours?'

He met her pleading glance with unreadable self-possession. 'At first, yes,' he said. 'The day I met you again I rang New Zealand and got someone to check his birth certificate. You didn't put the name of his father, but you called him Nicholas Patrick. And he reminded me so much of the way I was as a kid—as "Black" Pat used to be—his almost obsessive interests, even the way he tilted his head. Of course I thought he was mine.'

Her heart broke. Kate felt it quite clearly, shuddered at the sudden rending, the agonising pain as her hopes shattered, each jagged shard cutting her into shreds. She'd lied, but so had he—he had pursued her because he wanted the boy he'd thought was his son. 'I called him after you because I wanted to give him something of you,' she whispered shakily. 'It was all I had, all I could do for him. But it was a lie.'

Still speaking with that rigid, dispassionate composure, he went on, 'And you didn't seem very upset when you told me about being raped. In fact you were very calm.'

White-lipped, her voice barely under control, she said, 'Apart from a therapist, you're the first person I've ever told. The only way I could say the words was to cut myself off from any emotion.'

He swore—raw words delivered in a flat monotone—and then fell silent. Even when he spoke again he made no movement towards her, didn't touch her. 'I never know what you're thinking, how you feel.'

Anger splintered through her, eating up the adrenalin. She shouted, 'Why would I have made up a story about being raped?'

'To punish me for marrying Laura.' Suddenly, he smashed his maltreated hand onto the bench. Kate's breath hissed through her lips as he said evenly, 'I should have known—God, I should have seen that there was something fundamentally wrong with you at that last meeting in May when you told me you didn't love me any more! I was so lost in my own problems, it never occurred to me that...'

To her horror she saw that his eyes were wet.

She exclaimed, 'No! How could you? I made sure you didn't! I tried so hard to seem normal—and you were under such pressure yourself. Patric, don't blame yourself.'

He said savagely, 'I'll blame myself until the day I die.'

Her fury collapsed into dread. 'When did you realise that I'd told you the truth in Surfers' Paradise—that Nick isn't your son?'

'I realised you *had* been raped when I drove you up to the Bay of Islands for dinner. You said so simply that you couldn't marry me when you were carrying another man's child.'

She remembered then—that glimpse of his face in the headlights, the way he'd forgotten to dip the car lights.

'But I didn't know the rapist was my cousin, another descendant of ''Black'' Pat, so I still believed Nick was mine.' He spoke without inflection. 'There's a photograph of ''Black'' Pat taken when he was five in an old album—they could be twins. I thought that some miracle had made Nick mine.'

Pain squeezed Kate's heart, dimmed her vision.

'I felt murderous—and ashamed,' Patric continued almost soundlessly. 'I was bitterly glad that the man who'd done that to you was dead. And I knew that I had to go very gently with you, that you might still distrust men—that you might never be able to want me as I wanted you.' Some emotion broke through the bronze mask of his face. 'Why didn't you tell me when we met that last time at Tatamoa? Surely you didn't think I'd discard you because Sean raped you?'

Past weariness, Kate leaned back against the counter. She wanted him to go before she abandoned herself to grief at the destruction of all those shining golden hopes, but she owed him an explanation. 'I went into a deep depression and I wasn't thinking at all straight. I knew you despised him and—I felt dirty, demeaned, no fit woman for you. I was sure you'd never accept his child. Your father was dying; if I'd told you you'd have confronted Sean, and it would have ripped your family apart. In the end it was all too much. I loved you, but I wanted to get away, to be free of everything that had happened.'

His mouth twisted. 'He raped you because you were mine, because he hated me. He went around with a smirk for months, and I didn't realise—it barely bloody registered! And I still didn't realise when you told me about it. How can you forgive me for such blindness?'

Tensely, urgently she said, 'There's no question of forgiving you, of blaming you. I can imagine how hideous those months must have been for you. Anyway, Sean's sins are his, not yours.'

Patric said quietly, 'You're infinitely more forgiving than I am. I'd like to kill him.'

'I was afraid of that,' she said quietly.

'Is that why you didn't tell me?'

She flushed at the incredulity in his tone. 'Partly.'

'I'm not a murderer, Kate.'

'I know,' she said quickly, 'but you—I didn't know how you'd react! *Why* does he hate you so much?'

He looked past her, his expression bleak. 'Sean feels that because Aunt Barbara was older than my father she should have inherited half of Sutherland Aviation, and probably he's right, but "Black" Pat was an unregenerate chauvinist and so was my father. Instead of a share in the business she got a trust fund which her husband persuaded her to waste on speculations that invariably came to nothing.'

There was more to it than that, Kate thought, her anger dying and leaving her hollow, emptied out of emotion. Sean hated Patric because he was everything Sean was not.

Still in that distant, deadly voice, Patric said, 'I put up with Sean for years, but when he tried to blackmail his mother into handing over money from the new trust fund I'd set up for her it was too much. You'll never see him again.'

Exhausted, Kate said, 'But he's still Nick's father—nothing can alter that. I think you'd better go now.'

'Kate—'

She couldn't bear to listen. 'Patric, please go,' she said wearily.

He had betrayed her as she had betrayed him; he'd courted her to claim the boy he'd believed to be his son.

'Kate, I can't leave you now,' he said urgently. 'I can't abandon you—'

Something snapped inside her. Summoning every atom of strength and determination she possessed, she said, 'You are not abandoning me; you didn't abandon me all those years ago. I'm now a grown woman, and at the moment I need to learn to cope with the fact that you deliberately pursued me to get your hands on a child you believed to be yours. I need to be alone to do that, Patric.'

'All right,' he said between his teeth. 'I have things I need to face too, but I'll be back. I'm at the hotel. If Sean tries to contact you again, ring me there.' He looked at her, the dark eyes turbulent and angry. In a hard voice he finished, 'If you need me, ring me. I'll come, Kate—you only have to call and I'll come.'

It wasn't until Nick had gone to bed that Kate was able to sit down and face what had happened. Pain ached through her heart, clogged the back of her throat, throbbed in her head. If only she hadn't succumbed to the temptation to give her son Patrick for a second name she'd probably have convinced Patric right at the start that she'd been raped, and he'd have left them alone.

Was there any hope for them?

Don't give in, she thought grimly. You've dealt with pain before and survived. You can do it again.

But this was something more than pain—this was the defilement of her hopes and illusions, a keen agony she'd never escape even though the years might smooth over the raw edges of the scar.

When the telephone rang she was tempted to ignore it, but the possibility that it might be Patric galvanised her to her feet.

'I thought you might like to know,' came Sean's hateful, gloating voice, 'that I'm applying to the courts tomorrow for access to the brat. I think it's time I got to know my son—taught him a few things.'

Numb with horror, Kate slammed the receiver down and crept back to the sofa, pleating a corner of the throw with shaking fingers while her thoughts whirled in jumbled, terrified fragments around her head.

Eventually, however, her movements stilled. Abruptly she sat up and straightened her shoulders. 'No!' she exclaimed to a silent room.

Sean would never get his greedy, corrupt hands on Nick. Never. If he persisted she'd deny everything. DNA testing would be the only way anyone would be able to tell for certain who Nick's father was. And if Sean suggested that she'd make plans to run—

The telephone burst into her plotting. Stiffly she rose to pick it up and spat, 'You come anywhere near him and I'll be at the police station tomorrow morning accusing you of rape.' Lying, she added, 'My aunt will give evidence. I told her at the time. I mean it, Sean.'

There was a second of silence before Patric said in a low, furious voice, 'I'll be up straight away.'

Patric arrived within ten minutes. He looked just the same, except for a feral danger in his eyes she'd not seen before.

'Tell me exactly what he said,' he commanded as soon as he got there.

Word for word she repeated Sean's threat.

'He's trying to bluff you,' he said, then shook his head. 'No, it's me. He's blackmailing me. He'll demand financial support in return for not going ahead with it.'

Kate said, 'But how can he believe you'd give in?'

He gave her a hard, ironic smile. 'He knows me well,' he said. 'He knows that I'd do anything in the world for you.'

In a cracked, unsteady voice she said, 'Patric, please don't. At least you didn't lie before. Don't lie now.'

After a second's hesitation, he said quietly, 'I didn't realise it, but I wanted you to admit that you loved me before I told you how much I love you. Perhaps it was a petty revenge for not marrying me all those years ago. I hope not. If it was I've been punished, because you haven't said it.'

Kate plopped down on the sofa, huddling into the throw rug. Colour burned through her skin. 'You must know how I feel about you.'

'I know I can make you want me,' he said roughly, 'but it's not enough, Kate. You see, I've always loved you. I never lost hope that one day I'd find you again. In fact I knew I would, because you're the only reason I breathe. Yes, I was sure Nick was mine, and at first I thought I was cold-bloodedly pursuing you for my son, but it only took a few days for me to realise that nothing had changed. I didn't care whether you were lying or not—it didn't matter. I've never stopped loving you, and I never will.'

It was impossible not to believe him; the truth was stark, non-negotiable—in his tone, in the autocratic features clenched in intolerable emotion, in the dark, uncompromising eyes.

Transfixed by the stripped, aching need she saw there, Kate whispered, 'Patric, I love you so much I can't bear to think of exposing you to Sean's malice.'

'I can deal with him.' His tone sent shivers the length of her spine. 'I'm finding it very difficult to deal with the knowledge that Sean abused you because you were *my* lover. You were raped, forced to endure such degradation, because I loved you.'

She said succinctly, 'And because I made him look a fool when he tried to kiss me. Remember, I hit him in the solar plexus. He hated that.'

'It was my love that brought you horror and pain and years of loneliness. I left you this afternoon because I needed to be absolutely sure that I could still love Nick knowing he's Sean's, because I know you won't marry me without being convinced I'd make him happy.'

A bubble of emotion stopped her breath.

He walked across the room and took her hand carefully, smoothing away its tension. Dark, intense, his eyes held hers as he said, 'I *am* sure. I can never right the wrong that Sean did to you and I'll carry that guilt all my life, but I love his son, Kate, for a whole variety of reasons: because he's yours, of course, but most of all for what he is—a charming, interesting, lovable, strong-minded little boy, a son any man would be proud of. I'll be a good father to him, and to any other children we have. And I swear I'll try to be the best husband for you.'

Over the huge lump in her throat, she whispered, 'I love you.'

It was surrender and he knew it. His smile was tender and triumphant and relieved, as though he hadn't been sure.

Lifting her, he sat with her on the sofa. Cradled in the strong haven of his arms, Kate drew a deep breath and turned her face against his chest.

'Patric, I meant what I said before. You mustn't blame yourself for Sean's actions, because nobody but Sean is responsible for them.'

'You're too generous.'

His revulsion and remorse could be a problem. 'Oh, well, agonise, then,' she retorted. 'Perhaps you should never go anywhere near a woman in case your wicked cousin rapes her.'

After a moment's startled silence, he laughed with a note of genuine amusement. 'You're good for me,' he said, kissing the top of her head.

'And you are good for me. Don't ever forget that, Patric.' She hesitated, then said quietly, 'Your mother's not going to be happy about us.'

His answer was blunt. 'You're certainly not the wife she'd choose for me, but believe me, my darling, she's learned her lesson. She wants grandchildren and to see me happily married, not necessarily in that order.' He tipped her head and looked at her with gleaming, narrowed eyes. 'Being married to you will make me happy.'

'We'll keep each other happy,' she said, determined to enlist his mother's support and learn how to be the very best wife she could be for Patric.

He dropped a swift, scorching kiss on her mouth, and said, 'Trust me, Kate. We'll make it.'

'I do trust you.'

His unsparing eyes searched her face. 'Yes, I think you do, at last,' he said, and his arms tightened around her in a brief, fierce hug. 'I trust you, too.'

Dreamily, Kate thought she'd remember that precious moment all her life.

He said, 'We'll get married in three days' time. And we'll get DNA-tested. After I left you this afternoon I rang a friend of my father's to find out how it works, and apparently there could be enough similarity between Sean's test and mine to confuse the issue. So if Sean does press for access we can wave the results around the courtroom. Also, I have several other documents he won't want published; they'd ensure that no judge would grant access.'

'If he makes any move at all,' Kate said, shocked by the vindictiveness in her voice, 'I'll accuse him of rape. It will be awful, and I know your aunt will hate me for it, but I'll do it.'

'You won't have to. If he shows his face in New Zealand again I'll crush him.' It was said with such icy dispassion that she shivered. Instantly he demanded, 'Does he frighten you?'

'No,' she said contemptuously. 'Sex is nothing when it's stolen and forced. He wanted to humiliate and shame us both, but it would be giving him too much power to let him succeed. Actually, meeting him again helped me. I realised what a contemptible thing he is. But I do worry about Nick. I don't ever want him to know that Sean is his father.'

'We'll make sure he never does,' Patric said with lethal menace. 'I can control Sean. Our best revenge will be bringing up a son who is happy and successful and honest, and you've made a very good start on that. Between us we can make sure that Nick is nothing like the man who fathered him.'

He lifted her chin and looked at her, his hard face at last open to her. 'So now,' he said, 'may I stay the night with you, my darling? I need to hold you and make sure you're safe.'

Her eyes filled; nodding, she got up with him and went

into the bedroom, not worrying in the least that it was furnished with cast-offs.

This had nothing of the edged urgency of their last coming together; Patric undressed her slowly and sensuously, telling her how beautiful she was to him, how he ached for her, what he planned to do, how he hoped she'd feel.

Kate did the same for him, and when at last they lay together in bed she thought that this was how it had been the first time—profoundly, heart-stoppingly tender.

Although she'd been much shyer then, and Patric hadn't complained about the bed!

'Just as well I've got a decent-sized one at home,' he grumbled as they lay heart to heart, her face pressed into his neck, her body singing with anticipation. 'We won't live in the apartment—I want to buy you a house by the sea.'

Kate laughed silently, and ran a questing hand down the indentation of his spine and across to his hip. Her whole world, she thought exultantly, was blooming like a garden in spring.

A garden with a snake, but she trusted Patric to deal with his cousin.

'You don't need to make love if you don't want to,' Patric said, although his chest lifted suddenly at her caress. 'I meant it when I told you it would be enough to hold you.'

Kate lifted her head. 'Why?' she asked.

He kissed the vulnerable spot where her hair met her temple. 'The other night,' he said curtly, 'was it the first time since—since you conceived Nick?'

At her nod he went on, 'I tried to be gentle, but I made no concessions.'

Her heart started to jump. 'Neither did I,' she said stoutly, kissing along his jaw, lips tingling at the raw silken texture of his skin. 'It was wonderful because it was you. I'm not made of cotton wool, Patric. I love you and I want to make love with you. What happened with Sean was horrible, but it has nothing to do with us.'

His arms tightened. 'God, I love you,' he said, and kissed her, pressing her back into the pillow.

And what started with restraint ended in wildfire intensity, in untamed, exquisite fulfilment.

EPILOGUE

'OH, IT'S so hot!' Kate took off her hat and exhaled heavily.

'It *is* summer,' Patric said from behind her.

Laughing, she turned to kiss him. He returned it with interest and enthusiasm.

'Why do you do that all the time?' Nick asked teasingly, emerging from his bedroom, the same room Kate and he had shared the night they'd come back from Australia—only four months ago! 'When I grow up and get married will I have to kiss the lady all the time like you do?'

'Almost certainly,' Patric said, smoothing Kate's thick hair back from her face, 'but you'll find it feels good.'

'I don't think so,' Nick said cheerfully. 'Did you find us a house, Mummy?'

'I might have,' Kate said, resting her head a moment on Patric's broad chest before pulling away. 'The agent said she has a glorious place overlooking a tiny private beach on the North Shore. It has a jetty and a mooring.' She smiled at Patric. He had decided to change the sleek racing craft he already owned for something more suited to cruising holidays with a family. 'Are we interested?'

'I am.' But Patric sounded non-committal. 'What about you?'

'We can view it tomorrow morning at ten. Will that be all right?'

'Very,' he said.

Kate gave him a keen glance. Although she was getting better at reading his face, he'd reverted back to the poker-faced man who'd wooed her and caught her in the silken nets of love.

Tension plucked at her nerves, but she had a confidence now that she hadn't had then. He would tell her when he was ready.

He waited until after Nick had gone to bed. Then he sat down beside her on the big sofa in the sitting room and said, 'Brian Pierce rang me today.'

Kate looked up sharply. Brian Pierce was the specialist who'd conducted the DNA testing. She reached for Patric's hand. It had happened; now he had to say goodbye to the last particle of hope that Nick might not be Sean's son.

Patric's hand twisted, clasped hers. 'It's a perfect match. Kate, Nick is my son.'

Kate's mouth dropped open. 'I had a period,' she said numbly. 'Between when we made love and—and Sean. I had a period—a proper one. Nick can't be yours…'

He lifted her hand and kissed it, holding it to his mouth as he said, 'Was it lighter than normal?'

'I—yes. Yes, I think it was. But it was a proper period.'

Very gently he said, 'Brian consulted a gynaecologist. She said it can happen like that—you get what appears to be a lighter period, but it's really the fertilised ovum embedding itself.'

Dread suddenly vanished from the hidden reaches of Kate's heart. She whispered, 'Oh, thank God. Thank God. I used to pretend—and now it's true.'

'Darling Kate, don't cry.' He gathered her into his arms, holding her close while the storm of weeping shook her. When she'd choked back the last sobs he tipped her chin, looking into her face.

'It wouldn't have mattered,' he said, so decisively that she blinked. 'Of course I'm delighted, because this means that Sean hasn't any sort of claim, but Kate, I told you I'd never allow him to shadow Nick's life.'

Kate bowed her head into her hands. 'I don't deserve you,' she said shakily.

'You don't deserve someone who thought you'd lied about being raped?' He spoke with raw self-contempt.

'Who cold-bloodedly set out to woo you so that I could get my son? I even organised the upgrade to first class on the way back from Australia so that my son would be more comfortable. I lied, Kate.'

'And I didn't tell you that Sean was Nick's father. I lied about the man who stole the car. It doesn't matter,' she said, lifting her head. 'You know it doesn't matter now.'

His expression lightened. 'We'll make those lies up to each other. We had to wait a long time, you and I, but it's been worth it for me.' His voice was deep and sure, rich with love.

'And for me,' she said, hugging his hand to her breast. 'It was *all* worth it, Patric.'

'Sweet Kate,' he said huskily, 'my treasure, my dearest girl, let's leave it behind us now.'

'Yes.' She pulled his head down and they kissed, a kiss that closed the door on the past and opened one into a future more filled with joy and happiness than Kate had ever hoped for. That future stretched out in front of them, a shining, wide path. All they had to do was step out onto it without looking back.

And it was suddenly so simple to do.

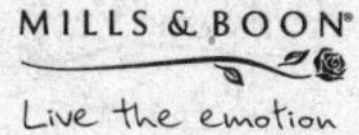

0405/01b

Modern romance™

AT THE SPANISH DUKE'S COMMAND
by Fiona Hood-Stewart

Georgiana fell for Juan Felipe Mansanto, Duque de Caniza, even though he was supposed to be her guardian. And it seemed that, try as he might, Juan couldn't resist her. But Juan was about to make a marriage of convenience to another woman…

THE SHEIKH'S VIRGIN *by Jane Porter*

Lots of women have enjoyed the benefits of being Sheikh Kalen Nuri's mistress – but they have all bored him. Now Kalen has discovered beautiful Keira – but she's refusing to be his, even though she has been chosen as his virgin bride!

THE ITALIAN DOCTOR'S MISTRESS *by Catherine Spencer*

Successful neurosurgeon Carlo Rossi has a passion for his work – and for women. And he desires Danielle Blake like no other woman. He insists they play by his rules – no future, just a brief affair. But when it's time for Danielle to leave Italy can he let her go?

PREGNANT BY THE GREEK TYCOON *by Kim Lawrence*

After a passionate whirlwind marriage to Greek billionaire Angolos Constantine, Georgie is pregnant. She is sure Angolos will be delighted – but instead he tells her to go away and never come back...but he'll have what's his – by whatever means necessary.

Don't miss out…

On sale 6th May 2005

Available at most branches of WHSmith, Tesco, ASDA, Martins, Borders, Eason, Sainsbury's and all good paperback bookshops.

Visit www.millsandboon.co.uk

0405/14

MILLS & BOON®

Live the emotion

ARM CANDY *by Jo Leigh*

Marketing whiz Jessica Howell needs some "arm candy" – a deliciously sexy man by her side to keep her married playboy boss in line. Dan Crawford fits the bill: he's handsome, discreet and available… Pretending to be in love with gorgeous Jess isn't difficult for Dan – except there's no pretence after they share one night of sizzling sex. But can their hot fling lead to the real thing?

INDISCREET *by Alison Kent* *www.girl-gear.com*

gIRL-gEAR vice president Annabel "Poe" Lee needs a change. That means telling her recent fling, Patrick Coffey, that it's over. However, Patrick's *the* best lover she's ever had, so saying goodbye is tougher than she thought. But it's time to move on; after all, falling for Patrick isn't in the cards…is it?

"Kent's gIRL-gEAR series triumphs with story and complex, rich characters whose scorching chemistry will keep readers guessing!" —*Romantic Times*

***Don't miss out!* These sexy reads are on sale from 6th May 2005**

Available at most branches of WHSmith, Tesco, ASDA, Martins, Borders, Eason, Sainsbury's and all good paperback bookshops.

Visit www.millsandboon.co.uk

EVER AFTER

by Fiona Hood-Stewart

"An enthralling page turner—not to be missed." —*New York Times* bestselling author Joan Johnston

She belongs to a world of wealth, politics and social climbing. But now Elm must break away to find happily ever after...

Elm MacBride can no longer sit back and watch her corrupt and deceitful husband's ascent to power and his final betrayal sends her fleeing to Switzerland where she meets Irishman Johnny Graney. When her husband's actions threaten to destroy her, Johnny must save not only their love but Elm's life...

ISBN 07783 2078 2

Published 15th April 2005

0405/03a

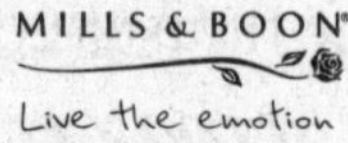

Medical romance™

HER EMERGENCY KNIGHT ***by Alison Roberts***

(A&E Drama)

When her light plane crashes, leaving her stranded on a New Zealand mountain, Jennifer must turn to fellow passenger Guy Knight to survive. The last thing rural GP Guy needs is a city surgeon to slow him down in the wilderness! But Guy soon realises that the real danger Jennifer poses is to his heart…

THE DOCTOR'S FIRE RESCUE ***by Lilian Darcy***

After avoiding pharmaceutical millionaire Niccolo Conti for the entire conference, doctor Alison Lane gets on the tour bus to find the only seat left is next to the tall, dark Italian. The last time she'd been this close to him she'd been in Italy, thinking he was to be her future husband. Irritatingly, the intense attraction between them is still there…

A VERY SPECIAL BABY ***by Margaret Barker***

(French Hospital)

Although her biological clock is ticking, and her daughter is asking for a baby sister, A&E doctor Debbie Sabatier believes she'll never have another child. Her ex-husband's betrayal has left her wary of commitment. But then consultant Marcel De Lange offers to father her baby…

On sale 6th May 2005

Available at most branches of WHSmith, Tesco, ASDA, Martins, Borders, Eason, Sainsbury's and all good paperback bookshops.

Visit www.millsandboon.co.uk

UNTAMED
by Merline Lovelace

Trapped by her own game of seduction…

Orphaned at a young age, Lady Barbara Chamberlain and her brother have been forced to live off their wits. Now Charles's schemes have landed him in prison and funds are desperately needed to help his escape.

Barbara devises a plan. Playing on her beauty and fine Society manners, she will save her brother by seducing Lieutenant Zachariah Morgan. But the devilishly handsome Zach knows that she has lied to him with every breath and, suddenly, she is caught in her own seductive snare…

"…it reads like great gossip.

…a compulsively readable tale."

Publishers Weekly* on *A Savage Beauty

On sale 6th May 2005

Available at most branches of WHSmith, Tesco, ASDA, Martins, Borders, Eason, Sainsbury's and all good paperback bookshops.

0405/03b